Reading-for-Men

NELSON DOUBLEDAY, INC.
Garden City   New York

Reading-for-Men

A Complete Novel

PAX

by MIDDLETON KIEFER

EDITOR'S NOTE

Pax is a highly explosive novel about the American drug industry.

The Raven pharmaceutical company, formerly known for their successful worm killers, has now come up with something really big—a new tranquilizer which they label "Pax." It brings peace of mind for everyone from expectant fathers to cancer patients; at least, that's the sales pitch. Raven feels they will make a real financial killing if they can get "Pax" marketed directly over the druggist's counter, bypassing the doctor's-prescription stage.

A shrewd and ruthless sales manager and his advertising stooge team up to sell "Pax" like bubble gum. But when they try to draw their public relations genius and an idealistic young Army officer into their scheme, the side effects are devastating.

This unusual story is an eye-opening blend of business, sex, and politics, with the powerful qualities that made *The Hucksters* and *The Last Hurrah* so popular.

Pax is the work of two free-lance writers: Harry Middleton, who has written for the Associated Press and been associated with the public relations organization of a major drug and chemical corporation, and Warren Kiefer, also a former reporter and public relations production supervisor for the international division of the same company.

1

WITH ONE IMPERIOUS white-gloved hand raised high while the other snapped open the taxi door, the doorman signaled for a bellhop lurking behind the plate glass of the hotel entrance. The tanned and well-tailored young officer who stepped from the taxi went briskly up the hotel steps, leaving the driver and the bellboy with two billowy canvas suitcases, a brief case and a duffel bag, all neatly stenciled in black letters that spelled CAPT. BEDFORD MONTROSE, US ARMY.

The captain moved with parade-ground step to the registration desk, where he signed in, and then to the elevator where the two bellboys transporting his effects were waiting to bow him aboard. In the unguarded privacy of his room, however, with his tunic removed and his tie loosened, he relaxed his bearing and moved more easily.

He carried the telephone as close to the window as the cord would permit. He found the number he wanted and gave it to the operator. While he waited for the connection, his eyes searched the world outside.

The thin blue haze which traveled upward to where he stood was a civilized fog, not rolling in over the distant mountains he had left behind, but through the canyons of the city, giving a luster of soft loveliness to stone and steel, and stirring excitement in him as distant fogs had never done.

Emily Klinger, secretary to the director of public relations of the Raven pharmaceutical company, turned her face to the door as her boss walked in at ten forty-five. He had made the trip from his midtown apartment to the plant on the outskirts of New York in a record thirty minutes. Relief showed in her eyes outlined by greenish shadow and protected by thick, moist lashes. "Well, thank goodness," she said. "I've been trying to get you everywhere. You must not have been home last night."

"If you're going to jump to conclusions," Joe Logan said, "don't do it so loudly. What's up?" He walked into his office and she followed him, carrying her notebook with her.

"Mr. McRumen's office called. There's a meeting in the conference room at eleven o'clock. Urgent."

"What's it all about?"

"Officially, I haven't any idea," she said. "But there's been a hubbub over this." She handed him a copy of that morning's *Daily News* and with a vermilion fingernail pointed out a brief paragraph in Eugene Carson's "World in Review" column. Logan read it:

> We hear another drug company—Raven—has a new "happy pill"—or tranquilizer, as it's known to the men in white. . . . Pretty soon worry will be as old-fashioned as gout. . . .

His face showing his surprise, he returned the newspaper to her. He spoke not to her but aloud to himself. "What's this all about?"

"Maybe you'll find out in the meeting," his secretary said.

"All right, Emily. What else?"

"Well, you have a lunch date. With Captain Montrose."

"Who?"

"You remember. The man from Asia. You asked me to make the date when he called. And he called first thing this morning. He just got back."

"Good." Logan picked up a letter from his desk and began scanning it absently. "You've had a busy morning."

"He said if it's all right he'd like to have his fiancée join you."

Logan looked up from the letter. "Oh? And what did you tell him?"

"I said I was sure it would be."

"Good girl." He smiled at her.

"He gave me her name," Emily said. She flipped a page on her notebook. "It's . . . Let me see . . . Craig, or something like that."

"It's Crain," Joe Logan said.

"That's right. Here it is. Isn't she a senator's daughter or something?"

"She is indeed." He patted her on the head and walked toward the door.

He proceeded slowly along the corridor to the building's opposite wing, and then, rather than take the elevator, he walked up the three flights to the conference room adjacent to the president's office. He was late but it was precisely the right kind of timing for the public relations director. It showed a casualness appropriate to a creative man, but not so careless a casualness that it was out of harmony with the company's team spirit.

A dozen men representing every part of The Team were gathered around the heavy, brightly polished table. At one end sat Lloyd Mc-

Rumen himself, the president of the organization, a portly little man with thinning gray hair and a round face that usually presented a mask of jovial well-being to the world about him but now was set in stern lines. At the other end of the table Alonzo Shively, a vice-president and the manager of Raven's sales organization, stared speculatively at a folded newspaper. His well-cared-for face was a study of thoughtful sadness. The other men, who flanked either side of the table, studiously considered the table area directly before them.

Silence surrounded the table as Logan took his seat. Finally Lloyd McRumen coughed and everyone looked in his direction.

"I think, Al," McRumen said, "that you might as well start things off by passing that newspaper around."

Alonzo Shively nodded. With his pen he drew a circle around the paragraph in the column in the *News*. "Some of you may already have seen this," he said.

The newspaper made the rounds at the table, drawing from most of the men expressions of puzzlement, and, from a few, astonishment.

"First of all," Shively said, when the paper had been returned to him, "I wonder if any of us here can tell how this story leaked out."

Lloyd McRumen said, "I don't think that's necessary, Al. I'm sorry those of you who didn't know had to learn about it this way." He paused, conscious that every eye in the room was on him. "The point is, gentlemen, that we have a new product—we think we have . . ."

"We know we have," Shively cut in.

The president continued. "We've been keeping it under wraps while the experiments were going on. We didn't dare take a chance on tipping off the competition, so nobody's known about this except those who absolutely had to. Now it's out, the news has broken, and we've got to move fast. That's why we've called you all together. Do you want to take over, Al?"

Shively stood up and beamed at his audience. He was a man who could change moods quickly, and now he turned with alacrity to the role he liked best—that of the great persuader. With a practiced flourish he took a fashionable pair of brown-rimmed glasses from his breast pocket and dangled them idly in his left hand while with his right he flicked the newspaper lying on the table in front of him.

"Having read this item," he said in a balanced masculine voice which carried an infectious friendliness, "you know we've found a tranquilizer." The wonderful salesman's smile he turned on them was soft and benevolent. It was kind and warm and disarming. He held it silently and allowed them to speculate aloud on what had been said. He stood and waited confidently for the murmur to subside. In his less than fifty years Alonzo Shively had sold hair tonic, glassware, insurance policies, corsets and contraceptives. He had managed the work of lesser men, needling, praising and threatening his way to a reputation of sales genius. He never forgot a name or a face. When he had come to Raven three years before, he had come high. After six months he had been rewarded with a vice-presidency, and no one who knew him doubted that when death or retirement overtook Lloyd McRumen, nothing would stand between Alonzo Shively and the throne. Some thought he might claim it even sooner.

Now as he sweepingly surveyed his audience, his smile dimmed and his face took on a look of serious concern. "You gentlemen know what this means for Raven," he said soberly. "Last year more than a hundred million dollars' worth of business was done with tranquilizers." He paused and let his voice drop a decibel to assume a more confidential tone. "And if our preliminary tests are correct, our product has properties that will give it a bigger appeal market-wise than any of the others now available." He leaned forward and spread his palms on the table. "This may well be, gentlemen," he said, deliberately spacing his words, "the biggest step yet in the growth of our company."

There was a silence in the room broken finally by Joe Logan. "I don't get it, Al. What are we doing with a tranquilizing drug? That seems pretty far afield for us."

Shively looked at McRumen, who cleared his throat and said, "It's not really, Joe. Not so far afield as it seems." He toyed with a gold fountain pen. "So we can get this thing off the ground properly," he said, "we're going to play it straight with everyone here. I'm going to ask Ambrose to fill you in on everything."

Dr. Ambrose Garibaldi, Raven's dour medical research director, was a big man, and at the president's nod he heaved forward in his chair and placed his elbows on the table. Peering over his spectacles at McRumen, he asked, "Everything, Lloyd?"

McRumen nodded with deliberation.

"All right," Garibaldi said. "We discovered this compound while pursuing our new intensive research screening program."

"What were you doing?" Logan asked. "Looking for a new pinworm purge?"

A laugh went around the table, which subsided quickly under the stern stare of Alonzo Shively.

Dr. Garibaldi barely was able to repress a smile as he continued. "You are not so far off as you might think. You may not know that some tranquilizers are basically antihistamine-type compounds, and that the

basis for most antihistamines is the versatile chemical we call piperazine."
His over-the-spectacle glance traveled along the table. "Everyone in this
room, of course, knows that piperazine salts make some of Raven's best
products." He paused and with a sweeping finger directed their attention
to a row of glass exhibit cases arranged along one walnut-paneled wall of
the conference room, each containing a Raven package.

They were all there—the purgatives with which the tiny company had
begun its commercial venture a half-century before, the modest line of
specialty pharmaceuticals with which it had grown, and the worm killers
with which it had established its reputation. A long black and orange
banner fixed to the wall above the cases carried the legend which now was
a proud part of the Raven logotype: THE WORLD'S LARGEST PRODUCER OF
VERMIFUGES. Directly below it hung several large colored-plaster models
of some of the frightening enemies vanquished by the power of Raven
drugs: pudgy larvae, sinister nematodes and slippery flukes.

With obvious relish, Dr. Garibaldi proceeded with the task of explaining the circumstances which brought the executives of the world's largest
producer of vermifuges together to hear their company's marketing plans
for a tranquilizing drug.

Raven had built compounds other than vermifuges around the piperazine chemical in the past—not always with successful results. One such adventure had come several years before, when the public appetite for
antihistamine drugs was dictating the market. At that time, in an effort
to find a place in that market, Raven scientists had come up with a compound called phitherdimethyldine. . . .

"Sneezone!" one of the men exclaimed.

"That's right," Garibaldi said. "We marketed it under the name
Sneezone."

"A real turkey," another said disgustedly. "It was a complete bust."

Garibaldi's mouth showed the smallest trace of a smile. Sneezone had
indeed been a bust, and because it was unprofitable the company had
dropped its promotion of the drug and had not, in fact, been manufactur-
ing it for the last year. Some bottles still remained on drug-store shelves
and forty crates were gathering dust in the company's warehouse.

"Do you know," Garibaldi asked, peering around the room, *"why* that
product was not successful?"

"There were drawbacks—drowsiness, and others . . ."

"Exactly. Even though the public had come to expect a certain amount
of side effects in antihistamines, the side effects in Sneezone were remarkable. Drowsiness was just one, although it was an important one. Even
where drowsiness did not exist, there was a relaxing effect, a sense of

well-being. The public rejected it. They were looking then for something that would work against the symptoms of the common cold. They hadn't yet been conditioned to seek euphoria in their medicine cabinets."

"You mean," Joe Logan asked, "that we had a tranquilizing drug and we were trying to foist it off as a sneeze-stopper?"

Garibaldi nodded. "That's not the way it would be phrased in the professional journals, but it's close."

"Does that make sense?"

"Of course it makes sense. Many antihistamines have some tranquilizing effect. Ours happened to be a good deal stronger in that direction than the others. It appears to work on the hypothalamus, but we're still trying to trace the course of action."

"In the company's search for an all-purpose vermifuge," Dr. Garibaldi continued, "laboratory scientists reinvestigated a number of old piperazine compounds. When they came to phitherdimethyldine they found quickly enough that it had no special vermicidal activity, but they became interested in its other effects. The drug was administered to a nasty-tempered dog and a cymologus monkey, one of the fiercest strains available. The dog became docile, and the monkey just sat and watched the lice romp in the fur on its belly, while a female in heat capered around in the adjoining cage. After two more months of animal work, the research staff knew it had something big."

Horace Blivet, the assistant to the sales vice-president, frowned after Garibaldi had finished his report. "That doesn't sound like much to work with," he said.

"Don't underestimate the importance of that animal work, Horace." Shively turned to Garibaldi. "Doctor, why don't we *show* the group how dramatic the response can be? Let's bring the dog and monkey up here so everyone can see what kind of a drug we really have."

"Well . . ." Garibaldi hesitated. "I don't think it's a very good idea to take those animals out of the lab."

"Is that right, Doctor?" The smile left Shively's face. "Well, *I do*. Now, let's get them up here." He motioned to Horace Blivet, who picked up a telephone and directed the chief of the pharmacology laboratory to have the animals brought to the conference room immediately.

Shively's demonstration was followed by an uncomfortable stillness before Garibaldi continued his report. "We are now retesting this drug in the clinics. Physicians have administered it to fifty patients suffering from some form of minor anxiety. Eighty percent have reported some varying degree of release from tension and worry."

"What about the others?" Logan asked.

"Most of them were unaffected or they simply went to sleep. One shut himself up in a deep-freeze. Whether the drug had a curious effect on him or whether this was his idea of relaxation, we have no way of knowing."

"But every time it has proved absolutely safe," Shively interposed.

"No instance of toxicity has been reported," Garibaldi said. "But that is not to say we don't expect some trouble with the drug. Sedation may cause us to reduce the concentration of the active agent. There's considerable laboratory work still to be done. . . ."

"Well, there you have it," Shively cut in.

"What kind of trouble do you expect?" Joe Logan asked.

"Well . . ." Dr. Garibaldi began.

"The few bugs that remain aren't worth discussing at this meeting," Alonzo Shively said. There was an angry intensity in his voice. "We've got no time to screw around with details. We're trying to show you the big picture."

He picked up a heavy pointer that stood against a sales map covering one wall, and carried it to a glass exhibit case. He held it by the light end as if it were a baseball bat and pointed the butt at a display of Raven vermifuge.

"This is *not* another worm killer we've got now." He swung the pointer back and with one quick violent motion slammed it into the case. The glass shattered to the floor and several of the men started from their chairs. Shively reached in and held up one of the vermifuge vials. With a triumphant smile he regarded his startled audience.

"Up till now we've been happy bumping along with small-time products like this—two hundred thousand a year in sales from this item. But it's a goddamn antique!" He straightened his fingers and let the bottle bounce harmlessly on the carpet. Then he turned and strode back to the conference table. From his pocket he slowly fished out a tiny capsule of phitherdimethyldine and held it delicately up between his fingers. *"This,"* he said in a tone so low that all leaned forward to catch his words, "is worth ten times ten what that ever brought in, in its best year! Ten, twenty million dollars of sales are in this product."

He stepped back from the table again and raised the pointer once more as if it were a club. "We're at the threshold, gentlemen, at the threshold. Our vermifuges have whipped these nuisances, one at a time." He raised the pointer and deftly smashed the first plaster worm model. "This—and this—and this . . ." He pulverized each one in succession. "We're through leading the world in vermifuges. We've flushed intestines long enough." He reached for the Raven banner and tore it from its moorings. Like a shelled and shredded flag it hung limp and defeated from one tack.

He looked at the shocked faces around him with an authority that bordered on contempt. "Do any doubts remain, gentlemen? We're going after the mind now. The *human* mind." He tapped his head with his finger. "That's the way we've got to think."

He took his seat at the table again. "We can't waste a day now. Where we planned to get on the market with a new name and new dosage forms in three or four months, we've got to do it in two."

"Aren't there already half a dozen tranquilizers on the market now?" Joe Logan asked.

"The market saturation point on tranquilizers of all kinds won't be reached for a long time yet," Shively said. "Drugs like reserpine and chlorpromazine can take care of the real psychos. But we are not interested in that. We're going after the *normal* human mind, the everyday neurotic, the common tension case. But we're going to have tough competition, all right. That's why we've got to come up with a sales promotion and advertising campaign that will knock them all dead."

He stopped, letting his mood change once more. His voice became gentle and persuasive again. "The most important thing"—he emphasized each word—"is that *first* we've got to make Raven famous. We may be big in worms, but we're not known for anything else. We've got to get the name of the company before the public in a big way—and then the name of the product, once we have a name. We'll need people with *ideas,* gentlemen—dynamic, atomic ideas."

The door opened and a white-coated laboratory assistant came in, leading a passive bull mastiff on a leash and trying to bounce awake a drowsy monkey on his arm.

"*There* we are," Shively said. "Put them up on the table."

The lab man laid the sleeping monkey on its side. Then, with the help of two of the executives, he lifted the dog, which stood on the gleaming table top blinking at the faces around him.

Shively walked to the side of the table, where he could reach the dog, and poked him violently in the side. The dog regarded him stoically. "You see? Nothing happens. This dog was practically foaming at the mouth when he was first treated." He poked him again, then turning to the sleeping monkey, he pinched its skin. "Kind of lifeless," he said.

"He went to sleep on the way up here," the laboratory assistant said. "He's been taking three hundred milligrams a day."

Shively poked the dog once more, and returned to his chair. "All right," he said. "Let's get back to business. Any questions?"

"Do you think this is the best timing, Al?" Joe Logan asked. "With the government about to investigate the whole industry, shouldn't we be moving cautiously?"

Shively looked at Logan tolerantly. "What better time for us to jump in with a big new drug?" he answered. "The sooner the whole world knows us, the stronger our position is. We'll worry about investigations when we get to them. Right now, we're worried about publicity."

"Al is right, gentlemen," Lloyd McRumen said. "You all know the problem. For all of our past successes, Raven is still a somewhat obscure company. Before our next meeting, I would like every man in this room to sift his imagination for ideas which might help solve this problem."

Shively had been nodding vigorously as the president talked. "Absolutely," he said. "Now that you all have a sure-footed grasp of the situation, let's see you *ideate*."

McRumen pushed his chair back. "I think that will be all this morning, gentlemen," he said. In a lower tone, he addressed Shively. "Al, why don't you and Joe and Ambrose come into my office and we'll take up another matter." He started moving toward the door, and the others in the room followed after him.

"Wait a minute, wait a minute!" Shively commanded. "Come back. Look here. This is what I wanted you to see." He pointed to the monkey, who was stirring now on the table. "Just a little nap, that's all. Now he's rested, you'll see what a docile little thing he is."

Everyone returned, and stood watching the monkey stretch slowly to life. He got laboriously to his feet, looking laconically at the faces in front of him. "Watch him now, *watch* him," Shively said excitedly.

With a dozen pairs of eyes fastened on him in entrancement, the monkey hunched into a squat, and grunting with small animal noises, defiled the polished mahogany surface of the table.

Then, a model of simian tranquility, he slowly lay down again.

The "other matter" which Lloyd McRumen wished to discuss was the forthcoming investigation of the drug industry by the Senate Subcommittee on Health and Welfare. It was no longer just a possibility, the president informed the three men as he closed the door of his private office and faced them. It was now a reality. He had learned this morning that the president of Placebo Laboratories had received his "invitation" to testify before the subcommittee headed by Senator Crain of Indiana, and it was just a matter of time before the other drug companies—Raven included—received theirs.

The news came as no surprise to Logan. For the last few weeks he had been filling out questionnaires distributed by the committee counsel, and he had provided the committee's investigators with a supply of Raven's price sheets and promotional literature—all ambitiously, if unsuccessfully, selected with the hope of settling the issue in the committee's mind before it ever reached the stage of actual investigation.

The issue, as the committee posed it, was a simple one: did competitive firms have competitive prices? For the millions of dollars spent on drugs each year by federal agencies, was the government getting its money's worth? Or was it paying luxury prices for commodity merchandise only because many companies conspired to keep their prices high? And what of the people? Was new legislation needed to protect consumer interests in the vital area of health?

"I want to be prepared for this," McRumen said. "I think Joe should draw up a presentation for us."

"Line the right pockets," Shively said, "and it'll never come to that."

"Not this time," Garibaldi said. "These people think they have hold of something hot. For that matter, they're right."

"That's a hell of a way to be talking," Shively said.

"I'm talking in the confines of this private office," Garibaldi said, "and I don't think it's going to help us any to ignore the facts."

"All right, then trot out some facts they'll be interested in, some that will steal the headlines right out from under them. Tell them about all the lives the drug industry has saved in the last fifteen years."

"That's the business we're in, isn't it?" Garibaldi suggested. "The pharmaceutical industry has been warding off criticism for a long time now by pointing to its lifesaving drugs. But that defense isn't going to last forever. And it's not much of a case when you get down to it. We can't claim some kind of corporate altruism on behalf of our products."

"There's a lot of truth in what Ambrose is saying," McRumen said. "But we can justify our position, and that's what I want Joe to work on. After all, we're in business for profit. We have shareholders to satisfy. No one can accuse us of any intent to defraud anyone. We put money into a product and we stay competitive. That's what keeps us all honest. You know what we need, don't you, Joe?"

"I think so," Logan said.

"More than just those points, of course. We run a noble business." McRumen's voice was defensive. "We're interested in the health and betterment of people everywhere. We have tremendous research costs and all that."

"Got a lunch date?" Shively asked Logan after they had left the president's office.

"I'm afraid I do," Logan said, looking at his watch.

"Too bad. There was something I wanted to go over with you while it's hot."

"Can it wait?" Joe asked.

"Well, let me throw it on the screen for you right here and see how it moves." He looked around him in the corridor cautiously. "Don't get too wrapped up in this thing for Lloyd," he said. "Give him what he needs, of course, but you've got another big job to handle, too, you know."

"The tranquilizer," Logan said.

"That's right. We're going to need everything you can give us. Here's what I want you to be thinking about. I'm going to want a press conference on this. The biggest. We need to give this product a real star-spangled introduction, and I want every son of a bitch who writes ten lines to be on hand."

Logan looked at him patiently. "We can have a press conference, all right, but don't expect too much. This *isn't* penicillin, Al."

"It's big."

"Maybe, but it doesn't sound like news. There are enough of those happy pills on the market now so the introduction of one more isn't likely to send off fireworks."

"Don't worry about that," Shively said. "We won't disappoint anybody."

Logan looked at him curiously.

"That's all I can say about it now, and I want you to keep that much in the safe. But you start dreaming up a big press do, one they'll never forget. Get 'em however you can and then blast 'em with a spectacular."

"We could hold it in a dirigible."

"You're thinking, boy," Shively said. "That's fine. Now burn rubber." He clapped Logan on the shoulder and hurried down the hall to his own office.

"No calls for about ten minutes," he said to his secretary. Inside his office he closed the door and went immediately to his desk. Too much time had been taken up with that committee investigation business. The leak to the papers about the new tranquilizer concerned him a good deal more than any Senate hearing.

Alonzo Shively was thoroughly angered. God damn it, this was *his* project. *He* was calling the signals, and someone on The Team had given away the play. He intended to keep this from happening again. He looked up a number in his private notebook. Abner Murphy was the most accomplished wire tapper in the business, but he was listed under "I" for "Investigator."

Shively placed the call himself, instead of giving it to his secretary. The confidential work that Murphy was doing, Shively intended to *keep* confidential.

"Things have changed a little," he told Murphy. "The story's out." He read aloud the item in the morning newspaper column.

Murphy grunted. "You want us to pull the bugs off now?"

"Hell, no," Shively said. "It's more important than ever for us to know what the other companies are doing. Maybe this news will smoke 'em out. What I want you to do now is bug about a dozen wires here."

"Your *own* company?"

"That's right." Shively was both amused and irritated by the hesitation in the other man's voice. A professional, for God's sake. Shively himself felt no squeamishness. Weeks before, when the idea first took hold in his mind to have the competition's wires tapped, he had debated it with himself, briefly and efficiently. He had decided that the urgent necessity of finding out about any new tranquilizer plans held by other drug outfits heavily outweighed any objection to the means employed. And once his decision was made, he had neither regretted it nor worried about it. He did not hesitate now to apply a logical extension of that decision. "Someone's running off at the mouth and I want to know who it is. You got a pencil? I'll give you the list. First, Dr. Ambrose Garibaldi, extension 753. He's a bigmouth and he might well be the one. Yeah, all outgoing and incoming calls. Next, J. H. Logan, extension 802 . . ."

He had, as a matter of hidden fact, acted wisely in making the call to Murphy himself. Although neither he nor his secretary Doris Krause would ever know it, the celebrated item which had found its way into the morning newspaper had started its journey from her desk. She had heard enough of a conversation between Shively and Lloyd McRumen to give her an interesting topic to pass on to a friend whose brother worked as a copy boy for the *Daily News*.

2

THE SENATE drug industry investigation was of considerably greater interest to Joe Logan than the new tranquilizer he had just learned about. He looked upon the product exploitation demanded by Shively as a routine publicity task, neither rewarding nor exciting. Since Shively obviously regarded the new drug as his own personal mission, Logan knew he could expect a relentless needling from the vice-president. Considering it, during the long taxi ride into midtown New York, from the Raven plant, Logan shrugged. Shively wanted a spectacular press conference; he'd get a spectacular press conference. Logan smiled wryly to himself. He had already embarked on plans for introducing a drug he didn't know a damn thing about. Nobody seemed to, for that matter, except perhaps Dr. Garibaldi. Logan reminded himself that he should ask the medical research director about it in the morning.

The Senate investigation was another matter. The issue was a live bomb for the pharmaceutical industry. It would not be difficult for Senator Barton Crain's committee to find disturbing similarities in drug prices, and even a cursory look at profits would show that most companies had grown strangely fat in less than a decade. With a drug-hungry public and a minimal three-to-one markup on the manufacturer's price, heavy dividends had come easily.

It would be the task of the lawyers and the public relations men throughout the industry to defuse the bomb or obscure it—at the very least to show that heavy profits were not in themselves evidence of collusion or gross irresponsibility. Logan expected the task to absorb a good deal of his effort. He did not resent the prospect; in fact, he welcomed it. There was a certain challenge in it, a promise of excitement, which was distinct from most of the assignments that filled his working day.

It was this sense of challenge which gave a special dimension to Logan's forthcoming lunch date. He looked forward, as eagerly as he could ever be said to look forward to anything, to meeting Senator Crain's daughter and her fiancé. He had no idea what advantage this would provide him, but—there was the challenge.

Before he had left the office, Logan's secretary had handed him a folder with all the correspondence pertaining to the man who had set in motion the events leading to this meeting. In the taxi he reviewed the pertinent details. Captain Bedford Montrose had been on a United Nations Civil Assistance team sent into the tiny Asian kingdom of Baopneng after it had been torn by revolution and divided permanently into two separate areas by the terms of a UN-arranged armistice. This was all outlined in the first item in the folder, a letter which Raven had received from the International Aid Commission. The director of the commission had written to request a free shipment of drugs for Captain Montrose. The letter explained that in the course of Captain Montrose's duty, an epidemic had broken out among the Baopneng refugees, and the officer had written to Senator Crain, his fiancée's father, asking help. Crain had asked the commission to handle the request, and the IAC had subsequently relayed the petition to Raven, the world's largest producer of the vermifuges which could halt the epidemic.

"I feel sure you will not hesitate to help us oblige this officer's request," the commission's director had written.

Raven had obliged, of course. Such requests could almost always be filled in a way that provided the company with a distinct tax advantage. In the folder was a slip of paper bearing Logan's scrawl which indicated that the retail price of the six crates of drugs shipped to Montrose might be estimated at $25,000, the book cost to Raven therefore some $4,300, but the *actual* cost absolutely nothing, since the drugs had outlived their expiration date and thus could not be sold in the United States.

The last item in the folder was a letter from Captain Montrose himself, acknowledging receipt of the drugs and accepting the company's invitation to visit its offices upon his return. "I'll be coming into the New York area as soon as I get back anyway," the letter said, "since my girl lives there." The last sentence read: "It will be a pleasure to make known my gratitude in person."

Logan closed the folder and returned it to his brief case. The prospect posed by this last message he found faintly unwelcome. Of all the vagrants who wandered through a pharmaceutical PR man's life, it was the do-gooders, with their frightening sincerity, whom he most strenuously preferred to avoid. Against most attitudes that were alien to him, Joe Logan had constructed reasonably effective defenses. But idealism—and Logan was coldly certain he was about to meet idealism personified—exhausted him.

He never expected total honesty from people because he himself seldom gave it. He looked for constantly, but rarely found, that quality in others which was most prized in himself: perception. Whenever he found it, he paid its owner respect. When he did not, he felt no compunction about using people in whatever way he needed.

There was nothing really commanding in Captain Montrose's appearance, Logan thought—no one single factor, that is—but the total effect was of a somewhat surprising authority. He was tall, slender, and well-barbered. His face carried earnestness and a suggestion of humility. He was four or five years younger than Logan, but Logan felt the gulf of half a generation between them.

The captain's handshake was firm, and his smile was both quick and warm. "Patty should be here soon," he told Logan. "I hope you don't mind waiting."

"Of course not," Logan said.

"Thanks. I haven't seen much of her lately."

Patty, Logan thought. It fits. Something pretty and frilly and sweet, and ready to give this gangling bit of uncertainty the mothering he needs.

They sat on one of the lobby's deep sofas while they waited for Pat Crain.

"I'll try to keep from bouncing," the captain said, "but I hope you'll forgive me if I gawk around. This is all pretty new to me still."

Logan hesitated. The war stories would come easily enough, he was sure of that. He had not intended to solicit one. Still, there was at the very least an hour and a half of conversation to get through. So he took the plunge. "Did you have rough duty over there?" he asked.

"Oh . . ." Montrose's smile was a small one now, and rather apologetic. "A little rougher than this, I guess."

"What exactly were you doing there, Captain?" Logan asked. "The information we had wasn't very specific."

"I know," Montrose said. "It couldn't be." He sketched in the story briefly. The kingdom of Baopneng was little more than an armed camp when Captain Montrose and the other four members of a UN team were allowed to enter the border city of Laophong immediately after the peace conference. Their mission was to process the people passing over the border from the Communist area to the free zone in the period of safe passage time permitted by the armistice. The American Army had furnished Montrose—a reserve junior officer, but one who had previously done some creditable civil assistance work elsewhere in Southeast Asia—in response to the United Nations' request for a U. S. Army officer to head one of the teams sent into the country. No sooner had he arrived and set to work than the epidemic had broken out and his job was

suddenly bigger than he, the Army, or the UN was prepared for: he had
to conquer the people's Communist-fed suspicion that the team had landed
in their midst as an instrument of bacteriological warfare. The only competent way to overcome this fear was to stop the epidemic, and the team
had neither a medical officer nor adequate medical supplies to try. Because of the terms of the truce, Montrose could get no assistance from
the Army. It was then that he had written to Senator Crain, who in turn
had found a way to help through the IAC.

He told it haltingly and with some reluctance, as if he did not want to
burden his listener but was having difficulty separating the highlights
from the trivia that surrounded them.

"Anyway," Montrose said, nervously fingering a button on his tunic,
"the supplies you sent did the job. And even though it probably can't
seem too important this far away, it was awfully important then. It was a
magnificent gesture for your company to make, and I'd like for your people to know. I feel pretty deeply about it."

Logan nodded briskly. He was strangely touched, and he strongly dis-
trusted experiences that touched him.

Pat Crain was not frilly, and if she had any desire to mother anyone
in the lobby of the Dorwick Arms, she managed to hide it well behind an
open friendliness. She was tall, with soft, close-cropped brown hair, and
a confident grace which Logan liked immediately. She embraced Montrose with restrained affection but she held onto his hand while the captain
introduced her to Logan.

Her gray eyes appraised Logan quickly and with friendly interest.
"Buddy's written me about your philanthropies, Mr. Logan," she said.

Logan smiled. "We'll put him on the staff." He turned to Montrose.
"Is Buddy your preferred alias?"

"I guess it'll dog me all my life," Montrose replied. "Bedford is quite
a mouthful. People think Buddy comes easier."

They arranged themselves around a corner table in the grill and ordered
a drink. Watching his companions, Logan wondered exactly what their
relationship amounted to. There had been some reserve in their embrace
in the lobby, which fed his curiosity. Pat's friendliness remained, but with
it Logan thought he sensed an unmistakable detachment.

"What do you do, Pat?" he asked midway through the meal. "Model?"

"That's very pretty, Mr. Logan," she said. "But I'm afraid it isn't anything nearly so glamorous. I'm a graduate student at Columbia. I study
and I teach a little."

"She's also a bleeding heart," Montrose said. "She sent me clothes that she had ripped off the backs of everyone on the campus—enough to keep half of Asia covered."

"Castoffs," Pat said.

They looked at each other silently, their eyes soft and eager. Montrose reached across the table and took her hand. Then, as if suddenly aware of the surroundings, he surrendered her hand and sat back in his chair. He seemed embarrassed. "Except for five quick minutes early this morning, we haven't seen each other for a year," he explained to Logan.

Pat shook her head quickly, making her smile bright. But her eyes were glistening.

Watching her, Logan said, "I'm sorry. I didn't know. We could have done this another time."

"Don't be intimidated by me, Mr. Logan," Pat said. "I'm a born weeper."

Logan had a sudden impulse to take her hand in his own. He envied Montrose the evening ahead and as his mind ranged over a montage of remote and improbable scenes involving himself with Pat Crain, he carried his share of light conversation.

Pat said she and Montrose had met three years before as students at Indiana University.

"In a classroom?" Logan asked.

Pat nodded and selected a cigarette from the package on the table. "Political Science 127. Democracy and Demagogues."

"Is that what you're studying now?"

She laughed. "Hardly. Political consciousness is for those who didn't have it with their breakfast food when they were growing up. I'm taking education courses for a teaching certificate."

"You know who her father is?" Montrose asked.

"I know," Logan said, smiling. He looked at Pat. "You probably come in handy during his campaigns."

"He won't use me," she said. "The only campaigning I ever did was for Buddy. I wrote him up for the college paper when he ran for president of the student council."

Montrose grinned. "I'd almost forgotten about that."

"But I didn't write these. You're famous in your own right, now." She drew an envelope from her purse and took some newspaper clippings from it. "These are from the Midwest City *Chronicle*."

Montrose took the clippings and looked at them. "The Army sure knows how to thump the tub," he said. He brought her hand up to his lips and kissed it.

"May I see those clippings?" Logan asked, self-consciously.

Montrose gave them to him and Logan read them over. They were front-page stories resulting from Army home-town publicity releases. The stories contained information Logan had not known before: Montrose had been personally decorated by the UN and the Baopneng government, and from the United States Army he had received the Distinguished Service Medal.

Logan looked at him with new interest. "That's quite a record, Captain," he said.

Pat said, "He's quite a guy, Mr. Logan."

Logan considered her words. Even if nothing else were accomplished, a photograph of Montrose would be certain to get some newspaper attention, with that record of valor to include in the caption.

"What are your plans now, Captain?" Logan asked. "Are you staying in the Army?"

Montrose shook his head. "No," he said. "I'm on leave now and I'll part company with the Army as soon as the leave is up. I really don't know what I'll do yet. If I had a choice, I'd like to go back to that part of the world as a civilian. There's a tremendous job yet to be done—in all those countries. But it isn't easy to get the funds or the sponsorship. Those poor devils over there need our aid desperately. Whatever I do —and this may sound corny, Mr. Logan—I'd like to be helping them in some small way."

Logan nodded quickly. He looked at his watch. "I wonder if I could prevail upon you two to come out with me to the plant for a little while?"

"What for?" Pat asked.

Logan looked at Montrose. "You said you'd like to thank our people for sending you your supplies. I'd like you to do it too, and meet our president, Mr. McRumen. We could have a picture of you two taken together."

Pat turned a worried face toward Montrose. "I don't think we can, can we, Buddy?"

"Why not?" Logan asked.

Pat looked at him and then back at Montrose. The reticence Logan had seen in her earlier had returned. "Oh, I don't know," she said. "Do you want to, Buddy?"

"Well, I . . ."

"McRumen would certainly appreciate it," said Logan. "You don't have any objection, do you, Pat?"

"It's not an objection really," Pat said. "I guess I don't understand this sort of thing very well. But it seems . . ."

"It's not just publicity," Logan said patiently. "The captain has had an exciting and stirring experience and to some extent my company was involved in it." He looked at Montrose. "What do you say?"

"Well . . . I think I owe you people a great deal." He studied Pat with hopeful eyes. "After all," he said to her in a half-pleading voice, "they did do a lot for me. I think I should."

"I suppose so," she said. She didn't seem at all convinced.

Logan paid the check and stood up. "Won't you come with us?" he asked Pat.

"I'm afraid not, Mr. Logan. Thank you anyway." She shook hands with him. There was no humor in her eyes now. "Thank you for the lovely lunch and good-bye." She turned to Montrose and kissed him lightly on the cheek. "Meet you here at seven." She walked quickly out of the room.

3

"CLOSE THE DOOR," Alonzo Shively said unnecessarily as Horace Blivet allowed it to swing shut with a bang. While Shively stood silently facing the window, the assistant sales manager in charge of advertising padded across the carpet and dropped his paunchy frame into a chair.

"Do you know what I'm looking at, Horace?" Shively said without turning around. Blivet strained to see around his chief, hoping to catch a glimpse of whatever it was.

"No, I don't, Al," he said apologetically.

Shively turned suddenly and pointed a finger at Blivet. The gesture carried a violence that made the advertising man recoil in his chair. "I'm looking at twenty million bucks," Shively said. He came around his desk and sat on the edge, facing Blivet. "Horace," he said warmly, "I said I was looking at twenty million fish and that's exactly what I mean. Twenty million. Maybe more. We're right on top of this boom in happy drugs. Our new product is going to *make* this company."

Blivet nodded enthusiastically.

"Your advertising is going to be more important than it ever has been before. I want to see a campaign that will stand right up and sing, promotion-wise."

"You will, Al. I'll . . ."

"I want to see our natural sales persuasion system succeed in your hands like it never has before. I want you to stay up every night *thinking*. I want to see gimmicks that will pry loose that twenty million in a hurry! Consider everything—radio, television, everything."

"For the doctors?" Blivet said with surprise. "For a drug that's going to be sold only on prescription, why television?"

"I said *consider* it," Shively said. "The idea I have about this product is a gold-plated dream, Horace. There are some bugs that have to be ironed out first and that's all I can tell you now. But you be thinking about the thousands of people who're going to be taking this stuff, not about who's going to give it to them."

"Fine, Al, but nearly everything we sell depends on prescription."

"That's policy, Horace," Shively said, "and you're not paid to worry about policy."

"I'm not worrying, Al. It's just that I'm inclined to be . . ."

"Well, disincline yourself. Just don't let any grass grow in the infield."

Shively walked with him to the door and shook his hand. "There'll be plenty in it for you, Horace. You have a real future as long as you make yourself necessary."

While Shively was stoking the fires of Horace Blivet's imagination, a staff of scientists and laboratory assistants less than a hundred yards distant labored over the new tranquilizer, attempting to correct the last remaining block to Shively's marketing plan. Silently and skillfully they carried out their duties, adjusting torts, tampering with microscopes, examining murky beakers.

Ordinarily, there would have been a running conversation in the laboratory, but now the cotton mask that each technician wore made all but the most necessary conversation troublesome. Periodically one would break away from his work, step quickly into the hallway outside the laboratory, and sag against the glass, breathing deeply. It was not sterile conditions that fatigued the laboratory workers, for their work was not performed under sterile conditions. Neither was it the threat of any dangerous contamination from the drug or any of the other chemicals they handled. It was the odor of phitherdimethyldine solution which drove them into the unpolluted air of the corridor.

Dr. Garibaldi had tried to talk of troubles with the drug in the meeting, but Alonzo Shively wouldn't have it. Potency, stability and color were all right; it was up to the research people to correct the smell.

The appalling odor of the new drug did not reveal itself until the powder was first put into solution. When it had been sold by Raven as an antihistamine, it had been safely sealed in tiny gelatin capsules. Dry, the hidden compound was nearly odorless. Wet, the exposed chemical took on the heavy fragrance of yak sweat in the spring.

Diligently the staff persisted in testing every chemical masking agent known to the pharmaceutical industry, but so far the assault on the olfactory system by Raven's new tranquilizer was undiminished.

Alonzo Shively's response was emphatic. The success of his plan depended on a compound free of disagreeable odor in any form, and he swore he would draw blood if the scientists didn't fix it fast.

CAPTAIN MONTROSE took a chair near Joe Logan's desk and studied the prints and photographs framed on the wall. "That the man we're going to meet?" He nodded toward the portrait of Lloyd McRumen.

"Right," Joe said. "And the old fellow with the whiskers is the founder, Ravenal Raven. He sold purgatives to the Army during the Spanish-American War." He pressed the buzzer for his secretary. "Raven's kept a lot of armies regular since then."

Emily Klinger appeared in the doorway and waited. Her eyes settled on the officer.

"Emily, this is Captain Montrose," Logan said.

"Yes, I know," she answered absently, her eyes still on the captain.

"Will you please get the president's office on the telephone for me?" Logan said.

"We've been waiting to meet you for a long time, Captain." Emily smiled at Montrose.

He mumbled an acknowledgment. She didn't move. "Emily," Logan said sharply. "The president's office." The girl nodded quickly and backed out of the room.

Logan smiled apologetically at Captain Montrose. "I don't think she ever saw an Army officer before," he said, waiting with one hand on the telephone.

Only two pieces of paper were evident on Lloyd McRumen's desk. One was a copy of the *Daily News,* turned to the page containing Eugene Carson's annoying column.

The other, which he held in his hand, was a copy of the current issue of *Business Fortnight.* It was turned to an article bylined "Lloyd R. Mc-Rumen, President, Raven Pharmaceuticals, Inc." The first paragraph read, "The pharmaceutical industry has become a symbol in modern America, taking its stand beside other symbols posed by other institutions from our past. Its medicines and drugs in two decades have revolutionized the medical history of man. That revolution is not yet over; it has, indeed, only begun. This is what gives the pharmaceutical industry its symbolic position in our worried world. A people beset with fears and anxieties and troubles looks on it now as the source of its hope."

Lloyd McRumen read through the article a second time. He was pleased with it, and the pleasure would easily have sustained him through the day if he had not been presented with grave problems.

He was deeply disturbed about the impending Senate industry investigation. Glancing distastefully at the folded newspaper, he wished that the new tranquilizer were already safely launched and the unpleasant business of the Senate hearings a thing of the past.

A figure was emblazoned across his mind, a dollar figure which had only become a reality that morning: $1,500,000. It was the sum he had tentatively approved for Shively's promotion of phitherdimethyldine. "It's only a budget," the sales vice-president had said. "Before we're through, we'll spend at least that to move this product." Lloyd McRumen was used to thinking in millions but not when it came to a promotional budget for one product. The combined costs of Raven's current advertising and promotion for all the company's products added up to less than what Shively wanted for the tranquilizer.

Ultimately the amount would have to be approved by the directors, of course, and McRumen also knew that Alonzo Shively could do a good job of justifying such an expenditure to the board. But what if it were a mistake? A seven-digit blunder? It could cause the loss of a year's profits.

Shively's sales talk would not alone convince the board. McRumen's sanction would have to be on it. Indeed, final responsibility for the expenditure would be his, not Shively's. Suppose it *did* backfire?

Shively had given the president an answer. "You'd be in worse trouble if we missed a crack at that market," he had said. "Remember Diettes, Lloyd? That cost us plenty."

His reminder left a bitter current in Lloyd McRumen's thoughts.

Diettes had been a hot-shot, sure-fire, plush-profit, cellulose reducing biscuit made from sawdust, which Shively wanted to market. McRumen's refusal to buy it for Raven's ethical product line had outraged the ever-pressing Shively. Placebo Laboratories bought it then, and through clever merchandising and sharp selling, had made enormous profits. Shively had never let him forget it. Shively had a better eye for estimating a market than the president. Sometimes it appeared as if his sales intuition was almost prescience.

The phone rang sharply and McRumen almost answered it, without waiting for his secretary. Sometimes, in moments of stress, he was likely to forget some of the subtleties which distinguished his position. He pushed the intercom button and waited impatiently for his secretary's buzz. When it came he picked up the phone and listened.

"Mr. Logan," she said.

McRumen switched another button and said, "Yes, Joe."

"I know you're busy this afternoon, Mr. McRumen," Logan's voice said, "but I wondered if I could snare about fifteen minutes of your time."

"What's up, Joe?" McRumen asked.

"I have an Army officer here," Logan said, "a Captain Montrose . . ." Logan described briefly who Montrose was and the circumstances of his visit. "I've got the photographer lined up and I think it would be a good idea to get a picture of you two together in your office."

McRumen tried to put a frown in his voice. "You know how I personally feel about things like this, Joe," he said. "But then, I have to leave them to your judgment."

"Yes, sir," Logan said. "Well, I think this is important. We can be over there in a few minutes if that will be convenient."

"All right, Joe." McRumen hung up, his feeling of satisfaction returning. Logan was a good man. He knew the value of good publicity. The president put aside his reading matter and prepared to receive him.

Lloyd McRumen had come to Raven twenty-seven years earlier from Passaic, New Jersey, where his father had run a drug store. Lloyd attended pharmacy college when it was still a two-year course and when he graduated, he went to work in the family business. It was there, behind the prescription counter, that he was spotted as a comer by the local Raven representative. A week later he was hired as a member of Raven's sales staff.

By 1945 Lloyd McRumen had become vice-president in charge of sales, and two years later, following a fatal presidential coronary, he was elected president. As president, he replaced the outdated don't-worry-the-family-will-take-care-of-you philosophy with the more progressive Raven team spirit.

With the success that came to Lloyd McRumen came the mixed blessing of Alonzo Shively as well. The new president regarded his sales chief as one of the keenest executives he had ever known, and he considered himself fortunate for having brought him into the organization to direct a shiny new sales philosophy which complemented McRumen's own program of expanding plant facilities and recruiting dedicated chemists, biologists, pharmacologists, physicians, engineers and technicians. Sales, profits and the price of Raven stock reflected the company's vigor and optimism. Raven became the world's largest manufacturer of vermifuges; ringworms, pinworms, flatworms, cutworms and glowworms all fell before their marvelously potent miracle drugs.

McRumen considered his meeting with Joe Logan to be one of the most fortuitous events in his life. Logan had come out on assignment from a news magazine to do a profile on him, and when he saw the portrait of himself that emerged from Logan's typewriter he hired him to take over Raven's newly formed public relations department. For Lloyd McRumen, immensely proud of himself, but having felt the sting of Shively's ambitious whip, was for the first time in ten years unsure of his grand design for the future. He was eager to become a public figure, and not at all certain how to go about it. In Logan, he saw a way.

He was right. In two years the name McRumen appeared frequently over such articles as "The Cultural Necessity of Business" and "Personnel Problems Aren't Necessary." He had in fact been so impressed by the public personality Logan had developed for him that in every way possible he attempted to live up to it. The effect in many respects had been to elevate him to a state of conscious dignity which many of his old friends and enemies within the company hardly recognized.

The first thing McRumen thought about Captain Montrose when he saw him was that if ever he had had a son, he would have wanted one like this. He immediately liked the officer's appearance, his manner and his attitude.

While the photographer stood in a corner making adjustments on his camera, Montrose and Logan took chairs near McRumen's desk at the president's invitation.

"So you know a little about our company already, do you, Captain?" McRumen asked.

"I think I know a great deal about it, sir," Montrose replied.

McRumen smiled at him fondly. "And you give a good report on us, eh?"

"Yes, sir." Montrose searched for the words to express himself. "I don't really know how to say this without making it seem awkward," he said finally, "but all my life I have said I believed in a system. We call it the American way. I've said I believed in it without really knowing how it works. But now I know. I've seen it work, and it was one of the most thrilling experiences of my life. And it is your company, sir, that gave me that rare experience. That's why I'm grateful."

"You do us a great honor," McRumen said, his voice unsure. "And coming from someone who has had your experience . . ." He let the words hang unfinished.

Montrose's gaze was fixed out the window behind the president's desk. "What I—experienced is not really important, Mr. McRumen," he said quietly. "When a whole nation is in torment, when something as vital as the cause of freedom itself is threatened, one man's experience is hardly important."

Suddenly the subject of their discussion seemed to be an enormously bigger one than that which had sprung up so easily just a few minutes before. It was as if, once Montrose had planted it, it grew with a will and a life of its own. The issue was no longer Raven, although Raven was part of it. The issue was made now of finer stuff. It involved freedom and it involved humanity.

Lloyd McRumen had dedicated the recent years of his life to the proposition that he was personally bound up in great causes, but he had never been able to surrender himself completely to that belief—until now. Under his encouragement, Montrose began to talk at length, telling them where he had been and what he had seen.

The slim captain's face was taut and controlled, and as his story took possession of him and he became only the agent of its release, his words lost their halting quality. His voice became confident and forceful.

He told them how he, an inexperienced junior officer who in college had studied the theories of the political systems men live by, had suddenly found himself caught up in some of the brutal realities behind the theories. Standing in the crossfire of conflicting civilizations, he had been deposited at a moment of crisis into a position of awesome responsibility.

"The people of Baopneng had known nothing but privation and want all their lives," he said. "And yet the urge to live free struggled inside them as it has struggled inside all men for centuries. Because it was strong, stronger even than the hunger which bloated their bellies, they were determined to escape the Reds. And more often than not, they had to literally fight their way out in the process—truce or no truce. I went there to help them—to tell them that freedom was just over the parallel if they could make it. They needed that help, for they are simple people and they haven't yet grasped the fact that the minds of human beings can be manipulated."

Montrose stopped and lit a cigarette. Logan's and McRumen's eyes never left him. The photographer in the corner of the room had quietly put his camera aside and was intently watching the captain.

Montrose inhaled deeply on his cigarette and then continued. "I grew half a lifetime in those few months. You know the story. Disease broke out and spread like lava over a people who had already suffered as men should never be forced to suffer. And there was I, a stranger in their midst, a witness to their agony. They were suspicious of me. Sure, why shouldn't they be? I was the only American they had ever seen, and the Communists' propaganda about Americans and the UN had spread far and persuasively."

The captain paused again and looked directly into McRumen's eyes. "You can see what happened. History made a symbol of me. I was America—*I* was America, gentlemen—standing unwanted amid a people in deep trouble. What was I to do?" His hand described a helpless arc in the air. "I did what I had to do. You got my appeal for supplies and you responded. And when those supplies came I went from hut to hut and I convinced them that this would give them new life. I told them this was America, this was American aid, this was the tangible proof of the love my nation had for them. It was—well, it was a selling job. It had to be. I'm no salesman, but I had to become one. I had to sell America to people who had never heard the word before except as part of a curse. I sat with them in the dirt in front of their hovels and I had your medicine in my hand and I took it myself to remove their fears. Finally, in hut after stinking hut, the mask of hostility slowly slipped away—and we were brothers. This went on for weeks, until the epidemic was over and the stench of sickness lifted from the valley. By the time I left them, our brotherhood had grown into something as splendid as I have ever felt or ever will again."

The buzzer on McRumen's desk rang. Its noise was as offensive and unwelcome as a rude remark. Reluctantly Lloyd McRumen moved his fingers to flick the button but he waited several seconds before speaking into the box. Tears stood unashamed in his eyes and he was not sure he could trust himself to speak.

His secretary's voice came through the machine. "Mr. Shively is on the line, Mr. McRumen."

"Yes," he said. He flicked the button again and sat looking heavily at the space in front of him.

Logan excused himself and stepped out of McRumen's office.

When the president finished talking with Shively and put the telephone down, his secretary buzzed him once more. With a trace of irritation he retrieved the receiver.

"Yes?"

"Excuse me, Mr. McRumen," she said quietly, "but Mr. Logan would like you to step into the outer office. He says it is very important."

"Yes," he said into the telephone. "I'll come right out." There was a force in his deep and thoughtful immobility as he turned a grave face to Montrose. "Captain," he said solemnly, "I wonder if you will wait here for me a moment."

"Certainly, sir," Montrose said.

"Thank you. I won't be long." The president rose heavily from his desk and walked toward the door.

The instant McRumen closed the door on Montrose, Joe caught the president's arm and gently held it. Logan had never seen him so moved as he was during the captain's talk. It was a sobering sight and one which had stimulated Logan's imaginative mind.

"Sorry to get you out here, sir," he said quickly, "but something important occurred to me in there." The idea, as he unfolded it to McRumen, took on shape and meaning. "The captain," he said, "is a compelling speaker. He has a story to tell and a way of telling it that will make people listen. He's already a hero though the general public have never heard of him. But *we* could put him on a nation-wide personal appearance tour and see that story reach a lot of people."

McRumen looked at Logan curiously. "I don't see . . ." he began.

"In the process," Logan said, choosing his words carefully and looking directly at the president, "he could help to give us just the kind of institutional publicity we need to break the ground for that new tranquilizer."

Lloyd McRumen's expression held a doubtful frown. "Well—I don't know, Joe. The captain only came out here to thank us. It seems as if . . ."

"He's getting out of the Army and has no immediate plans," Logan said. "We'd never find a better ambassador. It's a great story, Mr. McRumen. Raven would be performing a real public service in many ways."

"You're right there," the president said. "I'd like to see it spread. But I'm not sure we could consider . . ."

"It's the American way in action," Logan told him. "And he certainly wouldn't do or say anything that wasn't in keeping with what we've already heard from him. Just that. The Raven mention in something as powerful as his tale would be worth a thousand pages of advertising anywhere."

McRumen thoughtfully stroked his chin. "That's not publicity we're trying to buy, Joe. It's just the result of the bread we cast upon the waters."

"Maybe we *can* buy it, Mr. McRumen. Maybe this time we can." He lit a cigarette, carefully looking into the flame of the match. "It wouldn't do us any harm before that Senate hearing either. I don't know whether you remember, but Captain Montrose is engaged to Senator Crain's daughter."

The president's eyes showed quick interest before he looked away from Logan. "That throws a different light on it," McRumen said. "I'm not sure I like it."

"That would really be beside the point, though," Logan hedged. "The real reasons would be for public service and the enhancement of Raven's reputation. Just as he was the symbol of America out there in Baopneng, Raven is the symbol of free enterprise at work for the public good."

"I like that idea," McRumen said. He repeated Joe's symbolic designation of Raven to himself and nodded thoughtfully.

Logan could see that he had finally found the responsive chord he was after, and he knew that McRumen's thoughts now were moving quickly along with his own.

"Do you think he'd want to do it?" the president asked.

"We could find out easily enough," Logan said. "It would be a fine opportunity for him, as well as for us. He could be big, if he's used the right way."

"You think this could be big, eh?"

"Yes, sir, I certainly do. That boy's got something. Believe me, I can tell."

"Maybe you're right, Joe," the president said slowly. "Certainly I agree with you that he is magnificent. But I wouldn't want to make a decision on it without Al Shively's opinion. For that matter I'd like to hear what some of the others have to say too."

"Let's get everyone together now," Logan proposed. "And let's ask the captain to talk to them—tell them just what he told us." McRumen thought about it for a moment, and then began to nod slowly. Joe turned to the secretary. "Pass the word. Conference room. Immediately."

Captain Montrose was standing at the window when Logan and the president stepped back into McRumen's office.

"Captain," Logan said, "do you suppose you could take another half-hour to tell some of our people the story you told us?"

"Now?" Montrose asked.

"Now."

"Well, sure," said Montrose, "if you want me to."

McRumen beamed at Captain Montrose and motioned the waiting photographer to begin his work.

Emily Klinger missed two or three sentences of Captain Montrose's speech more than once. There were times when she simply had to stop and daub the corners of her eyes or look longingly at the speaker. Most of it she got, however, and when she went over her notes, the shorthand characters came alive with the stirring words of the young officer.

"America was my market basket," he said. "With every drop of precious drugs that came from you generous people, the flame of life, the spark of hope was kept alive a little longer in those desperate souls. . . ."

Alonzo Shively leaned over to Logan. "That guy's *terrific*," he whispered.

"What do you think, Al? Can we use him?"

"Use him? Hell, yes, we can use him."

"Captain," Lloyd McRumen said, moving his chair back, "if you will join me in my office for a moment . . ." Captain Montrose smiled obligingly and left the table.

When the two were gone, Logan addressed the group of assembled executives. "We are going to ask the captain if he will consider a lecture tour if no one objects. I think he is—just the man for us."

The group was embarrassed by Logan's words, all except Shively. The intense sincerity of Captain Montrose had gripped them. Now the suggestion that this straightforward young man be used as an instrument for company advantage disturbed some of them.

Logan sensed this and continued, "I think it would be worthwhile doing this even apart from the obvious publicity we'll get. As you can see, Captain Montrose is a real hero. He isn't famous but he deserves some recognition for what he's done, even though he would be the last one to ask for it. He has a story that people should hear. We could make this possible."

He had given them their rationale, and now they were able to endorse it—most of them—enthusiastically.

When the meeting broke up, Ambrose Garibaldi approached Logan before he got to McRumen's office. "Are you sure you want to use this captain, Joe?" he asked. "He seems like a nice guy."

"Hell, Doc, we'll be giving him his big chance."

"What about the Army? Will they let him?"

"He's getting out of the Army."

"I don't know," Garibaldi said. "I'm afraid this boy might get the hell exploited out of him. The look on Shively scares me. On you, too, for that matter."

"Relax, Doc. Take one of those pills I've been hearing about." Logan gave him a slap on the shoulder and went into McRumen's office.

Logan spelled out the lecture-tour plan while McRumen smiled benevolently. Montrose was overwhelmed. He dropped into the chair by McRumen's desk. "Is it that important?" he asked.

"My boy," McRumen said, "you don't know how important it is."

Without warning, Logan found himself thinking of Pat Crain, wondering if he could manage any time alone with her. After all, a girl like that should not be allowed to wander in and out of a man's life all in the course of a lunch hour.

5

EMILY KLINGER drew deeply on her cigarette and looked toward the ceiling of the pastel powder room Raven provided for its office girls.

"You just never heard a man like that," she said. "I mean you really haven't."

Doris Krause extracted a comb and lipstick case from her purse. "I've heard 'em all," she said shortly.

"Not this one. He had me practically crying."

"That must of been a panic. Is he cute?"

"A doll," Emily said. "God, everybody was bowled over."

Doris grunted. "Not Shively. I'll bet on that."

"Oh, yes, everyone. Shively too."

"He must be a snake charmer then. No one ever gets him to calm down long enough to listen."

"Captain Montrose came all the way from Asia, you know. He cured a whole epidemic or something. Those people had nobody to turn to, so they turned to him and he helped them."

"He sounds like a hot-air artist to me," Doris said.

Emily looked at her in disgust and angrily stubbed out her cigarette. "That's a very intelligent thing to say and anyone can tell you know all about it. *I* think he's very *savoir faire*."

"Well, calm down, for God sakes. I was only kidding. Are you stuck on this character or something?"

"Will you just shut up, Doris? Will you do that, please? He just happens to be a highly intelligent person, that's all. But if people want to make smart cracks about it, that's their business."

"All right. All *right. God.*" Doris pulled her comb through a lock of metallic blond hair.

"I mean you don't meet someone like that every day," Emily said. "Not around here."

"You're right there, anyway," Doris said. "These old goats." She tugged viciously at the comb. "You haven't got it so bad though. I'd settle for him."

"Who? Logan? He's all right, I guess."

"Don't gimme that," Doris said.

"You're very funny, Doris, you know that? You really are. What about you and Shively? I don't see him making any big play for you."

"Sure, Shively. He'd be some prize all right." Doris laboriously traced her mouth with a purple-red lipstick and grimaced, watching herself in the mirror. "By the time he gets out of here at night, he wouldn't be worth taking on." She snapped her purse shut. "Back to the sweatshop. What are you going to do about your dream man?"

Emily exhaled her breath in an exasperated sigh. "I'm not going to do *any*thing. Good Lord."

"Well, just remember to watch those smooth talkers, honey. They're tricky." Doris left, closing the door behind her. Emily moved to the dressing table and sat looking at herself in the mirror. Carefully, deliberately, she relaxed her frown, replacing it slowly with a smile. She moved her lips. "Tonight?" she said softly. "Why, I think I can make it. I'd *love* to, Captain."

When Logan and Montrose finally left Lloyd McRumen's office it was nearly six o'clock. "I'll drop you off at your hotel," Logan said. "I don't want to be responsible for having you late meeting your girl."

"That's not until seven," Montrose said. "Why don't you have a drink with us?"

"I suspect she's seen about as much of me today as she's going to want to," Logan said.

"We're not going to be alone at first, anyway. Patty's father is going to have dinner with us. Wouldn't you like to meet him?"

"I sure would." While Logan hailed a taxi and they waited for it to pull up alongside them, he deliberated. His sense of propriety, which told him he should not intrude upon another meeting between Montrose and Pat, was not much of a match for his desire to meet Senator Barton Crain. "I'll stick around just long enough to say hello. Then I'll have to take off," he said.

Montrose sat quietly as the cab weaved through traffic on its way into the city. Logan thought Montrose was looking not so much into the stream of cars as into the hazy but exciting shadows of a new self-portrait that had begun to grow in his mind.

"There's one thing, Captain, that I haven't told you about," Joe Logan finally said. "It's not very important, but it involves Senator Crain, so you probably should know about it." He outlined the investigation briefly. "Your relationship with the senator might seem to complicate it in your mind, but I hope it doesn't. There really isn't any connection. What you'll be doing for us won't compromise the senator's work in any way because they're two separate areas." He stopped and lit a cigarette casually.

"It doesn't sound as if it would be much of a problem," Montrose said finally. "I'll check it out with him, of course."

"Fine." Logan smiled wryly to himself. The world had not changed. The predictable world was still predictable. "Now, let's talk." During the rest of the taxi ride and against the exaggerated plush of the hotel bar, he described what he had in mind for Montrose's immediate future. "The way I visualize it, we can keep you moving for about three months."

"I don't want to sound naïve," Montrose said, "but I can't help wondering just what good all this will do you."

"If you tell your story to enough people, some of the good feeling it generates rubs off on us," Logan said. "The Raven name, if repeated and repeated this way, becomes synonymous with God, flag and country. That's what we get out of it."

There was a thoughtful silence and then Montrose said, "And how do you know this will work? With me, I mean, in enough places."

"This kind of a build-up is no hit or miss, Captain. We start small and feel our way. We move carefully with the pulse of the people but we pick up speed. And before you know it everyone has heard the Buddy Montrose story one way or another—and they've heard of Raven."

"It all sounds pretty scientific," Montrose said.

"You're damn near right," Logan said. "The more earnest among the public relations fraternity like to be known as practitioners. It's the newest profession, you know, and except for the scientific part, it's got a lot in common with the oldest."

"Then we're on our way," Montrose said.

"We are indeed." Logan looked at Montrose closely. "One thing should bother me, I guess. But it doesn't, somehow. I'm assuming you can tell this story five or six nights a week—maybe even more."

"Well, I can try," Montrose said hesitantly.

"Sure you can. You'll do fine. You've just got to keep from getting tired of it yourself. That's all. Give it the same schmaltz each time." Montrose said nothing. "Don't get upset if I sound flippant," Logan added.

"Of course not," Montrose said.

"I'm not, really. It's all part of the game."

"Sure. Hell, I probably sound like a broken record anyway. All us save-the-world types do." He smiled awkwardly again. "It's kind of a new role for me."

"That right?"

"I always figured that the part of the world worth saving would save itself." Montrose turned a cigarette slowly in his fingers, watching the smoke curl upward. "Maybe I still do, but . . ." He stopped abruptly and looked at Logan. "You ever been in the Far East?"

Joe nodded. "Island-hopping during the war. Japan for a few months after."

"Then you know the Oriental idea—that you'd better be damn sure you know what you're getting into when you help anyone in trouble. In the act of helping you begin an association that carries a lifetime contract." Logan nodded. "Well, make that fifty, and a hundred, then several hundred, and pretty soon you turn in your wisdom for a missionary's zeal. Before I go to sleep now I've got to say good night to a whole army of scared hungry faces that crowd in on me. They're still waiting out there. And I'm damned if I can help it."

Logan continued to watch the captain, without comment. He felt a sensation not common to him, and he recognized it, in surprise, as shame. The captain was as intense as most evangelists, but Logan was forced to acknowledge that he had guts and he had sincerity, and the combination of the two was intimidating.

Suddenly Montrose became aware of the hour and jumped up. Logan followed him and paid the check.

"Incidentally," Montrose said as they moved out to the main lobby, "if you don't mind, I'd just as soon not say anything to the Crains now about this arrangement. I'd prefer to tell them later, when I can explain it in detail."

Joe nodded. "Whatever you say, Buddy."

Like most members who have served two terms in the world's most exclusive gentlemen's club, Senator Crain had a look of deliberate and well-cultivated dignity about him. He carried his tall frame with easy grace. He greeted Montrose, whom he had not seen since the captain's return, with enthusiasm, grasping him firmly by both arms.

"My boy, it's good to see you—skinny as you are," he said, fixing his eyes on Montrose's face. "Pat, we're going to have to put a couple of pounds back on him at dinner tonight." He chucked Montrose good-naturedly in the ribs.

Pat Crain, smiling beside her father, introduced him to Logan. The senator took Joe's outstretched hand.

"Mr. Logan is a public relations man," Pat explained, "with the Raven pharmaceutical company."

"Oh, yes." The grin was still there, but Logan saw the eyes in the senator's expansive face become a trifle more cautious. The senatorial wheels, he thought, are turning fast. *Raven. Vermifuges. Where are they on our list?*

"His company, you remember, sir," Montrose said, "is the one that sent me the drugs after I wrote you."

"Oh, yes." The words came slower this time and they had a different ring. Crain looked at Joe carefully, measuring him. "That was a generous gesture," he said. "I wrote your president to that effect."

"I know," Joe said. "He treasures the letter. I think he has a sneaking hope it will be the last he gets from you for a while."

The senator laughed heartily. "It's easy to see why they've got you doing their public relations," he said.

"Let's talk over dinner," Pat said. "I'm starved."

Senator Crain looked at his watch. "You all go on ahead," he said. "I'll join you a little later."

Pat frowned. "I thought you were going to have dinner with us."

"Of course I am," the senator answered. "I've got a small appointment to keep first, that's all. It won't take long. I'll catch up with you before you've finished your soup."

Logan waited until the senator was gone, and then he left too.

He bought two newspapers and began walking briskly uptown. He was relieved to be alone finally. Another half-hour, he thought, and he might have tried making a pass at Pat Crain, and that would have complicated things nicely. It would also have been a fine way to start life with Montrose, who had managed to leave a strong impression of his own. Logan hailed a taxi and had the driver drop him at a bar, a block from his apartment.

He spread his newspapers out at one end of the bar as the bartender mixed a Scotch and water. Logan was accustomed to visiting the bar with some regularity during the early hour before dinner or for a nightcap.

He scanned the pages of the papers and sipped at his Scotch, but this evening he found it hard to concentrate on the news. His thoughts were racing back over the day, sorting out those facts that his perception told him would be important in the weeks and months to come, returning again and again to the two persons he had just left in the lobby of the Dorwick Arms.

Why, he thought with some resentment, had they had so forceful an effect on him? Envy? Perhaps. Their relationship appeared to be one that Logan had long ago decided did not in truth exist, at least for him. But it would not be only that. Maybe it had something to do with the kind of person Montrose was. Perhaps relationships of value were possible only for men like Montrose, who were able to bring to them what certainly seemed to be undevious sincerity along with their enthusiasms.

A contradiction in terms, thought Joseph H. Logan, looking into the dark street beyond the broad window of the bar. There is no such thing as undevious sincerity.

Logan needed his faith in his own evaluations and he wanted no intrusion of ideas that would mock them or make them hollow. His evaluations were not ones he had picked up lightly or for the advantage they gave him over most people. They resulted from conditioned reflexes that the events of his life had awarded him. They were the scar tissue of experience, of the man on the prowl, the searcher satisfied only with the tenuous belief that what he sought did not exist, the emotional vagrant, building a vagrant's defense.

The vagabondage had begun thirty-three years before, in a well-fed, well-scrubbed normal time. His mother taught him life in Bible terms and his father put calluses on his hands with a hay rake, but Joe Logan derived his sustenance largely from dreams. He learned some lessons in the district schoolhouse and others behind it, from farm girls older than himself. In the reading room of the county lending library he nourished his imagination. By the time Joe entered high school, depression and dust had settled over Nebraska, and his father, who had pitted his unbending faith against the harsh judgment of nature, retired bankrupt and bitter, too subdued by his own misfortune to care what happened to his sons.

Joe's physical strength came to him early and before he had reached his eighteenth year he followed his older brother into the oil fields of Oklahoma to learn a new set of economic rules: two dollars bought a Texas whore and three made her come alive; roughnecking on a drilling rig brought more in a month than his father had taken from his last year's grinding labor on his crops.

College was not easy or consistent. He went to classes spasmodically and he learned the trade of news reporting on a string of Midwest dailies. He studied literature and read about the war until 1944, when, two courses short of his degree, he found himself in the Pacific, with corporal's stripes stenciled on his sleeves. He spent a sultry Christmas in the Philippines, considering his future and realizing that the only future he cared about was that which he would wake to in the morning. Nothing during the grim advance on Okinawa in the last paroxysmal months of fighting ever changed his mind.

After the war Logan got his degree, found a job with the Associated Press in Kansas City and took time out to go home for his father's funeral in Nebraska. Restlessness, the last symptom of his ragged dreams, finally drove him to New York. It continued to drive him after he got there, hounding him into success and the point of view that had become his only real comfort.

Joe folded his newspapers and pushed them aside. The need to move on stirred strongly in him now, as it always did when his defenses were assaulted. Dropping a bill on the bar, he walked out and turned in the direction of his apartment. He was not in a hurry and he had no particular place in mind for dinner. He had made the turn toward the apartment house from habit and now he walked, a prosperous, rootless vagrant such as only this American century could produce.

Senator Crain made his way to the men's bar downstairs, where Alden Root was waiting for him. The conference was an inconvenience and an intrusion, particularly at this hour. But Root had said it was the only time available to him, and after a man had traveled halfway across the country, he was entitled to a few minutes. The senator nervously looked at his watch. By God, it *would* be just a few minutes, too; he had planned to have dinner with Pat and her young man, and he was not going to change his plans for Alden Root, no matter how difficult he became. And Root would become difficult, Crain had no doubt of that. The very fact that he was in New York was evidence enough of the importance he attached to the delicate problem involving the support of one of the state's congressmen coming up for reëlection. So far as Crain could see, the disagreement between them on the matter was so complete, there was no point in any discussion at all. It was delicate only because Root, as a party force, had the power to make things difficult or easy.

Alden Root was a man who preferred to live in shadows. He was short, fat, and expensively untidy. He carried a surface heartiness which to the undiscerning eye masked the stern seriousness of his every thought and move.

No man feared him, but many in Indiana stood in awe of him. In thirty-odd years he had built a substantial personal power plant within his political party, and before that, he had made his fortune in real estate. Without ever holding office himself, he had managed to group under his wing much of the eager money in the party, and his voice was strong in councils he never had to visit. He lived alone in a Spartan suite in the Mainline Hotel in Midwest City, and he made his office in an overstuffed lobby chair. Only in matters of the most urgent importance—situations which carried in them a threat to the importance of Alden Root—did he find it necessary to venture far from the hotel. Whenever such an occasion arose he did not hesitate to move, but the strain it imposed on his jovial presence was severe.

It was such an urgency which brought him on a lurching Pullman to New York City to meet Senator Crain, and he was having some trouble keeping his face set in the happy frame expected of a fat man.

"Well, Bart, see you're making the papers these days," Root said when they had ordered a drink.

The senator smiled. "You're a voracious reader, Alden."

"That's a mighty shrewd idea, taking the drug industry apart. Lots of public sympathy."

"Actually," Crain said, "the investigation wasn't started to take anything apart. It's just a fact-finding exercise."

"Sure, I know, but looking like a crusader won't do you no harm," Root said. His flaccid cheeks rolled into a sly smile. "Look what it did for Kefauver and McClellan." He waited a moment without taking his eyes from Senator Crain. Then he said, "Now, Bart, about this little problem of ours . . ."

"I'm sorry you came all the way east to talk this Lockridge thing over, Alden. I told you in my letter why I can't go along with you."

"I know what your letter said." Root's eyes, too small for his fleshy face, focused intently upon his companion. "It was my hope that you'd change your mind."

"Alden, listen." The senator's voice was patient. "There isn't any reason why I should go back on my word to support Lockridge again. He's one of the best congressmen our party ever had. The people like him. They vote for him. They want to see . . ."

"There's this thing called loyalty, Bart." The voice, when deliberately kept low, had an unpleasant rasping quality.

"Loyalty, of course," Crain said. "But you can hardly call this a test of . . ."

"Yes I can," Root cut in sharply. "I made a simple request of him. The Midwest City postmastership. He refused. If that's not a test of loyalty, what is?"

"Damn it, Alden!" the senator said. "This man you wanted Lockridge to give the postmastership to is already in tax trouble with the government."

"The point is—I *promised* that job. And after I did, it was up to Lockridge to follow through for me. Midwest City wouldn't know the difference, or care. They've had worse men in the Post Office."

"He doesn't think so," the senator said quietly, "and neither do I."

"Well *I* do, by God. We've had a nice balance in the organization up to this point, but something like this could upset it forever. If I don't deliver on the promises I make, I might as well close up shop. And I don't think you'd like that any more than Lockridge would, Bart."

"I'm sorry, Alden, if that's the way you look at it," Crain said. "I can't change my position now."

Root clamped his teeth firmly on his cigar.

Senator Crain looked at his watch. "I don't have much time, Alden," he said. "My daughter's having dinner with her young man and they're expecting me."

Root nodded. "The soldier boy? I read about him."

"I'm late now," Crain said. "I suppose you want to pursue this later."

"No use, unless you're going to change your mind."

The senator's face flushed. He was standing now and he leaned forward and placed the flat of one hand on the table. "God damn it, Alden, this time you're wrong."

"Relax, *Senator,*" Root said slowly. His inflection carried the suggestion of a taunt. "And just remember that I'm not wrong very often."

"Alden, I'm a fair and reasonable man and there isn't anything I won't do for party harmony. But you should remember something else, too: Lockridge is the party choice. That's what he deserves. I'm going to back him. I think you'll be there yourself when the heads are counted."

"Don't push me, Bart," Root rasped.

"I'm not trying to," Senator Crain said, straightening himself and looking down upon Alden Root. He was struggling to keep his anger under control, but his voice was tight. "Before the primaries come along, I hope you'll decide that you're going to support Lockridge too, because that's the only decent choice any of us have. And it's the only way we can avoid a party fight."

Root looked at him silently. Then, without rising, without offering his hand, he said, "Good-bye, Bart."

"Good-bye, Alden." The senator turned and left the bar.

Crain's anger did not quickly subside and he paused in the lobby before joining his daughter and Buddy Montrose. He knew that a core of hard feelings would remain with Root, and he cursed the man's monstrous self-interest, which had led to the construction of the problem in the first place. Root did not forgive easily and there was no particular reservoir of good will between the two men which could be drawn upon to close the distance between their positions. They had never been close associates, however perfectly their separate political operations meshed.

Crain's anger had sought a deeper level and centered upon himself. He had been firm as he had intended to be, but he had also been apologetic. He had tempered his responses, and now he resented the tempering, which could only be construed as compromise. Had he followed his impulses he would have told Root precisely what he thought of his position. But he had not. Instead he had followed his political sense in not shutting Root out completely, knowing that to do so would only provoke more difficulty than already existed.

Crain knew that Alden Root had no discernible philosophy of government. He rarely took a stand on anything if it could be avoided. In his great shabby chair in the Mainline Hotel he plotted the strategy of local campaigns, receiving and dispatching unidentified subordinates behind a cloud of cigar smoke. And always there was the knowledge that he tailored opinion and sentiment to fit demand. Even those who did not trust him, even Bart Crain, had long ago come to respect first his perspicacity and then his power—indeed, in time, to depend on them while pretending not to.

The senator knew that therein lay the seeds of trouble, if trouble ever came. He and others like him in the party were grateful to him for taking over the pettier tasks and responsibilities that held a political organization together. If out of these tasks Root fashioned a personal power, the effect was beneficial to men like Crain, leaving them free to concentrate on their jobs in the government.

Until now, the balance Root had spoken of had worked well. This

was the first time it had ever been necessary for Senator Crain to disagree
with him openly, and the senator could not ignore the discomforting
realization that in Alden Root he might one day find a formidable op-
ponent.

Root's power was undisputed, but a United States Senator was not without considerable power himself, and if it ever came to a showdown,
Barton Crain could bring to bear enormous weight in the party. But with
the pressures of the current congressional session and the drug industry
investigation close upon him, he profoundly resented Root's intrusion of
infighting at home.

Root had been half-right in calling Crain's attention to the public
support he had found when the drug industry investigation began. Crain
himself had been aware from the beginning that such a crusade would be
valuable to him politically. But there was another motivating element in
it as well, which Alden Root would never believe, much less understand.
The senator had first become interested in America's pharmaceutical industry when he studied appropriations for the armed forces medical services. When he questioned what appeared to be excessive sums spent for
medicines, he found the government was actually getting few bargains
and in some cases was forced to pay prices far in excess of accountable
production cost and reasonable profit. His staff noted that penicillin,
upon which no one had a patent, had dropped to less than 1/100th of its
original cost in little more than a decade, while the more widely effective
broad-spectrum antibiotics, all of which were patented, consistently held
exorbitant prices. As taxpayers or consumers, the American public paid
a high price for its health.

The subcommittee had little in mind at the inception of the investigation beyond an examination of government purchasing policies, but as
evidence of industrial irresponsibility and self-interest accumulated, it
now was considering legislative recommendations which would impose
severe restrictions on obvious profiteering practices within the pharmaceutical industry. Barton Crain hoped that he would be able to recommend a just and intelligent program which would serve the best interests
of all, and most particularly the public.

As he made his way out of the bar, he did not believe a brawl with
Root was likely. Root wouldn't risk one unless he was sure of winning.

By the time he entered the dining room and started across to the table
where his daughter and Buddy Montrose were sitting, the senator was
able to tell himself with assurance that everything was going to work out
all right.

Alden Root, sitting alone at the table Senator Crain had just left, was telling himself much the same thing, but in a considerably different way. There was no doubt that everything would work out all right. He would see to that. But it was going to take a good deal of thought and effort that Root had not been prepared for.

He too was angered. Who the hell did Crain think he was? Holding his cigar between two fleshy fingers Root emitted a puff of smoke and considered what he must do now about *Senator* Barton Crain.

The problem was bigger than the issue of a congressional seat. Crain should have known that Root could abide no opposition on a matter that went so deeply into the structure of Root's prestige. Why, the son of a bitch wouldn't even be a county judge without me, Root said to himself. But Crain *had* opposed him. All right. Root would fight. Lockridge would not get the party's nomination again, with or without Crain's endorsement; Root would see to that. He would find a candidate for that seat, and he would back him with every resource at his command.

In the process of that victory he would teach the senator just who Alden Root was. And whatever else he was, Alden Root was a confident man.

Settled in a taxi after they had left Senator Crain, Buddy Montrose seized Pat and held her in a long embrace.

When she pulled away from him finally, he held both her hands tightly. "I was beginning to wonder when we'd be alone long enough for that," she said.

Montrose grinned and kissed her again. "This has been a day, hasn't it?"

"Dad at dinner and your Mr. Logan at lunch," Pat said. "I'm just not conditioned for it. You've been away too long." She squeezed his hand and leaned back against his arm. "Did he take you on a tour of his factory this afternoon? That must have been jolly on your first day back."

"You'll be surprised when I tell you what happened," he said. He described for her his meeting with Lloyd McRumen and told her about his talk before the Raven executives. As the taxi pulled up before Pat's apartment house, he broke the news of the lecture tour Raven wanted him to make.

Pat waited silently while he paid the driver and followed her up the stairs of the brownstone.

"That means you'll be going away again?" she asked when they were inside.

"Not really, honey. I'll be in and out of New York. It's a tremendous opportunity."

"For how long, Buddy?"

"Only two or three months. It's going to give me a chance to collect my wits and figure out where I go—*we* go from here, darling." She turned toward him and he put his arms around her. "Aren't you happy?" he whispered.

"If you are. If it's what you want to do. I just . . ." She clasped both hands behind his neck and looked up at him. Tears had formed in her eyes. "You've been away so long. I want you near me. I'm so tired of waiting."

"I know, darling," Buddy said. "But we'll see each other almost as much as if I were right here all the time. And as soon as it's over you'd better have your baggage packed for your honeymoon, Miss Crain. I'm tired of waiting, too."

She smiled weakly and they sat down at one end of the couch. "Why do they want you to do this, Buddy?"

"Well, mainly they think it's a story that everybody ought to hear."

"And . . ."

"Naturally, it's good for them, too. I'll be mentioning Raven's name as the good Samaritan who came to our aid with a small fortune in drugs. . . . I might even be able to stimulate some other private contributions."

"That's what I thought," she said. "Are you sure you want to promote their products this way? If you worked for them it would be different, but —I think they'd be getting more out of this than anybody else."

"Hell, honey, you talk as if it's something dishonest. They want me to say just what I want to say."

"I didn't mean that," Pat said. "I just think you might be sorry later that you did it."

"Don't worry," Buddy said. "Logan seems like a decent guy. And the president's a fine gentleman. You'd like him, Patty. Really you would."

"I'm sure I would. But what does this solve?"

"What do you mean?"

"What are you going to do with your life now, Buddy?"

"I'm going to become Mr. Patricia Crain."

"I'm serious."

"I don't know, sweetheart," he said. "Everything's still too fresh in my mind. This will give me time to decide."

"You *are* going to make this tour, then."

"What can I lose? They're not asking me to do this for nothing. We should have a respectable nest egg by the time it's over."

"All right," Pat said with forced cheer. "I'll promise to keep quiet."

She looked up at him reassuringly. "But not for long. I competed with the Army and won. And now that I have you back, I won't surrender you to the Raven company for long. You can tell Mr. Logan that."

"I've thought a lot about getting a privately sponsored aid mission together to go back to the Far East," Buddy said. "Raven could help, if the time ever comes."

"If you mean that, Captain, you're looking at your first recruit. Now tell me you love me."

6

WHILE MONTROSE was in Washington getting his separation papers, Logan worked on the transcript of the speech the captain had delivered in the Raven conference room, as Emily Klinger had recorded it. He had finished it by the time Montrose returned to the city, separated but still in uniform. The first afternoon Buddy was back, Joe sent Emily with a copy of the speech to the hotel suite Raven had reserved for the captain's New York headquarters.

"Mr. Logan says he will see you here about four," Emily told Montrose, looking past him into the room. "He said you needed this and I said I'd be only too happy to bring it."

"Of course," Montrose said. "Won't you come in—ah—Miss . . ."

"Klinger," Emily said. "Emily Klinger. Maybe just for a minute."

Buddy stood back from the door to let her pass. She kept her eyes on his, turning her head as she stepped inside the room.

"Well, this certainly is a wicked-looking room," Emily said. "I'll bet it just fits your personality." She handed him the envelope containing his speech and Montrose smiled uncertainly.

"Would you like a drink?" he asked.

"Well, maybe just one," Emily said. She moved past the chairs in the room and flopped languidly on the bed. "What do you do up here in this wicked room all alone by yourself?" she asked. "Don't tell me, I know. You're not alone very much."

"Oh, I wouldn't say that." Montrose laughed uneasily. He poured two drinks and carried one to her.

"Why not?"

He looked at her curiously. "Why not what?"

"Why wouldn't you say that? You said, 'I wouldn't say that,' and I said, 'Why not?' "

Montrose took a long drink.

"I'll bet you *don't* spend much time alone," she challenged. "Do you?"

"Oh—well . . ."

"I'll just bet," she said, looking at him knowingly. "After all that time in Asia and everything, you must be hungry for the bright lights."

Montrose nodded hesitantly, watching her carefully.

"I know just how you feel," she said. "I broke up with my boy friend a couple of weeks ago and I miss the bright lights so much I could die." She put her arms behind her neck and stretched lazily. Her breasts strained against her sweater. After a moment she reached for her drink on the night stand.

Montrose stood up quickly. "Do you mind if I have another drink?" he asked.

"Boy, you're a fast drinker," she said.

"I guess so." He stirred the drink slowly, absorbed in his task. When he had finished he looked hastily at the bed. Emily was holding a fresh cigarette in her mouth.

"Got a light?" she asked.

While he held a match for her, she placed one hand on his wrist. "I expect we're going to be seeing quite a bit of each other," she said, exhaling slowly.

"Oh? Well, yes, I guess we will," he said quickly.

The telephone on the bed table startled them both. Montrose grabbed the instrument gratefully.

It was Logan, in the lobby.

"Broke away early," he said. "Have you had a chance to look at the speech?"

"Not yet," Montrose said.

"May I come up?"

"Sure, Joe."

When he put the phone down, Emily was at the door with her coat thrown over her arm. "If you need any help or anything," she said softly "—secretarial, I mean—just call me." She opened the door. "I'm in the book, and—well, just call me, any time." The invitation in her eyes was frank and clear. Watching her, Montrose suddenly was quite sorry for the interruption of the phone call.

"I'll do that," he promised.

Logan and Montrose went over the speech carefully, one paragraph at a time, Logan explaining the changes. "It was perfectly all right the way it was, but it just had to be paced a little better. Some of the emotional passages were too close together. We've got to wring them for everything they're worth. I think this will fix it up fine."

Montrose looked doubtful. "What about this, Joe?" He indicated a passage which began: "I know from personal experience what communism can do to people. I know from experience what Communist torture can be. That's—well, that's hardly true," he said hesitantly. "There weren't any Reds brain-washing me or carving their initials in my hide."

Logan laughed. "Oh, come on. Just a little wound? Somewhere? What's that scar behind your ear?"

Montrose fingered the long thin white scar that ran along his neck and smiled. "It didn't have much to do with communism. A few of the mountain people thought I was unfair competition for their herbal doctor and they expressed their feelings with a stone shower. One had a jagged edge."

"You mean your Baopneng buddies did this?"

"Well, only a few were involved. You couldn't blame them, really. As I've told you, they were suspicious as hell of me, at first. That was one of the real problems."

"Okay, we'll tone down the Communist torture angle. That'll cost us a headline in Pocatello."

"Actually, Joe, I'd like to tone down the whole thing a little bit. All that business about knowing from personal experience what communism can do to people."

Logan looked at him with amused patience. "Look here, sonny," he said after a few seconds, "we on the committee got a few questions to ask you about your loyalty to these Yew-nited States."

"I stand on my rights as a confused, muddle-headed, starry-eyed visionary," Buddy said. He waited for a few seconds and then he said, "The thing is, Joe, I'd like to keep this as honest as possible. I'm no expert on communism. I know about it, all right. It was the enemy out there, the ultimate enemy, anyway, and it was a tough one. But I didn't see much of it. The enemies I saw were hunger and disease and even war itself. I know what those things can do to people. *Those* people know what communism does. They went to inhuman lengths to get free of it. But I can't with any real honesty say that *I* know."

"You can refine honesty right out of existence, too," Logan said. "I don't want to turn you into a crusader, but what the hell. You said yourself that communism was the ultimate enemy. These people that came to you, swarmed into the free zone—they were destitute and miserable. Right?"

"That's right," Montrose said. "Of course."

"Well, if it hadn't been for communism they wouldn't have been, would they? Communism stood somewhere back of all that mess, didn't it?"

"Sure it did. But so did the old king and the European colonials who carted off what little wealth that country had years ago. We know the evil that communism is, all right. It's been demonstrated in enough tragic ways in our time. But it's not a simple evil. It's a hell of a complicated problem. The desire for freedom is not something that communism alone brought. Those people have been exploited by one thing or another for a long time. That's given the Communists something to work with."

Logan lit a cigarette as he watched Montrose.

"The best we can hope for everywhere that situation exists," Buddy continued, "is that the people can see that communism offers them less hope of freedom than what they've been trying to escape from. With luck and patience and work, the people usually do see it that way. The ones that came into our zone in Laophong did. But it's no simple problem, and there aren't any simple answers—at least none that can or should be given by guys like me. It needs the attention of people who know what the hell they're talking about. Climbing aboard the I'm-against-communism train is a cheap way to win a personal advantage, and dishonest if you don't have anything more to offer than that. It's easy enough to exploit people's fears about this, but—well, I don't know. It's just not being very level if you pose as an expert when you're not."

Logan once again regarded him silently and with deep interest. "By God, you put me to shame," he said finally. "You literal-minded nipshitz, coming in here and making an old pro review his catechism."

Montrose laughed with embarrassment. "I'll settle for whatever you think is okay. I know less about speech-making than I know about communism."

"No, let's make it honest. You've converted me. How about this: 'I know from personal experience what violence communism can cause'? You think that's close enough?"

"Sure. That sounds fine."

"Think you can say it without choking?"

"Well, it won't be much of a choke."

"All right, then. Damn." Logan penciled in the corrections swiftly, then looked at Montrose again. "Now. Do you think you've won a point?" Montrose nodded gravely.

"Are you grateful?"

"Overwhelmed."

"You can prove your gratitude," Logan said, "by letting me win a point now. All I want you to do when you say this line is run a finger tip along that scar on your neck."

"Well, I'll be damned," Montrose said.

"Just a finger *tip,*" Logan said. "And you won't actually be saying anything about it. If the audience wants to draw its own conclusions, that's their business. Okay?"

"If I hadn't heard it with my own ears," Montrose said, "I wouldn't believe it." He ran his finger along the scar. "And may I say in conclusion, ladies and gentlemen," he intoned, "that I have proof right here of the way those godless gooks behave when they get the ideology of communism in their haids and a gutful of free vodka under their belts."

They looked at each other and laughed easily.

From Logan's point of view, the work with Montrose had gone exceedingly well. The captain had been coöperative, but more than that, he had been pleasant to be with. His honesty, his charm and his obvious sincerity were compelling.

There had been remarkably few difficulties of any kind in making the arrangements for the captain's tour. Even Senator Crain had posed no objections when his prospective son-in-law told him that he planned to stump the country for one of the companies on the senator's investigation list. As Montrose reported it to Logan, the senator saw no cause for embarrassment to him. The mention Montrose was going to make about the Raven company's magnanimous contribution to the cause of freedom was a substantially different story, Crain had observed, from the one the committee was pursuing.

The only objection—and Logan could only guess at the intensity of it—had come from Pat Crain. The exception she took had nothing to do with her father's investigation, but it had a good deal to do with the Raven company. She saw Raven, Logan realized, as a giant vulture, ready to gobble up her hero.

Montrose had a cocktail date with Pat the afternoon Logan and Buddy went over the speech. Joe waited with Buddy long enough to see her.

"We seem always to meet in the midst of leather couches," Logan said to her.

"Maybe it's the kind of life you lead, Mr. Logan," she said lightly. She was elegantly but casually dressed in an expensive tweed suit with a matching coat which hung loosely over her shoulders.

"I never argue with a lady," Joe said. "Come on, I'll buy you both a drink before I take off on my nightly round of carousing."

"I imagine your evenings are filled with all sorts of glamorous people," Pat said as they went into the bar.

"Ever since I was drummed out of the Elks," Logan said, "I've been at a loss for entertainment."

For a while their cocktail conversation was warm and light and Logan found himself consciously trying to temper his interest in Pat Crain.

"So your plans are all made?" Pat asked.

"All made," Logan said. "We've fixed Buddy's story. Now we'll work on the bookings."

"Fixed the story?" Pat said, looking at Montrose. Her smile had disappeared and her face was faintly troubled.

"Well," Montrose said cautiously, "there were a few things Joe thought should be done to it."

"I liked it just the way you told it to me."

"We all liked it," Logan assured her. "It's a great story and no one should try to change it. But there are some special techniques in speaking before large audiences."

"I see," Pat said. "I guess that's your job, isn't it, Mr. Logan?"

"That's a *part* of my job," Logan said.

"I think Joe's right, sweetheart," Buddy said. "After all, I sure don't know much about this sort of thing."

Pat shook her head and smiled brightly. "Well, I bow to the wisdom of the experts," she said. "I certainly don't know anything about speech-writing."

For half an hour, until Logan left them, they talked about the details of Buddy's tour. But watching her, Logan knew with certainty that she was upset, and the knowledge annoyed him.

Logan's plan, as outlined to and accepted by President McRumen, was to book Montrose for two months in towns and small cities in the East, across the Southeast, to the Northwest and California in clubs and conventions and gatherings of all sorts which were always pleased to have a speaker. Simultaneously, Joe would arrange for as many local radio and television appearances as possible. He intended to plant articles about Montrose in newspapers and magazines wherever he could. At the end of that time, if Montrose was the success that Logan thought he would be,

Joe would have enough impressive evidence of his performances to get the captain scheduled in larger cities.

And then the campaign would be accomplishing precisely what they hoped. Montrose would not advertise a product, he would merely endorse the Raven organization—again and again and again. He would be selling Raven as an institution. Raven's name would be known in every state.

If—Montrose was a success.

And Logan was sure he would be.

And Lloyd McRumen, remembering how deeply the young captain had moved him, enthusiastically agreed.

7

EMILY KLINGER was delighted to see Dr. Ambrose Garibaldi amble into the public relations office. The place had been a madhouse that morning with Logan constantly on the telephone speaking to a dozen towns across the country while she took notes on the extension. Now the first lap of Captain Montrose's speaking tour was plotted and Emily was ready for a rest. She knew she could get a few minutes if the medical research director managed to divert Logan's attention.

Garibaldi slid into a chair facing Logan's desk. "I know a belly dancer I'd like to get bookings for," he said. "Am I in the right place?"

"That depends. What else can she do?" Logan said.

"We have never established that," Garibaldi said as he picked up a copy of the Montrose speech lying on Joe's desk and thumbed through it. "Wonderful," he said. "What it lacks in beauty it makes up in blather."

"Come on, Doc . . ."

"I quote. 'I know from personal experience what violence communism can cause.'" Garibaldi looked at Logan. "You're weaseling, Joe. Why don't you try something really gripping? 'I was a member of a Siberian chain gang.'"

"Too fancy," Joe said. "Nobody'd believe it."

"How about 'I know what it is to have my speech loused up by a publicity angle merchant'?"

"It has to be dramatized a little, Doc."

"Oh, come off it. That kid had all the drama he needed without your help. A glance at this would indicate that you may have a low-grade infection from the Shively virus. Why say what you mean if hyperbole says it better?"

"All right, so I jazzed it up a little. It's still the truth. Montrose bought it." Under Garibaldi's gaze, Logan was conscious of the defensive sound of his words.

"Look, Joe. Be careful with this boy. He's good. Hell, we were all ready to make our decisions for Christ when he finished. But that speech sounds a little as if you're not only satisfying the sales office demands but pandering to some shabby public clichés as well."

"That's the way I make my living, Doc. Pandering," Logan said with an edge in his voice.

"Okay, okay. I didn't come in here to insult you. I only offer the voice of caution. I know you're going to exploit him. That's the assignment you've got. But you *can* be careful—and kind." He held the speech up with a shrug. "You make him an expert and you endow him with a certain power. And power is tricky stuff."

"Doc, I think you may be overstating the case. I *like* Montrose. I'm not about to compromise him in any way."

"Then watch this nonsense. We're going to have our hands full enough trying to control Madman Shively and his miracle mulch, without turning Frankensteins out of your office as well."

"You want me to change the speech?"

"No. Leave it alone. Just remember that when you start turning heroes loose with a lot of eyewash and no prescription, you can get into the same kind of trouble Shively may find with his panacea."

"Don't tell me that speech called forth this lecture."

Garibaldi drew a folded sheet of paper from his coat pocket. "Hardly. Have you seen this? Latest communiqué from Brother Alonzo." He opened the sheet and peered at it through his spectacles. "As an illustration of the vast potential market he envisions, here is a list Shively has dreamed up of fifty-one different medical situations to which our new drug can be considered applicable. Let me read you a few. . . . Arteriosclerosis, asthma, backache, cancer, cardiac erethism, coronary thrombosis, hyperthyroidism, migraine, nail-biting, nightmares . . ."

"I don't get it," Logan said.

"Neither did I, at first. He very kindly explained it to me. You see, it's simple. Victims of all of these ailments will be among our first potential customers."

"For Christ's sake," Logan said. "Cancer?"

"Shively pointed out to me that it is the *situation* which demands the drug, not the disease. He says—and I don't think I do violence to his position—that it's the anxiety associated with every disease that makes it beautiful for his purposes. That's what he said—beautiful." He flipped to a second sheet of paper stapled to the one he had been reading from. "This is a list of people whose activities make them natural targets for the drug: expectant mothers, nervous children, policemen, actors, mail carriers, expectant fathers, drinkers, nondrinkers, ministers and morticians. There are others. All of them are anxious. All of them need peace of mind."

"I'll be damned," Logan said.

"Millions of people are dying in the world every year," Garibaldi said, "and in every funeral there must be at least five dollars' worth of business. It would be a shame to miss it." He folded the sheet and put it back in his pocket. "I don't think I'll voice that suggestion, though, after all. He'd like it. I'm surprised he hasn't thought of it himself."

Logan looked at him closely. "You don't sound as if you're in favor of this product."

"My only objection," Garibaldi said, "is the speed and the manner in which we're pushing ahead. It's too fast. It looks like a beneficial drug but we've got to be careful."

"You said there's no serious toxicity in any of the cases that have come in."

"No, there's been no liver damage or blood dyscrasia or convulsions or anything of that sort. But there is much we don't know about the drug that will take us months to find out. Maybe years. We say it's not habit-forming, but we really don't *know* that; we can't yet. No one ever took enough of it. What does it do to the adrenal function? The kidneys? The nervous system itself? If we're going into this, we should do it soberly and with great attention and not in this carnival atmosphere of Shively's."

"He's a salesman, Doc. That's his business."

"I know. What I worry about is that his concern for sales is absorbing everyone else. The whole organization seems in a dangerous imbalance." He looked at Joe silently for a few seconds before going on. "Noting the reception my signals of alarm have received in this office, I would say his insidious influence has found its way even through these cynically constructed walls."

Logan looked at him disgustedly. "I don't care what the going philosophy is, and you know it. If they decide to give this stuff away for box-tops it's all right with me."

Garibaldi looked at his hands. "I don't think you really mean that," he said.

"All right. I don't. But it doesn't make any difference, anyway. We're an ethical drug house and this is an ethical drug. It's going to be sold with a doctor's prescription, so it's up to the doctor."

"So hooray," Garibaldi said.

"Moreover," Logan said, "It's going to be sold *in the same way all the other drugs like it on the market now are being sold.* We're not in this alone, you know, Doc."

Garibaldi sighed. "That's the argument for which there is no answer," he said. "I suppose it's more a commentary on the society we live in than on our industry, that so many people seem to need these drugs. So here we sit, the last great hope of earth."

"You worry too much," Logan said. "Hell, they used to sell it as Sneezone, or whatever they called it. It didn't hurt anybody then."

Garibaldi grunted. "No one with a cold ever took it for more than three days. We're talking about long-term use." He rose heavily from his chair. "Now you pay attention to the wise words of advice the kindly old doctor has offered you this morning."

"Quit worrying and start living," Joe said.

"You're right," Garibaldi said. "Maybe *I* need this tranquilizer. I'd probably take some if the smell weren't so awful."

"What *does* it smell like?" Logan asked.

"Buffalo chips," said Garibaldi over his shoulder as he walked out of the office.

The auditorium of the Daniel Webster High School in Meadow Hills, New Jersey, was selected personally by Joe Logan for Montrose's first public appearance. Logan saturated the area for three days beforehand with press releases and photographs. Raven's sales representatives were instructed to invite every doctor, pharmacist and veterinarian in the immediate vicinity, as well as all of their friends. It was made clear in the publicity stories that Captain Montrose was sponsored by the public-spirited Raven company. Logan asked for and received the coöperation of a committee of ushers selected from the local Meadow Hills American Legion post, and the mayor was going to be there to introduce Montrose. A program of locally recruited entertainment had even been built around the speech.

As the people trooped into the auditorium a few minutes before eight o'clock on the evening of the address, a nervous Logan took a head count while he waited for Montrose to appear. The auditorium would hold fifteen hundred if you counted the balcony, and already people were being sent to the balcony.

Montrose arrived finally with Pat on his arm. The brown warmth of her hair glistened under the bright lobby lights. Her nose and cheeks wore a sun-touched healthy look that no cosmetic could have duplicated. She was laughing at something Montrose had just said, and he was smiling too.

"I'm overwhelmed by the people," he said to Logan. "How did you ever get them all to come?"

"All set for the debut?" Logan asked.

"I hope I don't let you down, Joe. It's one thing talking to a handful of people, but I'm skittish with this kind of a crowd."

"They'll hear you in the treetops," said Logan. "Don't be nervous. These people are here because they're interested. Just tell it straight from the script, don't forget the voice pitch and they won't miss your message."

Montrose's face became serious. "I hope not, Joe."

Joe was glad Montrose had agreed to wear his uniform a while longer, just for the lectures. Meticulously pressed and barbered, Montrose carried his lean figure with the casual precision of a West Point instructor. Against the dull weave of his Army tunic two neat rows of colored ribbons stood out sharply.

"Isn't it about time to start?" Pat asked. She looked at Montrose.

"Might as well go in," Logan said. "We'll meet you right here, Captain. Relax and good luck."

He turned to Pat. "I had one of the ushers save seats for us in the back," he said. "May I take your coat?"

As they started in through the open door, Alonzo Shively rushed up. "Thought I wouldn't make it," he said, puffing. "This is a tough town to find. I went clear the hell to South Orange when I missed a turn."

Logan introduced Shively to Pat and the three of them went into the auditorium together.

Logan squirmed while ten majorettes self-consciously took their places on the stage. Only three dropped their batons before their performance was over. A marimba duet, billed as Meadow Hills' Own Furtweiler Sisters, persisted through two numbers and an unsolicited encore before the mayor got up to introduce Buddy Montrose. He thanked the town's citizens for coming—one at a time, it seemed to Logan—before he got down to the prepared introduction Logan had given him.

Montrose got to his feet, erect as ever, and walked to the center of the stage. He crossed his hands in front of him and, nodding at the mayor, waited for the applause to die down.

Shively leaned across Pat, who was sitting between him and Logan. "That's what I call real command presence. You teach him that, Joe?" he asked in a stage whisper. Logan shook his head and silenced Shively with a finger to his lips. That kind of talk, he thought, was all Pat needed to hear.

"Thank you, Mayor Peale," Montrose began. "It is I who am grateful for the opportunity to speak to you tonight. I have been brought here to tell you the story of a brave people and their flight to freedom in the Far East. But the record is not all heroic, unfortunately. It involves filth and starvation and wretchedness, too. It involves brutality, and it involves violence." His low voice throbbed. "I know myself," he said, "what violence communism can cause. . . ." His finger tip ran to the scar on his neck.

Pause, said Logan to himself, *that's the boy. Hold it for five seconds and let it sink in.*

Buddy Montrose appeared to search every face in his audience before he continued. "Nor are these things far from you tonight. The agony and suffering of a sick and dying child, the anguish of a mother separated from her baby, the desolation of an ancient mandarin searching for his wife and not understanding that she is dead—killed by enemy hands . . . Each of these has been helped at least a little by the small hand of hope which you held out whether you knew it or not. They are no farther from your doorsteps than we are from each other at this moment."

He explained to his listeners that his job had been to process those fortunate ones who could escape from the Communist area. "But it became, through no choice or desire of my own, a good deal more than that. I was a doctor because they had no doctor and I was a man of God because they had no clergy and I was whatever they demanded I be."

Pause. That's fine. They're sitting up. They're getting your message, Buddy Boy. Logan could feel the tension begin to build around him.

When Montrose spoke of brutality and agony and wretchedness, of poverty and terror inspired by the sight of sudden death, he spoke in terms that every doctor, housewife and secretary understood. "I have always hated the sight of blood," he said. "I hate it more now than ever, I have seen so much." He shocked and prodded them and made many of them weep. Through it all they were transfixed.

When he paused for a sip of water on the rostrum, there was a brief rustle as many shifted in their seats, never taking their eyes from him.

He sketched the frightening details of the epidemic which threatened the entire free zone, as Logan silently cued him on his pauses and on the volume of his voice. And then, in his warm convincing tones, he described his appeal to Raven, and Raven's overwhelming response. He told how, just in the nick of time, the miracle drugs from Raven's laboratories arrived to save a thousand lives a day.

Pat nudged Logan and he let her out. Without a sound she passed through the double doors at the back of the auditorium, letting in only a crack of the bright lobby light to mark her departure. He followed her, leaving Shively too preoccupied with the figure on the stage to notice.

She had stopped in the lobby and was fumbling in her purse.

"What's wrong? Are you sick?" He was alarmed and puzzled.

"Disgusted," she answered him. "And don't you come near me, Joe Logan."

"What is it? What's the matter?"

"I hate the sight of blood, too," she snapped, nervously trying to extract a cigarette from her purse. He handed her one.

"I don't like your script a damned bit," she said. "Some of it's not even true—Buddy wasn't scarred by Communist violence. You know it and he knows it."

"Oh, now, look, Pat . . ."

"And some of it's only too true. All that nonsense about the drugs you sent. Isn't there any such thing as a little honest-to-God charity in this world? Seeing him up there, telling that story to those people just so you get your money back in free publicity, seems like the cheapest thing I ever heard of. Suppose he had been killed. Then what would you have done, hired an actor? That would have fit right in with your marimba players."

The assault angered Logan, too.

"Look, Pat, let's not be unreasonable about this. Cool off long enough to listen."

"I know about all I want to know."

"That's a very intelligent answer," he said.

She turned to walk away from him and he held her arm.

"Pat, I know how you feel. But let me say this. You know what he's been through. You know how important it is for as many people as possible to hear about it, and maybe when the time comes be better equipped to do something about it. These people will never walk out of a schoolroom or a church with the awareness that Buddy will give them."

He released her arm. She said nothing, but she did not move her eyes from him.

"It makes us look good, and rightly so. But it makes *all* of us look good. Buddy's going to be a bigger hero than you or I can imagine. He's good enough to give a lot of poor imprisoned housewives an emotional jag, but who's to deny them? He's also good enough to get people aroused about helping a million poor devils who desperately need that help."

The anger had gone out of her expression but she was not convinced. "It seems as if he's *selling* something up there," she said.

"Well, he's not," Logan said. Gently he took her arm again. "Let's go back in. He'll be through soon."

"Go ahead. Tell Buddy I'll meet him out here when it's over. I don't really want to hear any more tonight."

He left her and went back to the auditorium.

As he sat down in the darkness he realized there was not a sound in the vast shadowy hall. Montrose had apparently reached a dramatic point close to the end. He was standing dead center on the stage, looking down again as if he were trying to come up with a word he had forgotten. After a few seconds Logan heard him say, "I've told you what I saw and felt. I have told you what I did—what you would have done—and what I would do again. In spite of all the terror and the horror, I would rather be there now than here or anywhere." He dropped his voice to its conversational pitch again. "I want to go back—and I intend to if I can—back to lend my one small hand, to advise, to help, to comfort; in any way I can. I want to go back just as you would go back, because in all good conscience you could wish for nothing else. . . ."

For a moment he stood where he was and then slowly retreated to his seat on the side of the stage after pronouncing a barely audible "Thank you." And for another moment nothing stirred in the room.

Then like the sound of a thousand drums, the applause broke loose. It roared and deafened until there seemed to be no end. Bedford Montrose sat quiet and grave as the mayor rose and turned in his direction, applauding with the rest. Some of the people in the first few rows stood up, still clapping, and then more, until the whole audience was on its feet.

Logan saw Montrose only long enough to congratulate him that night after the speech, but the next morning he took the Meadow Hills paper to Buddy's hotel suite.

"It was magnificent," Logan told him. "The whole thing was. I was moved myself, and I'd heard it all before."

"It was a good audience," Buddy said.

Logan leafed idly through the paper. "Are you really serious about wanting to go back to the Far East?"

Montrose was silent for a moment, and then he said, "Yes, Joe, I am."

"I can't pretend to understand it," Logan said.

Looking directly at Logan, Montrose said, "If you believe in something, Joe, you have to live it and act on it. I think you understand that, even if you pretend you don't. You'd do the same thing if you were in my place."

Logan shook his head. "Not me," he said. "You're talking to an ex-mudhound who learned one thing in the Army, and that was that after a man did what he had to do he just got his ass the hell out and back to something cushy. You baffle me, Buddy." He grinned at him. "Just don't get any ideas about taking off before this tour is over."

For the best part of his thirty-three years, the only thing Joe Logan had trusted was mistrust. And now, with Buddy Montrose sitting across from him, the rule no longer seemed to work. Montrose wore his idealism on his sleeve, that was true. But there was a warmth in that idealism that got through to a man—even to a man who all his adult life had kept idealism at a safe distance.

EXTENSIVE TESTING of phitherdimethyldine had to be carried on with the old dry powder capsules, because the odor problem, which prohibited the use of any other dosage form, had not yet been solved. But the drug was testing nonetheless, and it did the job. The tests established clearly that phitherdimethyldine had some relaxing effect on most patients. Under its influence, worries evaporated, tensions disappeared and life became tranquil for an ever-growing number of anxious citizens. (If for some patients there appeared to be too much tranquility, few at Raven worried about that.)

Alonzo Shively was the first to say it, and then the message became gospel. *"It's peace of mind for everybody,"* Shively boomed, and his words described a future in which the world and Raven would prosper together. This was the agent that would bring a calm spirit and an untroubled mind to anyone who ever became worried or tense or anxious —and who, in mid-century America, did not? This would be the you-and-me drug, offering tranquility in a tablet.

This would be the peace pill.

The laboratory's continuing difficulty with the odor problem remained the only flaw. And then, finally, even that fell before science's tireless patience. After the research staff had labored many hours above and beyond the call of increased dividends and were working solely for the cause of chemistry itself, they were able to solve the problem of phitherdimethyldine's unbearable smell. Nearly every masking agent known to man had been tried, alone or in combination, and with no success. The persistent fragrance of the drug defied every chemist's skill until one of them reversed the approach. In a distillate of crab claws and myrrh, he found a faint, delicately deceptive odor which successfully anesthetized the nose, and the way was open for Raven's new drug to conquer the medical markets of the world.

Shively was in ecstasy. He had a marketing plan, carefully worked out, considered from every angle, and ready now at last to spring on a captivated board of directors.

He had a product, and what a product. Product, hell. It would be more than that. It would be a *social necessity*.

And he had a name for it. Horace Blivet had come up with one, and Shively was in love with it:

PAX

Sweet, simple, pure, a name that all sorts of brisk slogans could be built around. FIND PEACE IN PAX was one Shively liked particularly.

Blivet had achieved one other piece of good work in which Shively found solid satisfaction. He reached for the report the adman had given him that morning and thumbed through it again. A remarkable document. Blivet had culled all the reports turned in by Raven's veterinary researchers thus far and summarized them succinctly: *animals as well as human beings offered an incalculable market*. "Just as people lose their cares with this remarkable compound," the report read, "so do all the furred and feathered creatures of the earth. We see a splendid vista in the agricultural markets. Our studies tell us that under the tranquil influence of this drug a hen will lay more eggs, a cow will give more milk, a steer will grow fatter."

Shively pressed his intercom button and said to his secretary, "Have Blivet come up. And call Mr. Logan's office. See if he can join us."

Horace Blivet hadn't been getting much sleep in recent weeks and it told on him. He was as prompt as ever, and outwardly alert. But otherwise, the impression he made today on the meticulous Shively was not good. There were times, he thought, when Blivet looked more seedy than tweedy.

"Horace," Shively said solemnly, tapping the report on his desk, "this is a splendid job."

Blivet nodded, deeply moved and not in the least troubled by the knowledge that the advertising agency had had a generous hand in the preparation of his report.

"It was a long time in coming, but it's splendid. What I want you to do now, Horace, is add another hundred men to the special sales force you're getting together."

Blivet looked surprised. After a few seconds of reflection he said, "People-wise, Al, that'll make three hundred."

"I know it," Shively said.

"That's a good deal more than we had counted on."

"I know that, too." Shively let silence hang in the room for a while and then he said, "I'll explain it to you later."

"While I'm here, Al, I'd like your help on something," Blivet said. "The agency's got a problem I meant to tell you about before but . . ."

"What is it?"

"Well, it's about whether Pax induces sleep. We want some promotion that'll show it does bring sleep, for those who *want* to sleep, but on the other hand we don't want to scare off anyone who wants to stay awake."

Shively frowned. "I see."

"We've got clinical evidence to back up whichever side we want to take," Blivet said, "but it's pretty tricky to try to work them both together. We can't say it puts you to sleep *and* keeps you awake."

Shively stared at the wall in front of him for a few seconds, drumming his fingers on the desk. He shut his eyes tightly and then opened them. He opened them as wide as he could and then closed them again. He blinked them, open and shut, in rapid succession half a dozen times as Blivet watched patiently.

"Say it's got eyelid control," he said finally.

"Eyelid—control," Blivet repeated, marveling. "By God, Al, that's terrific."

Shively took the response appreciatively. In a sudden expansiveness he said, "Don't leave yet, Horace. I want to talk to you. Make sure that door is closed."

Blivet obediently tested the door and then walked back to the sales manager's desk.

"Sit down," Shively said.

Blivet sat down.

"A minute ago," Shively said, "I told you we were going to put a three-hundred-man sales force on Pax. You have any idea what we're going to do with all those men?"

Blivet shook his head.

"None at all? Think now, Horace."

Blivet's head continued to roll from side to side.

"Remember what I told you about concentrating on a promotional presentation that would include the consumer, rather than strictly an ethical medical pitch?"

"Sure, Al. I remember everything you told me."

"Well, I wasn't spinning my wheels," Shively said. "There's going to be a colossal shift in our policy, Horace." He leaned closer and looked Blivet squarely in the eye. "We're going to need those men to move that product over the counter. All the way."

"*Over* the *counter?*" Blivet asked in astonishment. "You mean sell that tranquilizer without a prescription?"

"That's right."

"But we can't . . ."

"Why can't we?"

"Why, Al, we don't have FDA approval."

"We don't *need* FDA approval."

Blivet continued to look at him blankly.

"You don't understand, do you? All right." Shively jabbed a finger at him. "What's our product?"

"Why, it's a tranquilizer."

"Not quite."

"You mean Sneezone? An antihistamine?"

"I mean its generic name."

"Phi—Phi—Phi . . ."

"Exactly. Phitherdimethyldine. Which is fully cleared by the government for over-the-counter sale . . ."

Blivet broke in. "But then it was for allergies and colds and . . . It wasn't . . ."

Shively extended his hand, palm forward, to halt the interruption. "What difference does it make? That's the essential question. And the answer is—not one damn bit. FDA gave us approval to sell phitherdimethyldine without a prescription, and so far as they're concerned, we've still got that approval."

Blivet looked as doubtful as he ever allowed himself to appear in Shively's presence. "What about the labeling and all that?"

"We change the name. Sneezone is dead. Pax is born. But we leave the same stuff about colds and allergies on the package as before, only

in the smallest possible print. Then it's still legal. We weasel-word a couple of new ones like 'tranquaid' and 'inner peace.' Who the hell could
pin us down on that? But that's all we do with the product. The important
thing is the promotion. Relaxation, peace, tranquility—all these go on
with a trowel, Horace."

"What about the Federal Trade Commission? Won't they scream about
misleading advertising?"

"They're always screaming about misleading advertising. They can't
really *do* anything—except go to court. And that's what we've got doctors
and lawyers for, to keep us out of trouble. That's one reason I've been
in favor of letting Garibaldi push his clinical testing. Anyway, whatever
the government can do isn't going to hurt our sales program."

"But suppose they just said to stop selling . . ."

"They can't forbid us to sell it unless it hurts somebody, Horace, and
they'd have a hell of a time proving that."

"They won't try to reclassify it as a new drug? As a tranquilizer?"

"They won't if we're smart," Shively said. "We don't specifically call it
a tranquilizer. We *push* it as a tranquilizer, but we don't really ever say
that's what is it. It's just Pax, that's all."

Blivet watched Shively with open-mouthed respect. "Al, that's pure
genius. We'll be the first with an over-the-counter tranquilizer, won't we?"

"The first with a *real* one," Shively said. "There are some phonies on
the market now, but they're not real tranquilizers. They're just weak
antihistamines and bromides. But ours—what about ours, Horace?"

"Ours," Blivet said, "is a powerful tranquilizing antihistamine which
we'll never call anything but Pax."

"Good boy." Shively's secretary called for his attention on the
intercom.

"Mr. Logan's out here," she said.

"Ask him to hold on just a few seconds longer." Shively flicked the
switch and looked back at Blivet. "One thing, Horace. You're to keep
your mouth shut about all this."

"Doesn't anybody else know, Al?"

"Nobody."

"Not even McRumen?"

"Not even McRumen. I didn't want to spring it on him until they
fixed that goddamn smell problem. Until they did that, the only dosage
form we could use was one of those horse pill dry-fill capsules with a
thick coat of gelatin around it. That's all right for prescription stuff. But
when I present a plan to sell this like candy, I want to make sure it's going to look like candy."

"You've had this in mind all along, haven't you, Al?"

Shively nodded. "From the beginning. What do you think this big promotion budget's for? Why do you think I wanted to get the company's name spread all over the papers? Why do you think I pushed the plan to have this Army guy out chasing his tail around the boondocks?"

Blivet nodded solemnly. "I see it all, Al. You think McRumen will go along with you?"

"I'll worry about McRumen," Shively said. "I'll worry about the rest of 'em, too. You just worry about that sales force, and about keeping your mouth shut."

"Oh, I will, Al. Don't you worry—I mean, I'll worry . . ."

"Okay." Shively flipped the intercom switch again and said, "Ask Mr. Logan to come in now, please." When Logan opened the door, he said, "Joe, I've been wondering how you're coming on that press conference idea we talked about. Time's getting short now."

"It's moving, Al," Joe said.

"That's excellent. When can I see it?"

"*Hear* it," Logan said. "I've got it all on tape. I told you this was a production."

"Terrific," Shively said. "When?"

Logan began to feel uneasy. He had spent one hilarious day in a radio studio putting the tape together, and he had taken enormous pleasure in recounting the entire presentation to Garibaldi. Now, however, seeing the enthusiastic interest light up Shively's face, he found himself wondering if he had gone too far. He shrugged. "Any time you want, I guess."

Shively looked at his watch. "How about in an hour? Where will it be? Here?"

"Well . . ." Logan considered. If he was going to go into it, he might as well go all the way. "The conference room would be better."

Shively winked at Blivet. "Sounds like Joe has something pretty spicy cooked up." He stood up abruptly, dismissing the two of them. "Okay then, an hour."

Logan left first. Blivet remained long enough to assure his chief, "I'm zeroed in, Al. I'll keep touching base with you." He padded softly out.

The door closed behind him, leaving Shively alone with his contemplation of the future. It was a future worth contemplating. It seemed to have no bounds at all for Alonzo Shively.

This would not be the first success that Shively had brought to Raven. When he had taken over as sales manager three years before, the company soon began to add a point a month on the big board at Wall Street. As the research staff turned in one worm success after another, the salesmen blanketed the country. Like locusts, twice a year they converged upon defenseless American cities for a mass canvass of every doctor, veterinarian and drug store within a ten-mile radius. Exhilarated by the half-time speeches of Coach Shively himself, the men rushed from hotel dining rooms brimming with hard-sell monologues—platoons of nice guys, battalions of smilers, hatted and clean-shaven, eyes bright and souls dedicated to proving the oft-quoted Shively maxim: "If a sale fails, we blaze no trails!"

Alonzo Shively had made his influence felt in every quarter of the company. He had had successes, but Pax would be the greatest of them all.

Shively expected opposition to his plan—from McRumen and from others. Garibaldi would be certain to oppose it; he had even stated misgivings about a hasty promotion of Pax as a prescription product. But Shively was confident that he could handle opposition; his confidence had almost a religious quality. Something fundamental was involved in the attention which he brought to the Pax campaign. There would be no rest for him, and little peace, until Pax was on the market.

"Get me Mr. McRumen's office," he said into his desk box. He stood impatiently, waiting for the signal. When it came he picked up the telephone and said only, "This is urgent, Lloyd. I'll be right up."

He had an hour. He did not expect complete capitulation—only enough to satisfy him and still leave McRumen the temporary face-saving solution he would need.

It took him little more than half that time.

"Of course I agree with you, Lloyd." The vice-president's voice was controlled and persuasive, but impatience was beginning to strain it. "No one has a bigger stake in the ethical prestige of Raven than I."

"It doesn't sound like it," McRumen said with a touch of bitterness. "We're an ethical house, Al. We've always sold to the druggist, who sells our product on a doctor's prescription."

"Lloyd," Shively said, "we make what makes money for us. If we sell Pax on prescription only, we'll make half as much as we will if we sell wide open and direct to the consumer. It's that simple."

"Deceit is never simple."

"What's deceitful? The only point worth our attention is that the government cleared this drug for over-the-counter sale once. That means it's still all right for over-the-counter."

"That's not the only point," the president said. "There is enough questionable clinical evidence for us to proceed very cautiously in marketing this as a tranquilizer. And the only way we can proceed cautiously is in the ethical market where we belong."

"*Whose* evidence? They're *our* cases. They go in our files. And that's where they stay."

"But *we* have them."

"That's right, we do." Shively's lips were drawn thin. "We've also got the sales forecasts for Pax. I've just shown them to you. They tell us where the real profits are."

McRumen retreated to his next line of defense. "We're not set up for it, Al. Our detail men are trained to call on the medical profession. Our distribution is . . ."

"What do you think I've been working on, Lloyd? I have every major wholesaler and all our direct accounts in the country ready and waiting for automatic shipments of Pax as soon as it's available. When they saw what our promotion campaign is going to be, they were all in our pocket. We've got a lulu of a sales training course outlined for *all* our old men and *three hundred* new ones."

"But we can't overextend ourselves that way. You know the stock is solid now. And our rate of growth has kept pace with the industry. We're not doing badly, Al. But if we start rocking the boat . . ."

"Rocking the boat?" Shively roared with forced laughter. "Jesus Christ, that boat sank a year ago. Don't you read my reports? We're going to do better than keep pace. We're going to *set* the pace. This is the beginning of a new era! I've waited for an opportunity like this for twenty years, Lloyd. If we keep the products and the rumors coming fast enough, our stock will swell like a boil. And if you're worried about your capital outlays, then start thinking about new financing, because we're going to be spending plenty."

The president stood staring at the top of his desk. "I just don't know," he said finally.

Shively leaned forward and his words were delivered with a slow crispness. "You know this, Lloyd. You know the board will buy this campaign, even if it is a departure from our policy. The sales forecasts are sound. Now I want to be able to tell them I have your enthusiastic endorsement."

McRumen waited again before he answered him. "I don't see how we can afford to take such a . . ."

"*I* don't see how *you* can afford *not* to," Shively said with finality.

The president sat down heavily in his chair and with deliberation turned half a circle. Then, without looking up at Shively he said, "I need time to think about it."

"Fine," the vice-president said, smiling. "I know you'll give it careful thought."

He left the president's office feeling radiantly confident.

McRumen stared out upon the Raven plant after Shively was gone. He felt lonely and strangely weak. His eyes moved over the rooftops of the production buildings and the warehouses, and his mind idly made note of those which had been part of his contribution to the company's growth. Out there, he thought, behind the dirty brick is an antiseptic world of clean machinery and white-uniformed workers, a world that I have helped to build.

The years had not been easy for him but they had been constructive. A man could buy a drug today with the expectation that it would do him some good. People who might have died were alive because of what was going on in those buildings, and Lloyd knew a small part of the credit was his.

In his own childhood, pharmaceutical chemistry had progressed little beyond the dark ages. Galenicals were the only weapons against disease. Strong-smelling herbs, mercury, bismuth and sulphur were still prescribed in palliative combinations invented by the neighborhood druggist. Today, Lloyd thought proudly, that was not the case. A drug was hardly out of the test tube before reliable machinery which would put it into the pharmacy, the sick room and the hospital had begun to turn.

In the course of his early career he had married a mild and barren schoolteacher from Brooklyn, the daughter of a pharmacist. Before they tried and failed, he imagined for himself a trio of sons, all white-coated professionals carrying on a family tradition.

Instead he lived alone with his wife and his unchanging bourgeois standards, amid the munificence of a four-story house with an elevator in Manhattan's East Nineties. But with the exception of his sterile marriage, all the inarticulate desires of his youth had been fulfilled. As chief of the world's largest manufacturer of vermifuges, he held in his hands the power to help people, which no combination of medical degrees would ever have provided. By the simple act of signing his name to a grant for private research funds, he might be helping dozens of deserving scientists, thousands of suffering people.

He had become a monument builder, and until now his most enduring work was the Raven company and what he thought it represented. His humor, his energy, his knowledge of drugs had all gone to the Raven service. Pound by pound, his whole being had been consecrated. His dedication to the company was a part of the Raven story now and an inspiration for all who followed. He worked tirelessly, relentlessly for the company's interest, as much as possible in keeping with his conscience. There were many times in his career when he had been unfair or dishonest. There were situations in which he had turned his back on activities he knew to be wrong but which would redound to the company's eventual advantage.

In the company's interest and in his own, he now had to meet the development Shively had presented and meet it quickly. Raven was an ethical pharmaceutical house, an important member of the health team which placed drugs in the hands of the physician. It was not a fly-by-night, hip-pocket operation. Dignity and character were as much a part of Raven as the laboratories and machinery which turned out its drugs. Profit was not the only ethic, as Shively believed, but the weight of power now lay with Shively. He controlled the sales organization upon which the company depended for its sustenance, and the directors liked the brand of bacon Shively's efforts brought in.

If his own position was untenable, McRumen reflected, it was not, in honesty, a surprising one. The hard truth was that much of Shively's power had been forged from raw materials provided by Lloyd McRumen himself. The troubled thought returned to him: *there were times when he had turned his back on activities he knew to be wrong but which would redound to the company's eventual advantage*. Indeed there were such times, many of them, but more than back-turning was involved. A tacit agreement to let someone else do the dirty work had provided Lloyd with both the appearance of a clear conscience and the opportunity to concentrate on his role of industrial statesman. And because the man who had done the dirty work was Alonzo Shively, Shively today had the strength to fight—and, perhaps, to win.

McRumen groped for an exit from his dilemma, and dimly one began to materialize on the outer rim of his consciousness. If he fought Shively and lost, the victory would be complete for the vice-president in the eyes of the board, and Shively would inherit the Raven prize. If he did not oppose Shively, then there would be no contest. Shively could carry out his plan with the temperate guidance of the president. If the vice-president's hopes for Pax were justified—and Lloyd McRumen was disconcertingly aware that they probably were—it could indeed produce enormous profits for the company, and in the process contribute toward the construction of a larger monument for the president than even Lloyd had dreamed of earlier. And Lloyd McRumen's conscience would once again be satisfied. It would be Alonzo Shively who would do the dirty work.

9

BLACK CURTAINS had been drawn to shut out the daylight, and the only light in the conference room came from the podium behind which Logan stood. On a table beside him was a tape recorder and a control panel with which he could switch the sound to any one of six loud-speakers concealed in various parts of the room.

Logan waited quietly while Shively and Blivet took seats. "This is just the first part of the program," he said. "It will start the press conference off." He began to read from a card before him: "You are about to enter into an adventure of the senses. You are about to see and hear compressed into a few short minutes the concentrated terrors of American life, the fears, the ghosts, the niggling anxieties that make up the pattern of your existence."

He switched out the light on the podium and the room was in total darkness.

"What the hell's this?" Shively's voice demanded.

"Part of the program, Al. You want to go ahead?"

"All right, all right. Go on."

There were several seconds of silence, and then the salving tones of a recorded narration spread through the room: "Imagine that you are part of a vast embryonic brain lying in the soothing quiet of nature's comforting womb. You have lived until now from natural inner direction. No shock has been visited upon you. You are in the husk of the seed of life and you are in a perfect undisturbed state of being. Let yourselves relax, forget your other being, steep yourselves in comfort." The voice stopped and there was only silence in the darkness. Then, slowly, the voice began again, lower still—sepulchral: "Prepare for the trauma of birth."

Another silence. Then suddenly, from a speaker in the back of the room, a woman's shriek cut through the silence, long and piercing. The only other sound was the clatter made when Horace Blivet upset his chair.

"You are now a part of America," the narrator's voice said, "living and breathing, playing and working, as child and as adult. From infancy onward, you are subject to a thousand tensions, a fearsome host of worries. You are assaulted and harassed but you try to relax. You try . . ."

The deafening wail of a police siren rose from another part of the room. When it faded, the clang of a fire bell began and was drowned out by the crashing noise of steel against steel as if a giant threshing machine had been started up, unoiled.

A child's scream was cut off sharply by the squeal of brakes which merged with the sound of an automobile horn.

"You try to relax," said the voice. "But who can?"

The voice was followed rapidly by bars of rock-and-roll music and the amplified noise of a jet engine. A dog barked, a whistle blew, and an inexpert trombonist ran up half a scale.

The voice began again against a background of an infant's cry, persistent and demanding. "The pressures of society are relentless. The thousand voices from every corner of your life will continue to gnaw on your state of mind until you are forced in all directions at once. Listen to these voices and feel the bind—feel the conflict they bring to play upon your lacerated nerves. . . ."

From the different loud-speakers came the voices—pleading, rasping, shouting, urging, bullying. . . .

"Pay up!"

"Sorry, old man, but you're just not pulling your oar."

"But, dear, we *need* a new furnace."

"Do pimples bother you?"

"Be an individualist, Mac. They can't push you around."

"I need a drink."

"You're too fat, too damned fat!"

"I can't go in there and face him now."

"My kid's a bedwetter? *My* kid?"

The voice cut in again. "The multifarious problems of the multitude, which find us terrified and defenseless," it droned. "The twisted daily dilemmas of our lives, which we must all face up to—or be hunted, hounded, and crushed by the forces which tear down our natural personalities, impede our efficiency, and make it all but impossible to find the *peace of mind* we crave.

"But now"—triumphal music could be heard from another loud-speaker—"there is a new hope, a new promise of peace for all." The music became louder and then diminished. The voice took on a brisk, urgent note.

"In Raleigh, North Carolina, last week, Doctor Ralph Rugg reported . . ."

Another voice: ". . . thirty-two patients of mine have found peace of mind."

"And from Doctor Warden Winthrop in Crankshaft, New Jersey . . ."

Another voice, rich with dignity: "Peace of mind was handed to fifty-one garden-variety neurotics under my care. . . ."

"In Los Cojones, California, Dr. Louise Bovary . . ."

A soft, liquid female voice: ". . . *I* gave peace of mind to twelve patients in one night. . . ."

"And how has this come about in an age of fast-paced, high-voltage living? The answer, brought out of darkness by the power of science, is a symbol of our native ingenuity and our creative resourcefulness."

From all the loud-speakers in the room half a dozen voices shouted:

"PAX!"

"PAX!"   *"PAX!"*

"PAX!"

"PAX!"

"PAX!"

as a shimmering light began to glow brighter and brighter on the center of the front stage, until a PAX sign in radiant pink and purple, ten feet high, lighted the room. Pastoral music was played softly in the background.

Logan switched on the wall lights. "Well, that's it," he said to his blinking audience of two. "I figure one of our scientists can make the actual announcement and answer questions. We can have the press kits passed out by models dressed in striped leotards."

Shively pumped Joe's hand. "Goddamn, that's it," he said. "That's *it!* Light, music, drama. It had—*soul.*"

"It sounded like a new religion," Blivet said.

Shively looked at his watch. "You fellows hungry? Let's kick it around over lunch." He led the way into the Raven staff dining room with Logan and Blivet trailing behind. He took his usual seat at the president's table and motioned them to chairs on either side of him. He shook out his napkin and looked thoughtfully at the linen cloth on the table. "Joe," he said, "you're going to have a real product to announce to those newspaper people." As Logan sat watching him, listening with deep surprise, Shively spelled out the details of his plan to sell Pax without a prescription.

When he was through, Logan considered it silently for several seconds, letting all of its implications arrange themselves in his consciousness, and then he asked, "McRumen has bought this, Al?"

"He's buying it," Shively said. "I haven't any doubts."

"I see. Well. It looks as if congratulations are in order. This is a big step for you, isn't it?"

"For all of us," Shively amended. "This is big."

Logan could believe that. He had been with Raven long enough, absorbing its philosophy, to know that the company was turning a corner now, one leading into uncharted territory. He tried to sort out his own feelings. He recognized some reluctance, the sentimental kind that accompanies break with tradition. But it wasn't strong—not nearly so active as Garibaldi's and some of the other professionals' would be. Far more powerful in him was a disposition toward excitement, the challenge of something new and untried. It was this feeling, he knew, that he would have to keep in deliberate check if he did not want to disturb the detachment which was his greatest advantage.

"Joe, that was good work on that press conference," Shively said. "Showed imagination, heavyweight thinking. Maybe you can help us out on some of our other problems. What do you think of television?"

"I don't know, Al. Since we've never tried to reach the public directly with a product before, I never gave it much attention."

"Well, I have," Shively said. "It's one of the best places we can put our advertising dollars. I'd like to use this new subliminal technique, but Horace tells me we can't get away with it yet, so I'm going to try some spot commercials. But we need gimmicks. That's what I want your help on."

"Not just straight announcer commercials?"

"Something fresh," Shively said. "Fresh and dramatic and human."

Logan considered. "You said it yourself," he told Shively. "Dramatic and human. Why not dramatizations?"

Shively watched him with interest. "Go on."

"Well, let's see. Why not dramatize some of our clinical cases, from the testing program? Garibaldi's got a whole office full of them."

Shively's eyes narrowed while he studied Joe's face. He drummed his fingers softly on the table. "Not bad," he said finally. "What do you think, Horace?"

Blivet's face was clouded. "Joe's no advertising man," he said petulantly, "but maybe there's some merit . . ."

"Where's Garibaldi?" Shively asked. "Is he here today?"

"Over in the corner," Blivet said.

"Horace, get him. Tell him to bring his coffee over to our table. I mean *ask* him."

Blivet hurried across the room and returned after a few moments with Ambrose Garibaldi in tow. Logan made room for him at the table.

"Ambrose, how many clinical cases have you got so far?" Shively asked him.

"Seven hundred, perhaps," Garibaldi said, looking from Shively to Logan, perplexed. "Why?"

"Covering how many conditions?" Shively pursued.

"That would be difficult to say. They're simple tension states, if that's what you mean."

"Yeah, I know," Shively said impatiently, "but how many diseases? Two, three hundred?"

"There are seven hundred separate sets of reasons why these people were tense," the doctor said. "They range from change of life to the tyranny of ill-mannered children."

"Wouldn't you say they probably cover our list of diseases which cry out for Pax? For the peace of mind promotional theme?" Blivet asked, trying to get the answer he knew Shively wanted.

"I wouldn't," Garibaldi said, "simply because they don't. That list is yours, not the physician's."

"But they *could,* couldn't they?" Shively asked with finality. "Give me a straight answer."

"The clinical trials speak for themselves. They only prove that Pax is effective in providing some anxious people with relief from anxiety. Anxiety can result from many things—including those on your list."

Shively looked at the doctor carefully. "Joe has come up with what I think is a splendid idea for getting some advertising mileage out of television." He described the plan briefly.

Garibaldi listened patiently, then turned wounded eyes on Joe. *"Et tu, Brute?"*

Joe started to laugh uncertainly. "Oh, come *on* now, Doc," he said. "Christ, it's only an advertising stunt."

"Indeed," said Garibaldi. *"Only."*

"Let's not get this cluttered up with crap," Shively said. "I want to know what you think of the plan."

Through the physician's mind ran visions of stick-legged Pax tablets dancing a jig and harmoniously joined in song—*oogeldy, oogeldy, pippity-pup, iggeldy-ziggeldy, gobble 'em up!* He looked from Blivet to Shively, noting the intensity with which they were studying him.

"Heresy though it may be," Garibaldi said, "we should not forget that it is to our advantage not to offend the medical profession with a lot of infantile promotion."

"Let's not worry about that now." Shively smiled tolerantly. "There must be at least a hundred satisfied patients with real testimonials we could use. The harried housewife, the broken-down schoolteacher, the reformed alcoholic, the frantic executive—all normal, everyday people saved by Pax. What I visualize are—vignettes."

"Normal, everyday people," the doctor said, "only they should all be coming apart at the seams."

"That's it! That's it, exactly," Shively answered. "And we only use one in each commercial. The first thing you see is this normal person coming apart—enough to get the audience interested, and then—boff!"

"Pax," said Garibaldi.

"I think we ought to have the advertising agency make up a commercial or two for us to see," Shively said. "Horace, you get together with Dr. Garibaldi after lunch and pick out a couple of cases you can use."

"We'll have to use fictitious names, of course, won't we, Doctor?" Blivet asked.

"Oh, I don't know," Garibaldi said elaborately. "Real names, like Alice and Tony and Jake, might be better."

"The cases ought to be the most universal, but they should also be the most dramatic," Blivet said. "Right, Al?"

"That's the idea," Shively said.

Blivet nodded. "You must have hundreds of everyday kinds of cases. What about juvenile delinquency?"

"I don't think you'd want those cases," Garibaldi said. "They're so rare."

"No siroony," Blivet said. "Everyone is concerned about juvenile delinquents."

"I hardly see why you'd want them, but there *are* two or three cases. One involved a high-strung young honor student—but I'm sure you couldn't use it."

"Thousands of people have high school age children," Blivet said. "What happened to him?"

"He was an outstanding student—consistently at the head of his class. His parents were alarmed, however, because he was always on the go—

a restless lad. His teachers told him he should slow down. And his father was continually telling him to take it easy. Finally, while seeing the family doctor about a virus infection, he was treated with Pax."

Blivet was puzzled. "I thought this was a juvenile delinquent."

Rising, Garibaldi heaved a great sigh as Shively watched him suspiciously. "Apparently that's what he became," the doctor said. "Peace of mind was too much for him. He wound up filching fruit to pay his gambling debts."

"That's absurd," Shively said.

"Of course it is," agreed the doctor.

"Look, Doctor," Shively said. "Let's cut this out. Horace will look over your cases and pick out what we need. I think you get the idea."

"Clearly," Garibaldi said.

"Well, fellows, let's get to work," Shively said.

Logan got up from his chair and went with Garibaldi into the hall. "Why are you shadowing me?" the doctor asked over his shoulder. "Do you have some more smart ideas about my clinical cases?"

Logan laughed uneasily. "You make it sound serious."

Garibaldi stopped and turned. "When my work is on Shively's sacrificial altar, you bet it's serious. Come on into the office for a minute where I can gripe in privacy." They had passed through the medical library and reached the door that carried Garibaldi's name. Inside, Joe dropped into a chair. "Is it still just a job, Joe?" the doctor asked.

"Why not?"

"You're handling it well. My compliments."

"I'm doing what I'm paid to do, that's all." Logan's words carried a trace of irritation. "I'm not making any decisions and I'm not taking any sides. They want ideas, I give 'em ideas."

"This last one was a crackerjack."

"Shively thought so."

"That's a rare honor. Pax to him means snake oil revisited. The medical profession exists only as a sales nuisance. In his book M.D. stands for more dollars."

"Look, Doc," Logan said, "I don't know whether you know it, but he's going for broke on this. He's planning to put this thing over the counter."

Garibaldi stopped, turned, and peered at Joe intently. "What are you talking about?"

"Just what I said." Logan repeated the information Shively had given him at lunch.

Garibaldi inhaled deeply. "I can't believe he can get McRumen behind him."

"He seems pretty sure of himself," Joe said. "And he's usually careful with facts like those. I think he's got Lloyd by the short hair."

Garibaldi slammed his fist against the desk. "Well, *I* won't stand for it, God damn it! This isn't bubble gum!"

"Isn't it? I got the picture from lunch that . . ."

"I should have read his mind a month ago. He'd be a narcotics pusher if it paid as well." Garibaldi rose from his chair and gazed through the glass partition which separated one side of his office from the library. "Well, well, here comes Horace. He isn't losing any time on his new assignment."

"Is this a convenient time, Doctor?" Blivet asked as he bounced into the office.

Garibaldi looked fully and carefully at Blivet. "Horace," he said, "I can't think of a more convenient time in the entire calendar of convenient days. They are all, every one of them, at your disposal. Don't go, Joe," he said to Logan. "As the rapist whose seed is responsible, you might find something amusing in this monster we are about to deliver."

"Got a date," Logan said hastily. He retreated from the room, closing the door behind him.

During the next hour, Blivet kept up a running commentary as he pawed through the folders of case histories which Garibaldi had silently turned over to him. As he talked, Garibaldi remained unresponsive, although his mind was depressingly active. The insidious influence of Shively's new scheme had fixed itself as a colored filter in his unconscious, and every clinical case Blivet triumphantly held aloft translated itself into a lurid television commercial.

"I probably should have had my secretary bring these up to my office," Blivet said after he had perused the first thirty folders. "There's a lot to this."

Garibaldi made no comment.

"Incidentally, Doc," Blivet said, "I didn't get a chance to tell you, but I'm going to get a new title."

Still the physician remained silent, partly because he didn't wish to encourage Blivet further, partly because he didn't trust his responses.

"Al's going to make me *director* of advertising and sales promotion," Blivet said proudly.

Garibaldi broke his silence. "Is *that* what he's calling his prat boys these days?" he asked, without turning around.

Horace Blivet, the new self-confidence born of his lunchtime recognition still intact, sucked in his breath heavily and demanded that Garibaldi repeat what he had said.

"Oh, come now, Horace. You heard me."

Blivet came around in front of his desk, bristling with outrage. "You think you've got all the answers, don't you?" he said indignantly. "Well, *we* don't think you've got very many. We know you haven't been on The Team for a long time and Al isn't going to humor you along much further."

"Look, toady," Garibaldi said, the accumulated anger of days rolling through him like a flood, "Al Shively has the brain of a retarded rhesus and you're a bag of wet wash and if I had half the professional integrity I should have, I'd stuff you down his throat. Now get the hell out of here!"

"Brains!" Blivet exploded. "Who do you suppose shapes the culture in this country, oddballs like you? No sir. It's done by men like Al Shively, some of the smartest men in the world. I'm wise to your kind, believe me."

"Good God—culture shaper."

"Go ahead, sneer," Blivet said. "That's about all you're good at. But I'm learning about people and I know a tin-plated quack when I see one. *Doctor?* Some doctor!"

Horace Blivet stormed out of Garibaldi's office. His great hulking shoulders sagging, Garibaldi leaned back in his chair. He had deserved Blivet's antagonism and he knew that the contempt with which the advertising man had voiced his feelings was his only defense. But in that contempt was the reverberating echo of Garibaldi's own conscience. How long could he keep it up?

He knew he had about all the *peace* his mind could stand, particularly after the news of the day. Then why not move? Now. He ticked off the reasons. *Conviction?* . . . Who cares? *Money?* . . . It was not a problem. *Pride?* . . . Before what? Raven? *Health, stability, security?* Words. *Professional inadequacy?* . . . Well . . .

Fear? . . .

His secretary gave him a sympathetic smile as she entered his office and put some papers on his desk. "Doctor, I believe that man depresses you."

"He demoralizes me."

"He and Mr. Shively make an energetic team," she observed.

"They ought to be joined at the hip," Garibaldi said.

10

LOGAN WAS never more right than when he predicted to Pat Crain the response Buddy Montrose would find in his audiences. During the next two months, in women's clubs and Rotaries, in Knights of Columbus halls and at Chamber of Commerce luncheons; in College Park, Maryland; in Enid, Oklahoma; in Casper, Wyoming; and in something more than fifty other communities in the path of his trip across the nation, a growing army of citizens experienced the thrill of participation in a human story that was bigger than their lives.

The intense young captain who stood before them, bringing them a message of lands they had never seen, sensations they had never felt, emotions they had never owned, took them into a world where headlines became real and the anguish of suffering peoples was a personal wound and the love that bound men together was something to feel and take pride in. The remote land he talked about became a neighbor's home—for half an hour anyway—and each of them carried some part of that land into the troubled, solitary moments of the night. The courage and privation that existed there existed here too, for all men are brothers and the torment of that brotherhood can sometimes be acknowledged best in the exquisite agony of tears.

I am your bridge into the world that lies beyond the events of your day, Buddy Montrose said to them; over me you may safely cross. I am your son and your lover and with me you can find a magnificence in yourselves. For together we have lived as men were born to live, knowing fear and finding courage.

In Enid, Oklahoma, and in Yakima, Washington, Buddy Montrose's mothers and his lovers wept. And their men felt the thrill of heroism in their chests.

The newspapers in the towns and cities where Montrose spoke reported on his addresses at length. Many of them ran an interview with the captain along with the story, some with photographs—either one of the pictures Logan had sent out with his press kit or one taken locally by the paper's own photographer.

Slowly, but with the consistency Logan had expected, Montrose's reputation began to build. It was still a bush-league fame, seldom extending more than fifty miles from the site of his latest speech. But this kind of solid localized attention was precisely what Logan wanted.

Although Montrose's reputation seldom carried beyond the places in which he spoke, it managed to reach Midwest City, Indiana, where it received a certain scrutiny. None of the newspapers there had yet bothered to pick up the activities of the home-town figure, but a clipping service had a long-standing contract with one of the city's residents to send reports from any newspaper in the country which contained the name of any prominent state citizen.

In no time at all the sheaf of clippings amassed on Bedford Montrose had grown substantially, and Alden Root, sitting in his quarters in the Mainline Hotel, looked through them carefully and thoughtfully.

After he had studied them all, he instructed an aide to find out from the Raven company when and where Captain Montrose was scheduled to speak. Then he made plans for a trip East to coincide with the speaker's return.

A clipping service also sent all the Montrose newspaper stories to Joe Logan, and as they came in, Emily Klinger pasted them carefully in the pages of a large bound book, on the cover of which she had mounted Buddy's picture and elaborately lettered "Montrose Campaign" in gilt. Periodically she took the book to Logan, who read through the new stories that had accumulated and dispatched a short memo to McRumen summing up the progress.

Logan closed the book, avoiding, as he always did, the preposterous cover. It irritated him to think that Emily could not bring the same devoted attention to any of her other duties that she brought so easily to anything connected with Bedford Montrose.

Reflecting on the clippings, Logan decided that Montrose was doing so well that it was just about time for phase two of the big build-up. Logan had it all worked out carefully in his mind. Once Montrose began speaking in communities with their own television stations, local TV interviews could be arranged. And if Buddy made a hit with urban audiences, Logan could attempt, with at least some hope of success, to interest a network TV show. He had already begun working to establish a beachhead on Gladys Constable's "People of Our Time," whose Sunday-night interviews consistently maintained top ratings. Joe had been able to persuade the first lady of TV news to let him buy her four pounds of prime beef and a pint and a half of gin, but his success had been distinctly limited. Gladys, whose television personality was built on a carefully retained Chicago accent and a willingness to insult anybody at all, told salacious stories about celebrities she had interviewed, and listened, chewing intently, while he presented the case for Montrose. "Maybe," she said, wiping a smear of cheese from her chin, "if he turns out to be anything. Get him out of the sticks and then we'll see."

Getting Montrose out of the sticks and into the cities was a tough job, and Logan had thus far met with resistance. To most city editors Montrose was still an unknown, or at best a rumor, and to the club and civic officials with whom Logan corresponded, only previous big-city attention would have made the speaker desirable. Logan knew that once the reaction to Montrose's first major address had registered, if it were anything like the response he was getting now, they would have the entree into every city they needed. But the question was, which one first and how?

Montrose would be returning in a few days for a swing through the East. Logan looked on the schedule and found that his first speech in the neighborhood would be in Babylon, Long Island. He would sit in on that one, he decided. Perhaps it would help him determine what should be done next.

Pat Crain's face crossed Joe's mind—crossed it and recrossed it. With some discomfort he was conscious of the frequency with which he had thought of her since the night in Meadow Hills. She had called him twice to find out what had been heard from Buddy, but he had not seen her. He picked up his phone, deliberately stifling the guilt impulse that rose up in him.

"Emily, call the ticket agency and get two for tonight to *A Soft Voice in Hell*, like a good girl. Make sure they're decent seats." He flicked the telephone button to dial an outside line.

Pat Crain answered.

"I've been looking over the book of press clippings we have on Buddy," he said. "It occurred to me that you might like to see them."

"That's very nice of you, Joe," Pat said. "I'm sure I would."

"Well, how about tonight?"

"Tonight?" Her voice was hesitant.

"As it happens, I have a couple of theatre tickets, and I thought I could bring the clippings by and then we could . . ."

"Thank you, Joe," Pat said, "but I really don't see how I can."

"Buddy wouldn't mind," Joe said. "You need some recreation. I had a long telegram from him detailing your recreational needs and how best I could supply them."

"I wonder how on earth he knows," Pat said.

"Let me bring the clips by, anyway. We can take up the theatre then."

"Joe, really . . ."

"What time?"

"Well—give me a chance to straighten this place up. But don't plan anything."

"See you in an hour," Logan said. He patted the telephone receiver after he had put it down. Once again he felt the pull of his conscience, and once again he was able to bring it quickly into control.

"Well," Pat said, turning the pages slowly, "he does seem to be getting attention, doesn't he?" They were seated on a long divan in her trim apartment, the book spread on a coffee table before them.

"He's the new Mohammed. I told you he would be."

"And, let's see . . ." She ran her finger down the column of one of the news stories. "Oh, yes, *here's* the name of the Raven company. I almost thought they'd been left out."

Joe crossed his arms and watched her in amusement. "How could we be left out? Don't you know each and every one of those editors is on our payroll?"

She turned more pages, ostensibly absorbed in her task. "I can't quite tell from the stories, so tell me, has he changed his speech any from the Meadow Hills version?"

"Only a few paltry facts," Joe said. "Now he's an FBI agent. He was imprisoned by the Reds and they cut his tongue out . . ."

"And now he has yours. Isn't that wonderful?" She closed the book and smiled at Joe. There was, he saw, no bitterness or displeasure in her face, only an open cheerfulness. "What about those tickets?"

Logan was surprised. "I thought I was going to have to talk you into it."

"You do, but hurry up, so we can make the curtain. I've been thinking it over and I *do* need relaxation. I hope you have something frothy in mind."

The play told the story of a young man afflicted with sexual infantilism who, goaded by the contempt of his father, sought satisfaction in alcohol and drugs.

Later, over a midnight supper in a French restaurant, Pat said, "Some relaxation. I should have stayed home and contemplated my troubled future."

"Maybe now it won't seem so troubled."

"Why do you suppose such unreal situations always provide the meat for drama?" she asked. "Can you imagine such a family in real life?"

"I came from one," Joe said.

She ignored him. "Every character was an institutional case. Now where would you find a family like that?"

"At evening prayers. Box suppers. Baseball games. It's the new form of togetherness."

"I could hit you," she said. "Why won't you be serious?"

"I *am* serious," he said. "Hell, those situations are commonplace enough. I've known lots of poor devils in worse shape than that."

"Really," Pat said disgustedly. "Well, I suppose if you seek out depravity . . ."

"The only difference in our approach," Joe said, "seems to be one of conditioning. I've been conditioned to expect certain results from experience. Not always the worst and not always the phony—but most of the time."

She rested her chin on her hand and looked at him. "Give me your rule of living," she said. "No more beating around the bush. If you don't have one handy, make one up."

"All right. Quick respect for anything is the cheapest kind of acceptance. It dulls the reason."

"And suspicion hardens the heart."

"Not hardens—toughens."

"This rule—it's all based on information you get from *inside* the camp, isn't it?"

Logan smiled widely. "Ah, Miss Crain, you're too obvious. I've been waiting for ten minutes now for you to turn the spotlight on my public relations."

"Well, now your waiting is over. The spotlight is on it."

"Do you suspect an inconsistency? There's one there, all right. I merchandise phoniness—some of it, and some of the time. That's why I say, look out for what *seems* to be. Poke the carcass with a question mark and see where the make-up chips off."

"How awful. Suppose it chipped off *everything?*"

"Careful," Joe warned her with some amusement. "That's the first step down to Logan's lower basement, where you can only see with a jaundiced eye. Rose-colored glasses aren't allowed."

"You're something of a fake yourself," she said.

"I'm a practical man."

"You're a phony, a charlatan, and just a little bit of a dreamer," Pat said, "and I find, after all, I can sit at the same table with you and not worry about my values getting completely distorted." She smiled at him.

Their conversation swept on through other pockets, buoyed by a succession of drinks and the friendly challenge they found in each other. Inevitably, by the time Joe returned Pat to her apartment, it touched briefly once more on Buddy Montrose.

"Be fair with him, Joe," she said. "Let him come out of this with his head up and his own rose-colored glasses intact."

The enthusiasm of Buddy Montrose's audiences varied hardly at all from night to night, from city to city. And the speaker, somewhat to his surprise, found the task of repeated delivery no chore at all. Because of Logan's warnings that he would begin to tire of the speech early and would have to guard against the dangers of improvisation or worse, he had braced himself after the first week for the onset of ennui and discontent. Neither came.

What did come, as his speeches grew in number, was a conviction of the significance of his message and his activity. It was a conviction abetted in no insubstantial way by the audiences who heard him and cheered him on. Standing before them, hearing their applause fill their auditoriums and their banquet halls, Buddy found himself believing in them —at least in their applause—just as they believed in him. The rustle of approval, stirring its way through a darkened chamber, had an electric quality which he came to wait for by his lectern. After he had felt it, he depended on it. He waited for it to touch him and then touching was not enough; he waited for it to engulf him. He found in their approbation something of the warm devotion of the people of Baopneng, which had nourished him through a dark and lonely time. Just as in Baopneng, it was a nourishment that fed the will to do the job at hand; it fed other needs as well, some of them more obscure and complex than simple devotion to duty.

Buddy looked upon the approval of the people as a gift which he accepted gratefully. Each time it was offered, his sense of well-being deepened.

An uncounted number of private citizens predicted a spectacular rise in his personal fortunes; some held to him urgently for the moment, as if to prolong his time among them or to take from him something that would endure.

In the glass and redwood palace of an automobile dealer and civic leader of Gadfly, California, where Buddy was guest of honor at a supper party following his speech, he heard the prediction twice. "You're going places, youngster," his cheerful and florid host told him. "Mark my words, you're going there fast, too."

The host's tanned and well-fed daughter laid a hand on Buddy's sleeve as she sat with him on a massive chaise longue before her father's amoeboid swimming pool. "You're going somewhere, you lovely thing," she said. "God knows where, but I wish you could put me in your chariot and take me with you." She spilled some of her drink on her white satin dinner dress and placed the glass carefully on the lawn beside her. "Come in closer," she said. "I want a better look at you."

The unreality of the monstrous pool, picking up lights from the sky; the pound of the surf in the distance, the sounds of civilized laughter from the house above them, the desperation of the girl beside him, created a moment of panic in Buddy, and he moved his eyes away from her, toward the house. "Shouldn't we . . ."

"It's all right," she said. . . .

Then, lying beneath the midnight sky, she cried out once and after a shuddering gasp relaxed limply and whispered, "Oh, you're going somewhere. . . . Take me with you."

She drove him to the station the next day where he caught his train for Los Angeles.

"Will you call me?" she asked him.

"I'll try."

"But you won't do it." She kissed him lingeringly, turned and walked back to her white Mercedes.

From the cool privacy of his compartment he watched her drive away before he checked his appointment book and made some special notes on the speech he would deliver that evening before the Long Beach Navy League. When he had finished, he wrote an eight-page letter to Pat Crain, and then he slept to prepare himself for the evening ahead.

Pat found Buddy's letter when she returned from her classes two days later and hurried up to her apartment to read it. She hadn't heard from him in over a week.

Stripping down to her slip, she stretched out on the end of the bed and opened the letter. It was scrawled in pencil on hotel stationery.

Dearest Patty:

I've been away too long this time, but it certainly has gone fast, I've been so busy. Last week eleven speeches and this week seven in three days. But everybody seems to like them. I've found that these people really want to know what it's like to see suffering and try to help, to experience Communist violence and survive, to participate in an experience that's as vital . . .

Pat put the letter down, anger and alarm rising inside her. *Oh, Buddy,* she thought, *look what is happening.* Didn't he remember any more that the Communist violence idea was Logan's contribution? She crumpled the letter viciously in her hand and let it fall to the floor.

Poor impressionable Buddy. He no longer knew himself what was line and what was color. He had to get away from it to get his perspective, to lose this growing acceptance of unreality. And she had to help him. Somehow.

Buddy Montrose arrived in New York before lunch the day of the Babylon speech, his suitcase stuffed with press clippings and honorary service club membership scrolls tendered by the West Coast communities he had visited.

He went to his hotel upon arrival, and after a shower he sat in his shorts and ate his lunch from the cart that had been rolled into his room. He arranged himself comfortably with the telephone at one elbow. The first call he made was to Pat Crain.

"It's about time," she said cheerfully.

"Look, honey, I don't know whether I'll be able to get over this afternoon. I've got the speech in Long Island at eight and Logan to see and a million things to do first. I'll have to meet you out there, I suppose." When she was silent on the other end of the line, he added, "You understand, don't you, darling?"

"Yes," Pat said wearily. "You can see me any old time. Logan may not get another chance at you."

"Look, honey . . ."

"I'm sorry, Buddy, that was mean. I'm just tired. Let's forget it. I'll see you tonight."

"You'll be there?"

"I'll be there."

"I have to get out there early," he said, "but you're going home with me. Logan . . ."

She cut in. "Please. I'll see you tonight." She put the phone down heavily. The vision that filled her mind was not Buddy Montrose, but Logan. Damn him, she thought. Why does he have to confuse things?

That night in separate parts of the auditorium, three listeners sat detached from the responding mass surrounding them, receiving Buddy Montrose's message to the world with antennae separately attuned.

Logan listened, half absently at first, his eyes wandering over the dark-ened auditorium, searching for the outline of Pat Crain, but he did not find it. All was murky and indistinguishable against the lighted figure on the stage. Unconsciously, Joe Logan hadn't missed a syllable. Even with the distraction of his search, Joe heard Buddy Montrose's words. Dramatic and powerful, warm and compelling, they came to him. And before it was over, Logan, too, was intent upon the young man's words, almost as if hearing them fresh and vibrant for the first time, and for the first time realizing that with Buddy Montrose as its spokesman, idealism no longer alienated him.

Another watched through narrowed eyes that took in at once the cap-tain's dynamic presence on the stage, and listened to the stirring drama in the young man's voice and words, and the gasps and muffled sobs and thunderous clapping it touched off in the attentive crowd. Alden Root watched and listened and chewed thoughtfully on the stump of a dead cigar, working in his mind a hundred small political sums and equating them all to the lean young speaker before him.

Pat Crain sat off to one side of the auditorium, quiet and tense, tears standing in her eyes. There were tears in other eyes around her, brought forth by the telling force of tragic fact and passionate rhetoric. But hers were alien tears, made of anger, disappointment and indescribable pity.

The tears had disappeared when Montrose took her home, gone as if evaporated by the brisk night air. But the mood that caused them re-mained. Buddy noticed and asked her what was the matter. She wanted to tell him but she could not. In her mind, the currents of the past several weeks seemed to have taken him so far that it was as if they inhabited different sides of the earth. Unhappily, she sat back while he told about the wonderful people he had met in San Jose and Fresno and the warm response they had given him.

"They treated me like a celebrity," he said. "Patty, what on earth is the matter with you? Did I say something I shouldn't have?"

"No, go on. I'm sorry, Buddy," she said, taking a piece of tissue from her purse. "I just don't understand. . . . I don't like what's happening. Can't you give up this tour?"

"Now, honey, you really don't mean that."

On the steps of the old brownstone apartment house in which she lived, he took her awkwardly in his arms. She tucked her head down against his shoulder and for several seconds neither of them said anything.

"You know what I'm trying to do, darling," he told her finally. "I know it isn't much but it has to be done. In a little while, this will all be over. Now brighten up and act like you're glad to have me back. Come on." He put his finger under her chin and tilted her head back.

She took his kiss with gratitude, hoping it would quiet the disturbances that whipped inside her. She clung to him, trying to find the assurances she needed.

When he left her finally, she went in and sat alone in the tiny living room, thoughts racing crazily over the speech she had heard, over Joe Logan and his damnable drug company, and above all, over what they were doing to Buddy. *What has happened?* she thought desperately. *What is going to happen to him now?*

Dressed only in a frayed terry-cloth beach robe, Alden Root arranged himself comfortably on his hotel bed and turned the bed lamp so that it shone directly on the folder in his lap. He lit the stump of his dead cigar, flicked the glowing ashes on the rug, and settled down to study the papers he had brought with him from Midwest City. The first was a biographical sketch prepared by one of his aides. It was short, but it contained all the elements Root desired to see.

Buddy Montrose had been born in a crossroad village ten miles from Midwest City, the second of three children in the family of George Cabell Montrose, tenant farmer. His father had died when Buddy was attending college, and his mother now lived with a married daughter in Angola. Buddy's other sister was married to a county school superintendent in southern Indiana. The boy had been educated in the rural school system near Midwest City, the county consolidated high school, and the state university. He had been an Eagle Scout, attended the Methodist church, made a "B" average in all his courses in college. He worked his way through, played basketball, won a debating medal, and, during his senior year, was elected president of the student council. Upon graduation with a degree in political science, he had also received an ROTC commission in the Army. He had never voted and he had three years of honorable Army service, most of it in the Far East, being relieved from active duty with the rank of captain. He held the Distinguished Service Medal from the Army for his most recent services, as well as other decorations. He was a moderate drinker and smoker, had never been in any kind of difficulty, financial or social, and was engaged to be married to Patricia Moore Crain, daughter of Senator Barton Crain.

He was in perfect health and had always enjoyed the highest regard of his friends, his teachers, his superiors and his subordinates. In the Midwest City Trust Company he had deposits totaling $4,800.

Alden Root put the folder down and puffed contentedly on his cigar.

Couldn't be better, he thought. *That and what I heard tonight. Bart Crain wants to make a stink? I'll cook him in his own juice.*

11

AMBROSE GARIBALDI'S experienced eye estimated the stack of case histories on his desk at eighty to ninety. He dropped wearily into his expansive swivel chair and began thumbing through them.

Under normal conditions, Dr. Garibaldi's workaday world seldom extended beyond the glass panes that walled in his office, except for his daily rounds of the Raven research laboratories. Since beginning the Pax clinical testing program, however, he found even those excursions less frequent and the hours spent checking the data received from clinicians increasingly more numerous. Each day he faced a mountain of clinical reports marked for his attention, for the results of the tests were coming in rapidly. He had advised the immediate abandonment of the clinical program when he learned of Shively's intent to market the tranquilizer over the counter. But the vice-president had insisted it be continued: if and when the government raised the question of Pax sales, he wanted unlimited ammunition in favor of the harmlessness of the drug. He also thought the clinical cases provided first-rate advertising fodder.

Now, as Garibaldi turned heavily to the study of the newest batch of reports, he realized that a good part of his scientific objectivity was slipping away. Shively's plan to market Pax as a proprietary drug had loosed in Garibaldi a pervading melancholy and a deep indignation. He was aware that the frankness with which he had expressed his earlier misgivings—over the hasty promotion of Pax even when he thought it was to be sold as an ethical drug—had reduced the effectiveness of his protest now. But he had tried, nonetheless. He had made clearly known—to Shively, to McRumen, and to others—his strenuous objections to selling Pax without a doctor's prescription. "It's a drug, it's a goddamn *drug!*" he had bellowed, exasperated, to Shively. He managed to make his comments to the others more controlled and professional, explaining over and over that although clinical tests indicated Pax to be effective medication for hundreds of patients, and so far perfectly safe, for others the benefits were less apparent. Such medication, he told them, simply should not be made available like popcorn to an indiscriminating public.

With growing regularity now, he asked just what it was he was doing at Raven. He knew why he had come originally, but why had he stayed? Why had he been afraid to try again, to go back to medicine and prove to himself what he thought he had failed so terribly to prove once before.

It had been a long time ago. He had changed. He was in command of himself now and had been for years. He could trust the fact that even his own mental scars had healed, so long as he didn't actually put himself to the test, so long as he didn't try once again to take a scalpel in hand and risk some poor son of a bitch's life. And maybe even, in time, he would be able to handle some of the surgery again. He had come a long way.

So had Major Ambrose Garibaldi, surgeon in charge of a field hospital unit on Anzio beach, come a long way. He knew even before he went on the beach that he should have accepted a transfer out of the combat area. His hands were no longer steady and his mind was dulled by long exposure to duty near the line. He found that only amphetamine would clear his head to allow him to operate. It did not always steady his hand. More than once he had to ask an assistant to relieve him when he could no longer hold an instrument. When he had not slept in twenty hours, Garibaldi would stiffen himself with the drug and spend hours more probing the tissues of a mortally wounded man, knowing the soldier would die and cursing God when he did.

One night in the surgical tent, under the portable operating lights, the end came with a force which broke Ambrose Garibaldi's life into two distinct parts. It came with a young officer who had taken a bullet in the throat and was carried into the tent, choking on his own blood. As plasma was poured into his veins, the throat obstruction was cleared, the man anesthetized, and Garibaldi and his team began their work. The bombardment that had begun early in the morning continued outside and the sky flashed with the return fire of the American guns.

The wound was deep and the bullet had exposed the surface of the carotid artery. The doctor's hands wavered as he began his work. There had been no amphetamine that day or the day before: there was no more.

He tensed himself and concentrated every muscle of control on the bleeding square inch at his finger tips.

A shell exploded twenty yards away and the litter shook, the lights danced, the hands jerked, and dirt and shrapnel rained outside.

"Major! Quickly, Major!" The terrifying death-red blood from the carotid spurted out where Garibaldi had caught the artery with the tip of his scalpel blade. His surgeon's reflex failed him and he fell back from the operating table with his arm raised to shut out the sight.

He did not remember how long he stood there or what had passed through his mind. Garibaldi knew only that he had been led sobbing from the tent when they had finished. It was the last operation he ever performed. Not until later did he hear that they had managed to clip the tiny slash in the artery and somehow save the man's life.

It had taken Dr. Garibaldi an excruciating year in a stateside Army hospital to break himself of the drug he had come to depend on. Then, with his secret buried deep, he had come to Raven. He thought he would gather the courage eventually to try to redeem himself in medicine. But first he had to redeem his judgment and his courage and to test them out.

His judgment—he had redeemed that, all right, a hundred times over. Raven's professional prestige attested that vindication in no small degree. But his courage? He had never been called upon, in his years at Raven, to put his courage on the line until now.

This was such a test, but Ambrose was not sure that the challenge, after all these years, would find him ready.

He had staked everything—his personal prestige within the company, his influence—on his initial effort to halt Shively's Pax plans, and his success had been so limited as to amount to failure. He had received solemn assurances that nothing would be done which did not meet with FDA approval. And everyone had ceremoniously avoided the central fact—that the success of Shively's plan lay squarely with the expectation that the FDA would let the product sell over the counter because it had once sold that way as an antihistamine. There was as yet nothing to invite government reclassification.

Lloyd McRumen's surrender to Shively's irresponsible cupidity had only buttressed Garibaldi's own resolve—at first. He had had no intention of reducing the force of his objections. He had told himself that he would oppose the plan until he prevented it from becoming a reality or until they fired him. But later, when Shively had finally had enough of Garibaldi's protests, the vice-president made it clear to the medical research director that his views were not, by God, going to affect the policies of the sales department.

To Garibaldi's total surprise, Lloyd McRumen had concurred with Shively. After more than a decade of association with McRumen, in which mutual respect and warm friendship had grown, Garibaldi was used to situations—although they did not come often—in which the president failed to decide an issue in his favor or refused to give him the research latitude and freedom he struggled for on behalf of the scientists in the laboratories. Garibaldi understood these maneuvers as the necessary exigencies of business.

But this time it was not the same. Lloyd's concurrence had been peremptory and without satisfactory explanation. Where once he had stood as a temperate influence upon the often intemperate policies of his sales chief, he had retreated to a position of permissive silence. Questioned closely by a shocked and disappointed Garibaldi, McRumen had responded with uncharacteristic petulance which all too clearly revealed the extent of his intimidation.

"Lloyd, I understand the profit picture well enough," Garibaldi had told him, after the president went to considerable trouble to make certain he did. "But if we draw the wrath of organized medicine down upon us, as we're sure to do, the profits from our ethical sales could go up in smoke."

"For every dollar we lose, we'll make up three," McRumen had said, echoing Shively's words.

"But this is get-rich-quick, and our ethical sales have always been the bread and butter around here."

"There are a number of factors you don't understand, Ambrose," McRumen had told him, avoiding his gaze. "Take my word for it, this is the only sensible way for Raven to move."

"And the hell with our responsibility to the public," Garibaldi had responded.

McRumen, bitter and angry, had told him with much the same finality Shively had employed that the subject would henceforth be considered closed.

Garibaldi saw no way to discharge his responsibility. . . . Responsibility? To whom? Raven? Himself? The answer, he knew well, was both. What was demanded of him now, after all these years, was an act of courage. It would take courage to leave. It would take courage to stay and fight. Only in submission lay defeat. And Ambrose Garibaldi was enormously weary.

He turned back to the clinical reports on his desk and struggled to direct some attention toward them.

A few days after the Babylon speech, Joe Logan received a telephone call from a man who identified himself as Alden Root of Midwest City.

He said he had something of importance to discuss with Logan and asked if he could come out as soon as possible.

Logan was curious, but an element of intensity in the man's voice kept him from asking questions. Instead, he told him to come whenever he wanted.

"Will Captain Montrose be there?" Root asked.

"I doubt it," Logan said. "Why?"

"I'll explain it when I see you," Alden Root said.

When he showed up in Logan's office an hour later, Joe's first impression was of a ludicrous little man. But beyond the broad hearty smile Logan saw the seriousness in the man's eyes.

Joe bowed him into a chair and waited patiently while Root lit a cigar with a wooden match.

"I took in Captain Montrose's speech in Babylon the other night," Root said.

"Oh?" Logan's curiosity settled deeper.

"Fine talk. He's a home-town boy, you know."

Logan nodded, watching his guest silently.

"I'll get down to business, Mr. Logan," Root said finally. "The point is that a lot of people back home are talking about the good job young Montrose has been doing on this speaking tour for you." He waited politely for any observation Logan might want to make, but Logan said nothing.

"What we'd like to suggest," Root continued, "is that maybe you'd like to set up a speech for him in Midwest City. Seeing it's his own home town, and he's a real unsung hero, we thought we might have a big Buddy Montrose Day in his honor." He clamped the cigar in his mouth and settled back in his chair, looking carefully at Joe through narrowed eyes.

Joe waited deliberately several seconds before replying. "Well, it might be a thought," he said slowly. He kept his face composed, consciously trying to let none of the surprise he felt show through.

A welcome home day for the returning hero had occurred to Logan early. He had written to the president of the Chamber of Commerce in Midwest City, but that body's lack of interest had forced him to drop the idea. Home town or no home town, Montrose had not been an important enough figure then for Midwest City booking.

Once the initial surprise of Root's proposition had passed, he began to consider the question of what authority this unspectacular little man had to commit Midwest City to such a scheme.

As if anticipating Logan's questions, Root opened his brief case and withdrew a sheaf of papers. "Thought you might like to take a gander at these," he said.

Joe looked through them. There were half a dozen letters from civic leaders—one from the very man who had rejected Logan's initial proposal —all attesting that a Buddy Montrose Day was just what Midwest City had been waiting for.

"That's quite a collection," Logan said, handing them back to him.

"When we get an idea, we don't let it get moldy," Root said. "I guess a big turnout in a town like Midwest City wouldn't hurt you people none either, would it?"

Logan ignored the boldness in his words. "I think it might work in very well with the captain's schedule," he said, "—subject to his agreement, of course."

"That's the way we see it too," Root said. "We already got the merchants and factories committed to a fund that'll take care of everything. We're going to have a school holiday and there'll be a parade and games at the park."

"Your citizens must certainly think a great deal of Montrose," Logan said. "That's quite an order."

"Nothing's too good for our boys," Root wheezed, "'specially when they done what that boy's done. We got the National Guard armory for his speech that night. All you have to do is see that he gets there for the fun."

"You mean you have a specific date in mind?"

"If it's just the same to you, we'd like to have it on the eighteenth of next month. That's two more weeks—Friday. I hoped we wouldn't let any more time go by."

Logan went through the motions of looking at his schedule, but he knew well enough that it could be sufficiently juggled to allow for an appearance on the eighteenth. "You people certainly don't lose any time."

Root bit the ragged end from his cigar and spat it out like a nail paring.

"May I ask, Mr. Root, just what your part in all this is?" Logan watched him with interest.

"Strictly unofficial," Root said. "I got no commercial gain interest, if that's what you mean. I'm just the mayor's emissary, you might say. Matter of fact, I was going to bring the matter up." He hunched forward in his chair and placed a fat forefinger on Joe's desk. "I don't want anything said about my part in these arrangements."

Logan raised a curious eyebrow but before he could phrase his question, Root went on. "There's nothing secret about it, of course, but the mayor and his people in Midwest City are the ones should get the credit for all this. I do a little volunteer work for them, like this, every once in a while. You see why it would upset the whole apple cart if this got to be anything but unofficial."

"I suppose so," Logan said.

"You don't need to worry about any arrangements," Root said. "The mayor himself or one of his boys will be in touch with you."

Logan nodded. Nothing more was said for several seconds. The interview seemed to be at an end. But Root made no effort to leave.

"I wonder," he said finally, "if while I'm in town I might see Captain Montrose."

"I should think so," Logan said. "How long are you going to be here?"

"I thought I'd go back this afternoon. Like to see the boy before I leave. I remember him as a young scamp and I'd like to talk to him a little."

"I don't know what his plans are for the day," Logan said. "Do you want me to set up a lunch date?"

"That would be dandy."

Logan reached for the phone and told Emily to call Montrose's hotel. Putting his hand over the mouthpiece, he asked Root, "Am I to keep him from knowing your part in the Midwest City arrangements?"

Root reflected for a moment. "It's all right to let him know, I guess," he said. "I'll explain it to him at lunch if he's free."

"Do you want me to go along with you?"

"Aw, no, it's not necessary at all."

When Emily announced that she had Captain Montrose on the wire, Logan spun his chair and began to talk urgently and persuasively into the mouthpiece.

Two minutes later he turned back to Root. "He's a little puzzled," he said, "but he'll be glad to meet you at his hotel."

"Fine. I'll explain the whole thing to him." Root extended a damp and grimy hand and assured Logan that he would next be hearing from the mayor's staff in Midwest City. Then he left.

After he had gone, the heavy malodorous fragrance of his cigar stayed in the room.

By the time Alden Root settled back for a leisurely cup of coffee after a too heavy lunch, Buddy Montrose was talking volubly.

"So after my father died," he said, "I worked a year to make enough to finish at the University. There I met Pat, graduated, went into the Army and—well, you know the rest."

Root put so much cream in his cup that the coffee spilled over. He did not appear to notice the steady drip from the bottom of the cup as he held it to his lips.

"I thought for a while," Montrose said, "that I might stay in the Army but the duty is too uncertain."

"Good thing you didn't," Root said. "You're on the edge of big things."

Montrose smiled and shook his head. "I really don't know where I am right now, Mr. Root. Once this is over, though, I'd like to go back to Baopneng. Those people over there need the help."

"That's fine, but don't forget you already done a lot for them," Root said. "You gotta look out for yourself now. But don't stop talking about going back in your speeches." He looked slyly at Montrose. "Ever consider politics?"

"Politics?"

"Why not? You got a way with people."

Montrose smiled slowly. "That's a long way from getting voted for," he said.

"Well, of course you'd have to have someone around who knew what they was doing. Somebody to give you pointers. Like your speeches, for instance. You know what's wrong with your speeches?"

Montrose looked surprised. "I thought they were going over well," he said.

"Beautiful," Root agreed. "Everybody cries and feels bad. It gets to 'em all right. But what you ought to try now is getting people sore. You're passin' up your best opportunity. You got a good issue and you're lettin' it go to waste."

Montrose looked mystified. "I don't understand."

"Well, let me explain a couple things to you." Root looked at his watch. He still had a comfortable hour. That would give him plenty of time.

The news of Buddy Montrose's forthcoming appearance in Midwest City pleased Shively. Impatience had taken hold of him regarding the Montrose tour, and he had been wondering if Logan was moving the thing along as quickly as it could be moved. Midwest City's Buddy Montrose Day dispelled his impatience and delighted him with the opportunity it offered to try out some particular ideas of his own.

"Miss Krause, get Blivet up here. Tell him to bring his advertising rate books along." Shively stood up behind his desk and with two fastidious jerks at his shirt, properly aligned his cuff links. He walked across his carpeted sanctuary and stood, hands folded behind him, looking vacantly at the factory grounds below, waiting. His thoughts ranged over a hundred aspects of the Pax campaign and the manner in which he would be able to utilize the further services of Bedford Montrose. He remained there until Blivet puffed into the office with two late editions of *Standard Rate and Data* under his arms.

"How many newspapers are there in Midwest City?" Shively asked him.

"Why—I don't know, Al. Why?"

"Look it up. And look up their advertising rates. Tell me how many there are and how much a full page is, cost-wise." Shively waited as Blivet nervously flipped through the pages of one of the books.

"There are two newspapers there," he said. "The *Chronicle* in the morning—and the *Evening Post*. We'd have to get a special quote on full-page rates. Probably run somewhere around a thousand dollars a page."

"Well, get it," Shively said, spinning the chair back toward his desk. "I want to run a full page in that *Post* on the evening of the eighteenth. That's the day of Montrose's speech there. I want that ad and I want you to set up Raven displays in the armory where he's speaking."

"What kind of ad?" Blivet asked. "Institutional?"

"I want Raven, Pax and Montrose in big letters."

Blivet was astounded. "Are you sure you want the product name in the newspaper, Al? I thought we agreed with Logan not to connect it directly with Montrose."

"Forget that," Shively answered him.

"But, ethically, it doesn't seem exactly the thing for us to do," Blivet said hesitantly. "Are you going to tell Logan?"

"You let me worry about that," Shively said. "You just take care of the advertising. Let me see the copy and you keep your mouth shut."

12

LOGAN ALLOWED HIMSELF an abundance of time. It was nearly two hours before plane departure when he pulled away from the front of the

Dorwick Arms and turned the Raven station wagon into Manhattan traffic. Montrose was riding in front with him. Emily Klinger and the luggage the two men were taking to Midwest City were in the back.

"If you keep this chariot over night," Logan said to Emily, "make sure you put it in a garage."

"I won't be keeping it out," Emily said. "I'll turn it in as soon as I drive it back."

Logan grinned at her in the rear-view mirror. "I thought while you had it, you might want to use it as bait for one of your boy friends. It's nice and roomy."

"For heaven's sakes," Emily said indignantly. "What a thing to say." She looked uneasily at the profile of Buddy Montrose. "Anyway," she said, measuring her words carefully, "I don't *have* a boy friend right now. I broke up with him and I'm foot-loose and fancy-free."

There was no indication that her words had registered on Montrose. Logan said, "Don't you worry, Emily. You'll find another one."

"Well, I'm not *worry*ing." She tossed her head to show her exasperation. *"Hon*estly!"

"Okay, okay," Logan said. "Give me the tickets now, will you?"

Emily drew two airline pocket folders from her purse and passed them forward. Logan handed them to Montrose. "Look them over," he said. "You'll see that we have some rather complicated travel arrangements. We go by air only as far as Indianapolis. We'll stay there tonight and take the train into Midwest City early in the morning."

"No, you won't," Emily said. "You go right to Midwest City on the plane."

"Emily, I told you air to Indianapolis and train to Midwest City."

"I thought you didn't know there was a flight to Midwest City," she said.

"Since when are you the goddamned traffic manager?" Joe said. Emily sat back in hurt silence.

"I don't see why these won't do, Joe," Montrose said. "The flight gets us in there all right."

"Into a real mess, that's where it gets us. They want to have a welcoming committee at the station. So what do we do after we come prancing down the ramp at the airport? The train was Mr. Root's specific instruction. The airport's too far out to pull a crowd."

"Maybe we can still get space on that train," Montrose said.

"I'll call the railroad as soon as we get to the airport," Emily said. "I'm awfully sorry."

"I'll do it," Logan said. "You just concentrate that steel-trap mind on getting the car back in one piece."

Emily sullenly nursed her wounded feelings as they moved across the Queensborough Bridge. By the time they were deep in the brick and concrete forest of Queens, she had begun to recover and was wondering how on earth she could manage to engage Captain Montrose in conversation. He seemed so quiet today.

Buddy's silence had registered on Logan too, who found the captain's withdrawal curious. Seeking to break the tension he thought existed behind it, he said, "Incidentally, I've been saving a beautiful piece of news for you. I outlined our Midwest City schedule for Gladys Constable and she's practically guaranteed us a night on her show. Top time, coast-to-coast hookup, the trimmings." Logan recalled his visit to Miss Constable's scented penthouse. While he had refilled his own glass a half dozen times from the crystal decanter of Scotch she set before him, the flabby queen of Sunday night television, arrayed in a green gossamer bolero and pantaloons, had sat opposite him on the couch and quietly knocked off a big shakerful of martinis. On the first round, Joe had got from her the agreement to use Buddy on her show, and on the fifteenth, he had clumsily tucked a pillow under her unconscious head and let himself out of the apartment.

Montrose showed active interest. "That's terrific, Joe," he said.

Logan nodded with satisfaction. "A pipeline into every living room in the country, give or take a couple of million. How's that for a place to tell your story?"

At the airport, Logan went directly to the check-in counter and then into a telephone booth to call the railroad.

"I wish I was going with you," Emily told Montrose as they walked along the terminal concourse. "I never get to take a trip anywhere. Except by myself, I mean. I went to Florida two years ago on my vacation."

"Maybe Logan will take you along one of these days," Montrose said.

"Oh, it's probably just as well. He can get so nasty sometimes. Here I thought I was doing him a big favor on those tickets and you'd think I killed his grandmother. I'd hate to be married to somebody like him."

"I think he's over that," Montrose said. "We won't have any trouble on the train reservations."

"Well, I'd hate to think I inconvenienced *you*, Captain. I hope you enjoy your trip, every minute of it."

"That's nice of you. I'm sure I will."

"I suppose you'd find it a lot pleasanter if Miss Crain was here to see you off. I mean, instead of me?"

"Oh, why, I don't—why, of course not."

Emily watched the little hydraulic-lift food truck pull up beside the airliner parked a hundred yards away. "You've been engaged a long time, haven't you, Captain?"

"Buddy," he corrected her. "Yes, since college, more or less."

"She's pretty, all right, I guess," Emily said. "At least from what Mr. Logan tells me. Kind of cold-looking, I gather, but pretty."

"Well . . ."

"That often happens with some kinds of pretty women, you know. Maybe that's a good thing about long engagements, for some people, anyway. Then you know exactly what you're getting into. I mean if a person wasn't careful they could make a dreadful mistake. You want to be awfully sure you know what you're doing, Buddy." Her eyes were fixed intently on him.

"What? Oh, yes, certainly," he said, nervously.

"Because sometimes if a person isn't, it's better to wait. Particularly if he's been away for a long time in the Army and all. There are lots of pebbles on the beach and, well, you shouldn't be forced to keep a promise you made before you went into the Army, if you don't want to."

"No, that's right," Montrose said.

"Someone in your position has to be sure, because the wrong woman could be an awful handicap—I mean if she doesn't understand you or anything. I think women ought to understand men, don't you?"

"Yes, certainly," Montrose said, looking down the corridor and relieved to see Logan returning.

"That was quick," Emily said tonelessly as Joe reached them.

"They'll give us the space, fortunately," Logan said. "Deluxe on the milk-stop special out of Indianapolis." He reviewed office details with Emily until their flight was announced. Then he said, "Let's go, Buddy. Be a good girl, Emily. Sorry I yelled at you." He picked up his brief case and walked briskly toward the gate. Montrose started to follow him.

"Buddy," Emily said. "Just a minute." He looked at her curiously and she said, "I just wanted to tell you good-bye."

"Good-bye," he said.

"And—and good luck."

"Thanks."

Suddenly she reached up, put her hands behind his neck and kissed him on the lips, pressing as close to him as she could. She released him and smiled. "That was pretty forward of me, wasn't it?"

"Not—not at all," he stammered. "I . . ."

"Don't try to say anything," she said. "Maybe when you get back . . ." She let the sentence hang provocatively open.

"I—why, of course," he said. "Well—uh—good-bye."

"Good-bye," she said softly. "I'll be thinking of you." She stood watching him as he passed through the gate with Logan and boarded the plane, feeling with delight the warm flush in her cheeks and the tremor in her breast. *That* would show Buddy Montrose that not all pretty women were cold types.

A crew of high school boys had helped the flag committee from the Midwest City Merchants Association put all the banners and bunting in place along the streets before eight o'clock, and before joining the crowd or dashing off to their respective posts, they all stopped by for the cup of free coffee provided by the early-rising ladies of the American Legion Auxiliary at City Hall. They watched enviously and joked as the National Guard companies formed in front of the building and they saw the mayor drive up. They listened to the sound of last-minute hammers and the aimless tootling of gathering bandsmen.

The police lieutenant told the sergeant to assemble all the motorcycle patrolmen and get ready to precede the mayor's procession to the station. The city's largest fire trucks wheeled slowly out of the central firehouse and parked on either side of the square in front of City Hall.

In the distance, along the coal-dust grass and auto-graveyard approach to the city, the Diesel express from Indianapolis sounded its low-throated air horn blast to announce the arrival of Captain Bedford Montrose, Midwest City's own.

Both Logan and Montrose, looking out from the platform of the Pullman car, were amazed at the turnout. The vintage railroad station was hung with bunting and a long banner reading WELCOME HOME BUDDY. The high school band, drawn up smartly before the Pullman, swung into a spirited playing of "Back Home Again in Indiana."

"You think they have the right train?" Montrose asked Logan quietly.

"I forgot to tell you," Logan said. "They think you're the new chairman of the Joint Chiefs of Staff. Wave, for Christ's sake."

Buddy smiled into the crowd and raised one hand in salute. A cry of approval rose from several voices in the midst of the group. Suddenly Montrose thrust both arms high above him and a cheer as from one throat went up from the crowd. The cautious and polite people became energetically friendly, whistling and shouting their welcome. The mayor, the police chief and the commanding officer of the National Guard unit met

Buddy as he alighted from the train. After each of them had posed for pictures with him, they sandwiched him into the mayor's limousine and sped him to City Hall. In a ceremony on the front steps the mayor invested him with an honorary mayorship. A solemn boy scout presented him with a scroll announcing that his old scout troop was changing the name of its summer camp to Camp Montrose. He received a gilded fireman's hat, and from the president of the D.A.R. an award for good citizenship and devotion to the highest American ideals.

At eleven o'clock there was a parade. Along six blocks of Central Avenue, past the closed houses of commerce, the high school band strutted, followed in turn by the boy and girl scout troops, Midwest City's veterans, the crisp and trim company of the National Guard, and in an open limousine, the mayor and Captain Bedford Montrose.

In the course of the six-block journey the band ran through "The Stars and Stripes Forever" three times. Brisk martial notes rang clear and brassy in the mild, early spring air. The citizens of Midwest City who heard them, lining either side of the street, moved their bodies in response, stirred by deep pride and excitement. They cheered with passion the young hero riding in their midst.

In his hotel room, Joe Logan punched a couple of pillows behind his head and settled down to wait until it was time to go to the armory for Buddy's speech. He had scrupulously avoided close contact with Buddy through the day, and he intended to hold to that policy until the festivities were over.

Alden Root himself had suggested by telephone call to Logan several days before—with hardly any tact at all, Logan had noted with amusement —that it might detract from the solemnity of the occasion if the guest of honor had a publicity man at his elbow. Logan had given complete assurance that he understood. So long as the Raven name sounded in the speech tonight and appeared in the newspaper copy, the day and its treasures belonged to Buddy and the celebrating citizens of Midwest City.

It had been quite a day. Logan, lost in the crowd, was heavily impressed with the way Buddy had handled himself. Accepting his honors at City Hall, making his communion with the people who lined Central Avenue to watch him pass, he had been a perfect guest of honor—poised and dignified, but never for a moment losing the easy, humble, boyish charm that made his presence electric in any group. And the people had responded with something close to adulation.

Logan pulled the chain on the fluted-brass bed lamp and began looking over the newspaper clippings and letters Emily had given him to read on the trip. They were from Chappaqua and Torrington and Bath and all the other eastern cities where Montrose had recently spoken.

The letters made it clear that the fervent attention Buddy Montrose had been getting was not restricted to the spectators lining the streets at a parade in his home town. There were requests for money and offers of money. There were also offers of food and clothing for the starving Asians and offers of marriage for Montrose. The overwhelming majority of the letters, however, consisted of a few lines penned or typewritten by a housewife or a businessman, a teacher, a storekeeper, a student or a clergyman, praising the officer for his courageous spirit and enormous heart, and indicating that because he had made these qualities manifest to them, because he had touched their lives with his own splendor, they were bound to him in devotion, but also in something more complicated than devotion—in gratitude.

After he had scanned fifteen or twenty, Logan decided he had read them all. The letters disturbed him in a way he could not easily identify. There was a frightening sameness in the reactions of these people. He was public relations and this was the public—the great mass that looked and listened and talked and, ultimately, decided the destinies of all the Buddy Montroses and the Joe Logans.

The newspaper clippings presented another but less disturbing consideration. There seemed to be some exaggeration of certain of the facts in Buddy's recent speeches. The native huts he had visited had doubled in number in some of the newspaper stories. Evidence of Communist torture inflicted on the fleeing peasants was more specifically detailed than Logan remembered hearing it. Apparently Buddy's speech, as it showed up in these reports, had changed subtly with its delivery in the last couple of weeks.

But this was hardly surprising, Logan reflected. Making as many speeches a week as Montrose had been doing was a chore, even for a professional. A tyro would naturally feel the strain and begin to stray from the text a little. Logan himself had once assured Montrose that under the pressures of boredom the temptation to improvise would be strong.

The rickety bed table quivered under the telephone as Logan groped for the receiver, looking at the bedside clock as he did so. It was nearly five.

Pat Crain's voice surprised him. "What are *you* doing here?" he asked. "I thought you weren't going to be able to make the festivities." Her plan, when Logan had last talked to her, was to meet Buddy the next day at her family's farm outside the city, where they were to spend the week end with her father.

"The pull was too great," she said. "I came in time to hear the speech. Where's Buddy now? Is he with you?"

"With *me?* We public relations types muddy up the scene. I imagine Buddy's caught up in a swirl of clubwomen and cops at this point. Do you want to try to find him?"

"Well—are there dinner plans for him?"

"I think the mayor is going to have a little private party before the speech. You could probably wangle an invitation easily."

"It sounds terrible. Are you going to eat?"

"Stay right where you are. I'll come after you. I want to know if you're as mean in home territory as you are in New York."

Pat arranged herself against the back seat of the taxi and looked at Joe. "All right," she said. "All the details. How did Buddy Montrose Day go?"

"Swimmingly," Logan said. "Your man is handling himself well. His old school teachers revised all his report cards upward for the record and his old boy scout troop gave him a lifetime supply of jackknives. Before Alden Root and these people are finished, they'll have a statue in the park."

"Alden Root?" Pat asked.

"Do you know him? He was somebody's messenger boy in all this."

She nodded. "I know him," she said. Her voice was curiously flat.

Logan felt uneasy. He had not talked to her about the Midwest City plans in detail before, mainly because he realized that her already well-documented prejudices about the tour itself were likely to become magnified if they were involved with home-town considerations; and he did not know how much Buddy had told her. Now that the subject was opened before them, he wished sharply that it would give way to another. He was relieved to hear Pat say, "I think I'd better wait to hear about it all until after I've had something to eat."

"And drink?"

"And drink. I want a cocktail and a steak—and lots of *relaxed* conversation."

"If you mean from me," Logan said, "you'd better know. I talk best in my sleep."

"That's too much of a price to pay for bright chatter," she said.

As the taxi cruised past neon-lighted gasoline stations and twinkling motel signs, heading for the heart of the city, Logan leaned back in the seat. He saw that she was looking at him. Her mouth carried the barest suggestion of a smile and he thought he recognized a warmth, deeper than the interest in her expression, that he had not seen before.

"Joe," she said in a low voice, looking at the flashing signs outside the cab, "let's make a pact, shall we?"

"Sounds formal," Logan answered. "I'm the spontaneous type at heart. What's the problem?"

"I want to talk about Buddy once more, right now, in this taxicab, and I want you to be perfectly honest with me. Then we won't bring up the subject again until his tour is over."

"I like that last part best," Joe said.

"He is changing, isn't he? You can see it as well as I."

"I can see some things," Joe said. "He's gained weight, made money, picked himself up a California tan . . ."

"The pact calls for you to be serious," Pat said.

"If I'm serious you'll find me ponderous," Joe said. "A man is bound to change a little, Pat—any man, in any given time."

"Yes, but I'm talking about one man specifically, and in one specific period of time. I think he accepts some of your stage business as the truth now. He's so convincing, he's convinced himself."

For the second time in the course of the taxi ride, Joe was uncomfortable. His thoughts swept back to the newspaper clippings he had been reading just an hour before, and he realized the explanation he had given himself would never satisfy Pat. "A few small deceits are bound to crop up in his delivery," he said. "It's nothing serious. Do you want me to do anything about it?"

"I think so." She looked out into the street, at the brightly lighted shop windows which the taxi was passing now. "He likes you, Joe. You have an influence on him. Try—try to keep him from taking any of this too seriously." She did not wait for him to reply, but leaned forward and kissed him quickly. "Thanks."

"Don't take advantage of me," he said, rubbing his jaw where her lips had touched him. "I haven't promised anything."

"Of course you have," she said.

Joe bought a newspaper on the way in to the restaurant. At a corner table, Pat read the story about Buddy on the front page.

"Hand me the sports page," Joe said. Pat did not answer him. She sat stiffly, her face expressionless, her eyes on page five of the *Evening Post*. Then she started to laugh. The laugh rose, spiraling and gathering force, as if it had been coiled inside her, waiting for release.

Logan looked at the paper. There, in the center of the page, was a four-column cut of Buddy Montrose in full regalia, and above it, in 48-point type, the name Raven fairly jumped from the bare white newsprint. Below the picture, in smaller, but by no means modest lettering, Logan read: "Makers of the world's finest health aids, and sponsors of the nationwide tour of Captain Bedford Montrose, are proud to announce that Peace of Mind will soon be here with. . ." His eye jumped to the bottom of the page where, bold and blatant, the word "Pax" stood out more prominently than all the rest. If the page was held up and away from the eyes as Logan held it then in disbelief, only "Raven," the unmistakable face in the picture, and "Pax" could be seen.

"I—I don't get it," he said, shaking his head.

"Don't—don't." She forced the words out between the sobs of her laughter.

Logan leaned back heavily in his chair. At first he said nothing, trying to thread his way out of the confusion in his mind. Then he said quietly, "I think you'd better stop that, Pat."

He waited patiently for her to compose herself. She blotted her eyes with a handkerchief. "You're too much, Joe Logan," she said. "You and that company of yours. Honest to God. And I wanted *you* to help Buddy keep his perspective." She started to laugh again.

"Now, look, God damn it," Logan said. "If you think this ad was my doing, you're wrong. This isn't my line. I don't club people, I nudge them."

"Oh, come now, Mr. Logan. This piece of effrontery is too good a thing to deny. If it wasn't your idea, whose was it? Aren't you running this tour?"

"When you have a good thing in a big company," he said, "all kinds of people are in on the act. Al Shively had something to do with this."

"And you knew nothing about it. Of course." She pushed her chair back and stood up.

"Where the hell are you going?" he demanded.

"Joe, let's forget the steak. Let's just settle for laughs tonight. I really have things I should be doing." She looked down at Buddy's picture and the stark message "Pax." "I don't suppose I'll ever be able to look at him again without seeing him just that way, with those absurd letters around his neck." She started to laugh again, the sound of it high and uncontrolled. She put her hand to her mouth. "I've got to get out of here," she said. "I'm going to disgrace myself." She seized her purse and left the restaurant.

Logan stood by the table looking after her, immobilized by the frustrated anger rolling through him. When he left, after a few minutes, he bumped into a waddling matron and passed on without apology or awareness.

The mayor's dinner for Buddy Montrose was a small and intimate affair, and it ended early enough to permit Montrose ample time to get to the armory. The mayor himself and two of his aides escorted him.

As they were leaving, the mayor asked Alden Root, "Are you sure you won't go with us?"

"No, no. You go on ahead," Root said. "There are a couple of things I want to do first."

"We'll be glad to wait for you," Montrose said.

"These might take a little while." Root laid a heavy hand on Montrose's shoulder. "Good luck out there tonight, now," he said, looking into the young man's face. "We're counting on you."

Logan's anger had not subsided when he arrived at the armory an hour before Montrose's speech was scheduled to begin, and the spectacle that greeted him did nothing to assuage it. As he stepped through the front door, he saw a giant orange and black Raven sign. Flanking the doorway on both sides were two newly designed Pax displays. One included a three-dimensional, multicolored, animated mural of a waterfall splashing down the side of a mountain. Fauna frisked in the spume directly above a delicately lettered legend which read: "Peace of Mind for All Mankind." The opposite display was less restful. Luminescent letters two feet high spelled out *"Pax*ify Yourself" against a fuchsia background.

Bending over in front of the waterfall was a young man Joe had never seen before. Behind him stood Horace Blivet.

Logan stopped and gaped. Then with the voice of an enraged drill sergeant, he barked, "What the hell are *you* here for? What's this display doing in here?" Startled and confounded, Blivet turned suddenly, started to walk away, then turned again and smiled weakly at Logan.

"Why—hello, Joe . . . I . . ." He raised his hand, and then let it drop limply to his side.

"What kind of a stunt is this?" Logan asked incredulously. "What are you trying to do, sink this thing tonight?"

"Of course not, Joe," Blivet said, struggling to keep his dignity. "Al and I thought what this place needed was a little Raven display. We thought it needed—brightening." He smiled thinly again.

"Well, this is no goddamn convention, Horace. Take it down and get it out of here. All of it."

Blivet brushed some imaginary lint from his sleeve and tried to look as self-possessed as possible. "Now, *just* a minute, Joe. Al Shively told me that . . ."

"I'll worry about Shively on Monday," Logan flared. "Now get this stuff out of here!"

"All this? What do you think I am?" Blivet asked, waving his hand at the waterfall. "It took eight men to carry it in here."

"Horace, if this garbage isn't out of here in ten minutes, I'll show you how heavy it is." Joe moved threateningly toward the advertising man.

"You can't talk to me like that," Blivet said. "I'm in charge of . . ."

"God damn it, get it down!"

"I'm not taking anything down," Blivet said stubbornly, folding his arms across his sagging front.

Logan started for the waterfall and before either Blivet or the young man could block him, he seized one corner of it. Two hundred pounds of papier-mâché and neon tubing wobbled for a terrifying instant, then crashed down around them all.

"All right! All right!" Blivet screamed as Logan headed for the Pax sign. "I'll take it down." But his protest was too late. "*Pax*ify Yourself" smacked loudly down upon the wreckage of the waterfall as the advertising director watched openmouthed.

"There's your goddamned display," Logan said fiercely. "You've got five minutes to get it the hell out of here."

Blivet looked dumbly at the wreckage about him, but he was careful to stay well beyond Logan's reach. Joe turned and strode into the main part of the armory, leaving the two men to stare after him in disbelief. When Joe was out of earshot, the young man with Blivet whistled softly. "Holy Christ. What's the matter with him?"

"He's sick," Blivet cried, tapping his hand against his head, "sick—sick—sick." He returned to his mute survey of the shambles on the floor. Some men, he thought, could never be team men.

By eight-thirty Midwest City's vast armory was filled to capacity. Backdropped behind the stage was a huge photograph showing Montrose in frayed khakis, kneeling in the dirt with a protective arm around a tearful waif. Television cameras mounted on the stage and pointed toward the vacant speaker's chair drew the animated attention of the crowd.

When Montrose came on the stage escorted by the mayor and half a dozen of the city's leading citizens, the Consolidated High School band played "America the Beautiful."

Captain Bedford Montrose had never been more eloquent. He told his attentive listeners how good it was to be home again and how he could stand with them and believe, almost, that he had never been away. "In a sense," he said, "I have always lived in the land of my boyhood, using the strength I took from it, and the principles and beliefs I hold in me today are the ones that began right here."

But he *had* been away from them, and now tonight he was returning for one dark and lonely hour to the place of his trial. And he was taking them with him, his neighbors, who had helped him to become whatever he was. He led them into an ancient valley, past moss-covered temples, past quilt-coated Communist soldiers. He reached inside them and released trapped hungers. He made them weep and he made them listen. Then, in the end, his voice growing sharp and brutal, he made them angry.

"The story," he said, "the *real* story of the people of Baopneng is a simple one. It is that of a dauntless people struggling against overwhelming adversity to fight the greatest evil of our time . . . communism." His voice dropped. "And the fight is not theirs alone, but ours as well. Yours and mine and everybody's in this great land we love. We cannot live in a world where evil is winning tragic victory after tragic victory and refuse to know the evil . . ." He ran his finger along the scar above his collar. "This is the message I bring to you tonight. In your acceptance and recognition of it . . . lies the promise of our return to greatness as a nation which sees its duty and is neither ashamed nor afraid. . . ."

When he had finished, an aroused people applauded wildly, stood and cheered, and the music of the band could not be heard above their clamor.

Joe Logan stood quietly to one side as people pushed past him. Gradually, as the mob thinned, he made his way along a side aisle toward the stage where Bedford Montrose was surrounded by well-wishers. Pat Crain was there, standing quietly with her father.

"They never turn out for my speeches like this," Senator Crain said to Buddy. "That was quite a—powerful talk."

Even without hearing the senator's words, Logan knew well the extent of the impression Buddy had made. It had indeed been a powerful talk, and the effect of its power was not likely to be lost on a politician. Once again, as he had listened to a Montrose address, Logan had been swept along in the reactions of the audience he was part of. He had been stirred, as they had been stirred, by the urgency of the message and the force with which it was delivered. The fierce anti-communism pitch at the end, which had given the speech its special direction, must have been a recent addition, Logan reflected. At any rate, he hadn't heard it before.

But even as he phrased the thought, he realized he *had* heard it, or something like it—not from Buddy, but from himself. *I know from ex-perience what Communist torture is.* These words had come out of his own typewriter. But they were words Buddy had refused to use then.

Uneasiness brushed Logan's mind. He found himself wishing that the forces at work, whatever they were, had not forced Buddy to change the speech Logan had heard in Meadow Hills and Babylon.

He angled himself into a position behind Pat and said, "It's a pleasure to see you when you're in control of yourself."

"Why, hello there," she said brightly. "You know as I was coming in, I saw the funniest thing. Some little man was carrying a neon sign of yours out of the building. What happened, didn't the electrical connections work? It would have been such a nice touch, flashing on and off during Buddy's talk."

Senator Crain extended his hand. "Nice to see you again, Logan," he said.

"I'm flattered you remember, Senator."

"Have you had much experience at *separating* people from their fan clubs?" Pat asked Logan. "We've got an hour's drive to the farm yet."

Buddy, hearing her, turned and winked. He removed himself deftly from the knot of people around him. "I'm ready," he said. "Let's start the caravan rolling."

"I'm afraid the week end is going to seem a little tame," Pat said. "No parades. And a minimum of ceremonies."

Buddy kissed her lightly on the cheek. "A week end of air and relaxation. And you. That's pretty tame."

Senator Crain said to Logan, "May we drop you somewhere?"

"I don't want to put you out," Joe said. "I can get a taxi back to my hotel."

"Not at all. You come right along with us."

On the ride to the hotel, the senator asked, "What's that company of yours likely to think if they knew you were riding around with me?"

"They'd think I was doing my job admirably," Joe answered. "You remember, Senator, public relations."

Crain boomed heartily. "I think you ought to go into politics. Do you know anything about farming?"

"I grew up on a farm in Nebraska," Joe said, "but I'm a city boy now."

When they pulled up in front of the hotel, the senator said, "Unless you have other plans, Mr. Logan, why don't you come with us? I'll show you a farm and a half."

Pat leaned forward from the back seat and rested her hand lightly on Logan's shoulder. "Joe, we really would like to have you," she said.

For several seconds Joe searched for the declining answer he thought he should make. Finally he relaxed and said, "Sounds good to me."

As the car left the city and cut through the crisp Indiana night, Logan found himself listening with pleasure to Crain's anecdotes. His mind turned up experiences long dormant. "In Nebraska, we used to . . ." he heard himself saying, and a part of his life was opened up again—one he had not thought about since his youth.

13

SENATOR CRAIN'S FARM did not remind Logan much of the dust-bowl depression land he had grown up on in Nebraska. This one was green and rich and bordered with hills.

Despite the differences, however, there was a similarity which stirred responses long untouched in Logan. The look of early morning sun straight on the earth and the feel of the wind before it is blunted by activity, he remembered as possessions of his boyhood.

Everyone around the table at breakfast was cheerful, reflecting the golden tenor of the warm spring day.

"What do you plan to do today, baby?" Bart Crain asked his daughter.

"I thought we might all pack a lunch and take the horses out," Pat said. "The weather's so lovely." She looked, Logan thought, like a part of this place. She was dressed in a blouse and whipcord jodhpurs, and the sunlight that streamed in through the window behind her gave her brown hair a golden shimmer when she turned her head.

"You young people go," the senator said. "I'm going to poke around the farm."

Feeling like an interloper, and suspecting that Montrose might be thinking the same, Logan said, "I'm not much of a horseman, and if you don't mind, I'd enjoy tagging along with the senator."

"Delighted," Crain said. "Come right along."

Before they were able to leave, however, a telephone call came for Montrose.

He was out of the room for several minutes. "I'm awfully sorry, honey," he said to Pat when he returned. "I've got to go into town for a little while." He made no further explanation and Pat asked for none.

"I hope this doesn't upset our picnic," Buddy said.

"We'll just eat on the lawn," Pat said curtly.

"This doesn't *have* to spoil it," Buddy persisted. "Look, I won't be gone long. Joe, why don't you change your mind and go on that horseback ride? You and Patty could go on ahead and when I get back I'll catch up with you."

To Joe's surprise Pat agreed, and it was decided that Montrose would join them when he returned.

Buddy took the senator's car and left the farm before the others. He followed the winding country road to the state highway and pushed the station wagon up, just over what the law allowed. In less than half an hour he turned into the gravel parking area of the Melody Farms Country Bar-B-Q and parked. There was only one other car in sight and he guessed correctly that it was Alden Root's.

"This is as good a place to talk as any," Root said, as they went into the deserted bar. "I ordered some coffee for us."

"I wasn't sure this was the right place," Buddy said. "It looked pretty empty." Root smiled and led the way to one of the imitation colonial tables. The bar room was sunless and chill, and the stale scent of long-contained tobacco smoke and draught beer hung in the air.

"That was a dandy speech last night," Root said.

"I'm glad you liked it," Montrose answered.

"Not just me. Everybody did. The boys that count." Root waited while a sleepy-eyed man wrapped in a dirty white apron put a pot of coffee and cups on the table.

"I own this place," Root said matter-of-factly, "in case you're wondering. But I don't come here much. Food's lousy."

Montrose laughed and Root waited again for several seconds, his expression deeply serious. "There's only one thing about that speech, now. It was good, all right. Better'n the others. But it was still a little weak."

"Weak?"

Root moved his head vigorously. "The people that listen to you aren't college professors. That's one thing you got to remember. And they ain't all interested in Christian uplift, either. You got to get away more from that foreign missionary hogwash and go after the things that worry 'em. You got to make it more personal."

"But I thought . . ."

"You can't leave any questions. They like to be slugged, you got to slug 'em." Root blew on his coffee and inhaled it noisily. "Well, we can take all that up later. We got a Red or two right here in Indiana you can take a shot at when we're ready. You're still a little green but you're learning. Now, let's get down to cases."

While Montrose listened, his head bent forward and a slight flush touching his cheeks, Alden Root talked. To Montrose, much of what was being said had no direct personal meaning. He did not know the incumbent representative named Lockridge, who figured so prominently in the discussion; he had never experienced an immediate association with such terms as endorsements and financial support. But the central message Root was giving him was clear enough: *Bedford Montrose, Congressman.*

The wild and seductive idea that had grown in his mind since his first conversation with Root was no longer just a tormenting conception. It was being presented as a probability. Montrose was lost in his speculations, and Root, looking at him sharply, asked, "You're paying close attention to this, aren't you?"

"Of course," Montrose said. "I still find it hard to believe you're serious, though. I mean—well, after all, this is *me* we're talking about, and it all doesn't seem very real." He grinned suddenly, his warm and engaging attention appealing deferentially to Root.

"It's real," Root said, studying him intently. "You got any doubts, you might as well get rid of 'em now. After last night, I got all the assurances I need. We're going to move ahead now." He lit a fresh cigar and, still watching Montrose carefully, he said, "You still like the idea, don't you?"

"Like it?" *Bedford Montrose, Congressman.* "Well, sure I like it."

"Okay. You haven't told nobody about our discussions so far, have you?"

"No," Montrose said, "of course not."

"Fine," Root said. "No one's to know about this one yet, either. No one."

Montrose didn't answer and in the small silence that grew around them the line of a frown began to crease his forehead.

"Any questions?" Root asked.

"Well . . ."

"You thinking about the Crains?"

"That's right," Buddy admitted, feeling both relief and consternation. "The senator's name hasn't come up in this at all."

"I know it," Root said. "I was waiting for you to bring it up. Now listen carefully." He leaned forward heavily on the table. "Bart Crain can't know a thing about this, yet." Seeing the shocked surprise settle on Montrose's face, he rushed ahead. "It's all going to work out all right, you take my word for it. But right now we don't want to embarrass Bart. You see, he's got himself into a spot where he's committed to supporting that fellow in office. He don't want to, you understand; he knows as well as any of us that Lockridge hasn't got a prayer. But—well, in politics, sometimes you got to give your word to something you don't want to and then you can't change it till later. You see what I mean?"

Montrose stared vacantly at the coffee spoon which he was twisting idly with his fingers. "I don't know whether I do or not," he said. "I never thought—well, it never occurred to me that we wouldn't be working with the senator."

"Later," Root said. "After we've filed, and we show our strength, he'll come around. He'll be relieved and grateful then, you can take my word for that. I'm betting Lockridge will even pull out and Bart'll be off that hook he's on. He'll be relieved and grateful then for what we've done, you can take my word for that. Right now, though, it couldn't do anything but embarrass him. You understand, don't you?"

Montrose continued to toy with the coffee spoon. Subtly and slowly his body relaxed. His face lost its look of shock, but it retained a slightly troubled cast. "I guess so," he said. "I don't know anything about politics, so if you say this is the right thing . . ."

"I'm sayin' it." Root pushed his coffee cup back with a gesture that declared the subject closed to further exploration. "Now there's one other thing." He took from his pocket the folded newspaper page with the Raven advertisement. He carefully unfolded it and tapped the page with a pudgy forefinger. "What's all this about?"

Buddy shook his head. "I only know what Logan told me. He said Raven's sales people put it in."

"Well, it's no good," Root said. "Not in these parts."

"Logan assured me it wouldn't happen again."

"Um. Well." Root drummed his fingers on the table. "It'll happen. They'll ring you into everything they can. How much time you got left with them?"

"A month."

"You got to be careful," Root said. "This publicity you're getting ain't hurting. It's helping. But only as long as the people don't get the idea you're working for this outfit. See what I mean?"

Montrose nodded slowly.

"Okay. Stay out of advertisements. Don't let 'em put the bit on you. I don't want anyone to get the idea you're sellin' drugs. You're a public figure. What have they got lined up for you? More of the same?"

"Just about. And one television program."

"Oh?" Root looked at him sharply. "Where?"

Montrose told him about the Gladys Constable interview Logan had arranged.

"That's dandy," Root said, considering it. "Couldn't be better. You be sure to give me all the information on that. I'll see to it that every set in Indiana is turned on that day. You can give them the business. I want to talk to you about it beforehand." He looked at his watch. "And one other little thing," he said. "Take off that soldier suit. If you're going to be running for office, people got to get used to you in ordinary clothes. You been wearing that long enough." He pushed his chair back and stood up.

"Remember," he said, after they had shaken hands, "no talking—to anybody. Yet."

Heading the station wagon down the highway, Buddy pressed the accelerator recklessly to the floor. As he raced along the smooth macadam roads, his excitement kept pace with the speedometer. He shot through a stop sign and across a state highway intersection, unmindful until he was past that he had done so. He glanced into the rear-view mirror but seeing no threat to his freedom he pushed confidently on. He had driven a quarter of a mile past the highway before the sharp sound of a police siren reached his ear. As he braked the car, a motorcycle officer whipped by him and waved him to a stop. Slowly, and with a deliberate, ominous movement, the policeman dismounted and walked back to the driver.

"Who you trying to kill, yourself or somebody else?" the officer asked angrily. "Lemme see your license." As Buddy started fumbling in his pocket, the officer, squinting down at his face, asked, "Say—ain't you Captain Montrose?"

Buddy nodded.

"Well, Jesus, Captain. If I'd known it was . . . I mean, I'm sorry I had to stop you." The hard mask dissolved on the sunburned face and the smile was almost apologetic. "You *were* driving at a real clip there, Captain. I clocked you at eighty-five."

"I'm sorry, Officer," Buddy said, returning his own smile of apology. "My mind was a thousand miles away."

"You better be a little more careful, Captain. These roads just don't take a lot of speed."

"I sure will, Officer, and I *am* sorry."

"If you don't mind, Captain, I'd like to ask a small favor." At Buddy's puzzled nod, the policeman brought out a notebook. He flipped it open and tore out a page.

"My kid read all about you in the papers and he thinks you're great. I mean we all do, but I'd appreciate it if you'd autograph this for me. He'd sure be proud to have it. His name's Bobby."

Buddy scrawled a good luck message for Bobby and signed his name. The officer accepted it with a grateful smile and touched his cap in salute.

"Thank you, Captain. Thanks very much. I'm sure honored to make your acquaintance."

"Thank you, Officer," Buddy said, extending a hand. "It's been a pleasure talking with you."

The policeman waved him cheerfully on his way and Montrose settled back in the seat, a sense of excitement growing in him. His thoughts, as he drove, were a jumble: Bobby and Bobby's red-faced father, who represented the one sure vote that made reality out of illusion; the cheering citizens of Midwest City lining the streets; the rapt and attentive listeners of Babylon; and with them, their faces dimmer now but the memory important, the people of Baopneng bowing from the dust of another roadside. Buddy Montrose looked into the rear-view mirror as he gained speed, and the reflection he found was alive with pride and a restless, overpowering hope.

During the first half-hour Logan spent more than one anxious moment with a heavy hand on the rein. Pat led the way and they followed a winding dirt road that took them back into the hills behind the farm. They clattered across a shallow brook and into an open field at one point, bounded on the far side by a low fence.

"Ever jump?" Pat called back at him.

"No!"

"Well, the horse has," she shouted. "Just give him his head, keep your weight up and forward and stay with him. Let him have the reins and follow me." Before he could protest, she was off at a run, heading straight for the fence. As if the animal had understood her every word, he leaped forward to follow and Logan held on with his knees.

Joe managed to stay put as his mount gracefully skimmed the low fence, and he was able with some effort to bring the animal up short on the other side.

"Wonderful!" Pat cried, drawing alongside.

"It's the horse," Logan said. "He understands me."

"Let's rest awhile," Pat said. She dismounted and Logan followed her.

They walked across the rising ground to a small clump of pine trees near by and tied the horses.

"That's where we'll eat," she said, pointing to a rocky outcropping silhouetted against the sky a quarter of a mile in front of them. "It won't take long from here." She lay on her back in the dry grass and Logan sat down beside her.

"Cigarette?"

She nodded and he lit one for her.

"Pat, I'm sorry I horned in on the week end," he told her.

"I'm glad you came. What would I have done today without you?"

"Get drunk?"

She smiled at him. "Don't try to impress me with your big-city ways."

"No, ma'am. I certainly won't. Would you like to hear the story about the farmer's daughter?"

"Farmer's daughter, indeed. You don't know any normal, wholesome farmers' daughters. The one in your story would be a moral cripple. Her sole function would be to point up the perversity of life."

"Not this one. She's a veritable tower of moral strength."

"Is she—confused?"

"Not a bit of it. Confusion left her in alarmed abandon when she was barely out of her crib." He watched her quietly for a moment. "She's also uncommonly lovely."

She looked away from him. "But she's not confused. Her story must be terribly dull."

"Pat, what's the matter?" he asked her. "What are you unhappy about?"

"Am I so obvious?" She looked at him again and smiled lamely. "I shouldn't be unhappy, should I? It's a lovely day, the world is green and new, and I've got everything I want."

"No, you shouldn't be," he agreed. "But you are. What is it?"

"You're not a doctor," she said. "You're a story teller. You're just collecting research now for your tales about farmers' daughters."

He did not answer her, but sat watching her, his eyes never leaving her. She stubbed her cigarette out on the ground beside her. "Why is anyone ever unhappy?" she said. "Because the world isn't green and new at all. It's a bramble patch. That's why."

"Not your world," he said.

"Oh, yes. Mine." She picked up a pine cone and began to dissect it. "Every day something changes."

"The gospel according to Logan says be fast on your feet."

"Oh, I try," she said. "I try very hard. I've done fairly well, too—until now."

"Things are catching up?"

"Perhaps. That sounds drastic, though. I think it's just change itself. I've changed, at least a little. Everyone in my bramble-patch world has changed a little, and because of all the changes, I find myself—lost in the brambles. Now, what do I do about that, doctor, or story teller, or myth maker, or whatever you are?"

"You want advice from me?"

"I don't—know what I want from you." She was looking at him as she started to speak, but midway through her words she turned away from him, shifting her body. He took hold of her arm, held it roughly, and then pulled her quickly to him.

"Joe . . ." Her voice was muffled against his shoulder. "This will only . . ."

"Be quiet," he said. He held her chin and pressed his mouth against hers. She met his kiss, finally, but when it was over she said, moving her lips against his cheek, "We can't solve anything this way. We'll only make things worse."

He kissed her again, searching for her with sudden longing. He felt her body respond to his urgent touch, then in an enflamed moment of breath on breath he found her.

They lay quietly in the deep shadows of the pines. Cushioning her head with his arm, he ran a finger along the line of her chin and smiled at her.

"I have no secrets now," she said. "No shame and no secrets."

He moved his head toward her and very gently kissed her on the lips.

"Shouldn't one of us say 'I'm sorry'?" she asked.

"Only if one of us is," he answered. "I'm not."

"I'm not, either." She circled his neck with her arm and drew him to her. "I like your world, Mr. Logan," she said, releasing him. "Your nice physical world where there aren't any problems that can't be solved with direct action."

"That doesn't describe it very well," Joe said. "I . . ."

She put her hand against his mouth and sat up quickly. "I'm not sorry about this, Joe," she said. "But we can't let it happen again."

He watched her carefully. "It may not be as simple as that," he said.

"It has to be. Turn your head while I dress."

He grinned. "Isn't it a little late for that?"

She looked in distress at the clothing scattered on the ground around them. "Well, how *do* people manage under these circumstances?"

"All right," he said. "I'll close my eyes. Wake me when the coffee's ready."

She was sitting on a rock near the horses when Joe joined her. Hearing his step, but looking away from him, she said, "Joe, we're both decent people."

"Not me," he said.

"Obviously there's something in us that attracts each other."

He smiled. "Obviously."

"You've just made love to me," she said. "I'd think you could be serious."

He sat down beside her. "Maybe you find this hard to believe," he said, "but I'm feeling awfully serious."

"I don't want you to fall in love with me," she said.

"My dear young lady."

"I know. There isn't any danger of its happening, anyway."

"Suppose I told you I *am* in love with you."

"No, you're not. I'm just another conquest. Another farmer's daughter."

"For Christ's sake," he said, "are you deliberately trying to mix me up?"

"It is confused, isn't it?"

He reached for her hand, covered it with his own. "Pat, we mean something to each other. Maybe it is a little confused, but that doesn't matter. Nothing is ever going to be quite the same again."

"You do make your declarations ring," she said.

"I'll say it any way you want to hear it."

"You're not used to situations in which you have to follow up with affirmations, are you?" She smiled, but there was less warmth in her smile now. "I'm female enough to want to hear one, and at the same time persuade you that we can't let this mean anything to us."

"Why can't we, Pat?"

She didn't answer him, and he asked, "Buddy?"

"Of course," she said. Before he could say anything more she stood up. "Let's don't talk any more about it, Joe. Not now. Come on, I'll race you again." Quickly she mounted her horse and Joe was left to follow her to the rocky slope she had selected for their picnic.

Buddy was there waiting for them.

After they had eaten their sandwiches, Logan stood and said, "If you don't mind, I think I'll wander on back."

"Can you find your way?" Pat asked without looking at him.

"Just follow the road after you cross the brook," Buddy told him.

"I can find it," Joe said. He remounted his horse awkwardly, but the animal was obliging and Joe was able to leave with some grace. As he passed the place near the pines where he and Pat had stopped, he gave it a long thoughtful look. *Go easy.* He turned away and managed to put his horse into a trot toward the brook, but he couldn't still the restlessness inside him or push aside the images that crowded his mind. He sensed that there would be no way to outrace them, and the knowledge offended him in the way all conditions which involved him but which extended beyond his control offended him. He had found what it had never been possible for him to find before, and what he had long ago relinquished hope of ever finding. And finding it, he had to lose it again.

She had said they could not allow love to grow between them. And in the depths of his mind he believed she was right. He resisted the belief, but he could not ignore it or dismiss it. She would never be able to forget that she was Buddy Montrose's woman.

Nor—and this recognition too was difficult but inevitable—could Logan. He had never known love before. He had never known respect for what belonged to another man. And now on the same bitter day he knew both.

"What did Alden Root want, Buddy?" Pat asked. She had waited for him to bring up the subject, but he had not.

He looked at her surprised, and she said, "I knew it was Root."

"What makes you think so?" he asked.

"Please, Buddy. No one ever does anything in Midwest City without Alden Root being in on it."

"All he wanted," Buddy said casually, "was to tell me he liked the speech, and to ask me if I could make a few more around the state when the Raven tour is over."

Pat looked at him thoughtfully. "And are you going to?"

"I suppose so," Buddy said. "That's pretty far away."

"Buddy, do you know who Alden Root is?"

"What do you mean?"

"He doesn't make a practice of running around the countryside recruiting inspirational speakers. He's a cheap dirty little man and every time he flicks his cigar ashes he has a thousand hidden motives."

"He's a friend of your father's," Buddy said.

"He isn't anyone's friend," Pat said. "He's a very big man in the party, although few people know who he is. He is shrewd, and he deals in people the way some men do in corn and hogs. The only thing he asks is power and the only thing he wants from the men he uses is unqualified obedience. He's a political pimp."

Buddy said, hesitantly, "That's hard to believe, Patty. I mean, he's such a nice guy and all."

She turned away from him. "Of course it's hard to believe," she said. "You've got other things to think about." Then after a moment, she said, "I'm awfully tense today. Nothing is working out as I expected it to."

"You don't exactly sound like yourself," he said.

Together they walked silently over to the horses.

Pat retired early that night, but sleep did not come easily for her, and wakefulness was a torment of conflict and guilt. It had been a day of the deepest disturbances and contrasts. From ecstasy she had moved into a shadowed depression where she was forced to face the fundamentals of a life that had gone awry. How on earth had she permitted this to happen to her, who all her life had quietly believed that constancy and clarity of purpose were her special virtues?

Love is not always simple. Had Joe said that? Or had she imagined his saying it? It did not matter. He was wrong. Whatever he had said, he was wrong. She twisted wretchedly on her bed and buried her face deep in her pillow. Why had he come along, with his warmth and his distortions and his easy control? *Love.* How do I know, she thought bitterly, what love is?

She knew that she must take a stand. Now and for all time she must declare herself and bring order and unity into her life again. There could be no more confusion. And she knew what her decision must be. Perhaps love did come suddenly and with fire, in a bolt of destruction that seared and discolored everything that had lived before it. But she would not take her stand here; she could not. Love must have honor, and loyalty even under assault, and wisdom. It could not be discarded in moments of doubt.

She had failed Buddy. The excitement of love newly found in passion could not diminish that knowledge, nor lessen its guilt. Even in her acute awareness of Buddy's need—for what? Whatever it was, it was hers to find and fill—she had failed him. And she had failed her own conception of what was possible in life and what was not.

She got out of bed and put a robe around her. Looking at her clock, she saw it was not yet midnight. She went to her father's room and finding him still up, reading, she sat on his bed and faced him.

"Have you talked with Buddy at all this week end?" she asked.

"No, I haven't, really," he answered. "Why? Is there something you want me to talk to him about?"

"No. I just wondered if you had been able to see—oh, I don't know. I really don't."

"What's the matter with Buddy?"

"It's so many little things. I want you to help me and I don't know how to ask you. It isn't really Buddy. It's everyone else. It's what they're doing to him."

"That drug company?"

She nodded. "Raven and its damned publicity. They've twisted him and used him and they've almost made another person out of him."

The senator looked at her tenderly. "Now, honey, Joe Logan seems like a reasonable and intelligent fellow. I'm sure he wouldn't go along with anything that wasn't right. Don't you think you're being a little strong?"

A mirthless smile was on her lips. "Maybe," she said, "but Joe isn't concerned about Buddy. Not really. And Joe *has* gone along with things that aren't exactly right."

"Now, Pat . . ."

"It's true!" she said. "Look at it. Buddy did something big and worth-while and—honest. And now he's telling the story of it for their purposes. Joe doctored up his speech for him. He put words in Buddy's mouth that he had never said before and stood him up in front of a lot of audiences and had him move people to tears just so Raven could sell more of its damned old pills or toothpaste or whatever." She caught her lip and swallowed hard.

"You're upset, baby," Bart Crain said. "You may lose faith in me too, but from what you've told me it doesn't sound so alarming."

She looked at him, desperation clouding her eyes. "But it's not the same story any more. You heard it last night. It's not his. There's more blood in it now, and more of the things that stir people up."

Senator Crain reached over and covered his daughter's hand with his. "Baby, Buddy's a grown man, and he's a little fascinated by the sound of his own voice."

"That's no answer," she said angrily.

"What *is* the answer? I can't very well tell this drug company to cancel his speaking tour."

She looked up and met his eyes levelly. "No," she said, "but there are other things you can do."

"What?"

"Buddy wants to go back to the Far East. You know people who could help him do it."

The senator looked at his daughter in surprise. "Do *you* want him to go?"

"I'd rather see him do that again than go through what's happening to him here. The only thing we'd have to fight then is distance. That would be a lot better than this. And—maybe I'd even go with him."

She looked at her father in distress, wondering if she could tell him of the new suspicion that was in her mind, but knowing she could not. She could tell him nothing of her vaguely formed but substantial fear that somehow Alden Root was going to try to make use of Buddy just as the Raven company had. It was possible the senator knew of Root's sudden interest in Buddy and wanted to avoid acknowledging it. Perhaps —perhaps he even condoned it and was part of it.

She stood up quickly. "We can talk about it some other time," she said. "I'm tired and I'm going back to bed." She kissed him on the cheek and left the room.

The senator sat looking into the empty room after she left. He felt very tired and suddenly old.

His daughter's words about Montrose had worried him, for in spite of his assurances to her, the speech he had heard in the armory the night before had been in his mind ever since. It was a moving speech, but a deeply disturbing one, too. It had had an obvious power over the people who had sat and listened to it. And it had what the senator reluctantly acknowledged were distinct evidences of demagoguery.

There had been in the speech, the senator thought, a curious alliance of truth and half-truth, an uncomfortable coupling of inspiring personal experience with shoddy clichés. Buddy had not only touched sympathy and respect in his listeners with his own rewarding story; he had gone further and stimulated their anger and fear with the anti-communism weapon. It was a valid weapon, certainly, and one not unused in the past. But in Buddy's hands it had not been employed with—well, with intelligence. The fact could not be blinked away. It had been too crude a presentation, too pat, too obviously tailored for thrills rather than information. The words were not those of a dedicated man, but an ambitious one, seeking an advantage from the crowd.

The fault was not Buddy's, the senator was able to assure himself easily. He was reasonably sure the boy was being used, and he felt certain that Alden Root's name would show up on the list of users. It was not likely that Root would let a spellbinder such as Buddy, from his own state, slip by without trying to take advantage of him in some way that would eventually work to Root's advantage. Nor would Buddy necessarily be aware of Root's intentions. The senator knew well enough the ways in which Root worked. A few words of advice would bring results: "The people around here go hard for the Communist issue. If you want to make a hit with them, work that in. Now here are a few ideas. . . ." And if the speaker succeeded, if he showed the talents with the people that Root was always looking for, Root would have a job for him sooner or later.

The senator sighed heavily. Pat was right. A young man like Buddy, with what he had to give the world, deserved better than crass exploitation. The drug company had had a hand at it—and now it might well be Root making his effort. There were too many people in the world who would see in a man like Montrose a vehicle to power and try to use him, and Buddy would probably remain completely unaware of it until too late. He had a proud record behind him. If he wanted to serve, he should be allowed to serve.

The senator considered the possibility of writing to the International Aid Commission. They should be able to help Montrose get the assignment he wanted, if anyone could.

It would be best, however, Crain thought, not to say anything about this to Pat until it was settled.

Or to Montrose, either, for that matter.

Sunday evening Logan returned to New York aboard the same plane as Pat and Buddy. Comfortably settled alone in a forward seat, he opened the bulky Sabbath edition of the Midwest City *Chronicle*. He scanned a picture page devoted to scenes of Friday's festivities, scenes showing Buddy with the boy scouts and Buddy shaking hands with his old high school principal, and Buddy at the armory lecture. At the bottom of the page, the *Chronicle* even ran a special poem by Letitia Mae Morse, its part-time poet laureate, whose efforts usually commemorated only the changing of the seasons.

Listen to the Hero's Voice

He's carried the sword and helped the sick,
High the freedom flag he's borne,
The man the Commies couldn't lick,
Fighting Reds through thin and thick,
He blows on Liberty's bugle horn.

Americans you have no choice,
Listen to the Hero's voice.

There was more and Logan read it all. *That,* he thought, *will make
one hell of a chapter in the "Montrose Campaign."*

14

LLOYD MCRUMEN was always at his desk by eight-thirty in the morning,
a full half-hour before the offices officially opened anywhere else at Raven.
It was a habit of many years and one in which he took considerable
pride. He enjoyed the opportunity it gave him to set an example, but
he had never been known to suggest that anyone else on the Raven ad-
ministrative staff follow it. That would have removed the distinction of
old-fashioned virtue which, in small quiet ways of this kind, he cherished
in his own reputation.

This morning, he waited nervously until nine o'clock. Then, acting on
his deliberately built rationale that the best defense would be offense,
he telephoned Alonzo Shively and told him he had the notes ready for
his next formal progress report to the board of directors. Shively said
he would come right in.

The vice-president's greeting was buoyant. McRumen handed him a
copy of the board presentation. "I'm soft-pedaling a few points as you'll
see," he said. "Let me have some of the advertising layouts for that meeting too, so they can see what kind of shape our campaign will take."
Shively nodded, fixed his glasses in place and began to read through the
pages while McRumen pawed some papers on his desk, waiting.

"Lloyd, I don't think this is exactly what we mean," Shively said before he was three-quarters of the way through. He turned a puzzled expression toward the president and removed his glasses.

This was the beginning of the action McRumen had been expecting.
"The figures are correct," he said.

"Yes, they are," Shively replied slowly, "but I'm afraid somebody
might misunderstand the basic concept here. There's not enough empha-

sis on our consumer sales hopes for Pax. That's the key to our volume."

"But too much attention to it might raise opposition," McRumen protested. "You know our board is conservative, Al, and I didn't want to alarm . . ."

"It's the *basic* concept, Lloyd, and it deserves a hell of a lot more attention than you're giving it here." He waved the pages of the presentation in McRumen's direction.

"I prefer to present it my way," McRumen said stiffly. "This is not the only subject I'll be bringing before the board. I expect to spend more time on the Senate investigation."

Shively rose and walked away from McRumen. A few feet from his desk, he stopped, turned, and studied the president. Then he smiled.

"Well, it's not a major misunderstanding," he said. "Nothing we can't fix right now. Let me rework this and I'll explain the whole thing so it's absolutely clear to all of them."

"It's perfectly clear," McRumen said in a low voice. "I plan to ease this before the board. After all, there's quite a bit of money tied up in it already."

Shively's expression hardened. "No, it won't be eased in, Lloyd," he said. "We'll splash it in—A–B–C—so everybody knows exactly what we're up to."

"It can't be that blatant," McRumen said, his voice rising, "without a very careful explanation."

"I told you I'd explain it. Don't worry about that. We're going to *blast* Pax, and the directors should know *all* about it now. There's no point in pussyfooting. What are you afraid of? Making a mistake?" Shively laughed contemptuously. "You're already committed. Why not face up to it?"

McRumen stood up, his face angry and excited. "I'll present it the way I want to present it. You're not running this company, not while I'm here." He turned his back on Shively and faced the window. His small shoulders heaved with quick and angry breathing, and he clasped his hands tightly behind him. Shively examined him and shook his head.

"Let's be sensible, Lloyd," he began slowly. "I don't think you've thought it out all the way. Between us, you'd look like a goddamn jackass going in there with a mealy-mouthed presentation in the face of what you've already poured into Pax. And you'd look like a double fool for pulling the rug out from under me at the last minute—and that's exactly what you'd be doing. Now, I don't think you want to do that, so let's be reasonable. . . ."

"I've had enough of your kind of reasoning," McRumen said sharply, his voice rising as he turned toward Shively.

"As you will," Shively said with a shrug. "But I tell you this, little man—we do it my way or I take it elsewhere. I don't have to remind you what Placebo did with the Diette wafers. And there's been a standing invitation for me to step over there any time I tire of the air around here." He paused and looked hard at Lloyd McRumen's eyes. "But that's beside the point," he said. "The point is that I'd take the whole Pax program with me."

"You'd do no such thing," McRumen said in disbelief.

"Oh, I'd leave you the name, Lloyd. That's a Raven trademark. But I'd take the ideas and idea men I need. I'd take the magic, Lloyd, and that would leave you with a half-assed bunch of vermifuge pushers who might sell a little volume through the doctors. In five years maybe you'd get back your investment. Is that what you want?"

McRumen was silent. Shively studied him for a few moments without speaking. He saw the anger which had etched the president's face gradually subside and give way to a look of confused and puzzled desperation as McRumen's reason slowly sorted out the facts. Inwardly, a smile of amused contempt took shape in Shively. *You've had it, Lloyd. You mull it over and you see you're sitting right where I've put you. You don't like it but there isn't a thing you can do about it. You're in a jet-propelled ejection seat, and one of these days I'm going to press the button that sends you spinning out of here on your ass.*

Shively rose with deliberation and leaned over the president's desk as McRumen's eyes followed him. "Sorry for what I said, Lloyd. We've got too much work to do to stand around here calling each other names. I'm glad we agree," he said, as he picked up the copies of the board of directors' presentation and held them for an instant with both hands before McRumen's curious eyes. Then, as the contemptuous smile broke through and lighted his expression, he tore the papers crudely in half and let them fall over the president's desk. He turned without speaking and walked confidently out of McRumen's office.

Until that moment McRumen had considered the office his haven. Nowhere in the world outside had he ever felt so safe and free of the forces which converged upon him and demanded something of his personality. Only in the office, in this carpeted womb, could life be measured, drawn up and looked at squarely.

Without the violent intrusion of an Alonzo Shively, a man could almost live independently inside Raven, secure in the one great fortress that was the corporation. Now the fortress was crumbling around him and Lloyd's hands shook as he brushed the torn pieces of paper into a wastebasket.

Later that day Logan spread a copy of Friday's Midwest City *Evening Post* on Shively's desk. "You place this ad, Al?" he asked, his voice calm and serious.

Shively grinned and turned to Blivet. "This is that newspaper piece you placed in Midwest City, isn't it?" Blivet nodded, mutely. "It looks good," Shively said with pleasure.

"Good?" Logan repeated incredulously. "Why in hell didn't you tell me you were going to pull something like this?"

"Why, I thought you saw it, Joe. Horace, didn't you show the layout for this ad to Joe?" Shively's voice had an edge.

The advertising man hesitated. "Well, no, Al. You said . . ."

"You know he's supposed to see everything on this Montrose campaign," Shively said sharply. "Sorry it missed you," he told Logan.

"We'd better get one thing straight all over again," Logan said. "The agreement is that we keep the product stuff out of Montrose's tour. We're selling this guy as a *hero* to people and not as a Raven representative. That ad put me in one hell of a spot."

"We *sell* products," Shively said.

"But not from the speaker's platform," Logan answered him. "That *was* the agreement."

"I'm sorry about that, Joe," Shively said, "but to tell you the truth, I decided it was about time we tied in a little more directly with Captain Montrose, now that he's so popular."

"*You* decided."

"That's right." Shively's smile was tight but unwavering.

"God damn it," Logan said, "Montrose is *my* project, at least for the moment. When you want your piece of him, we discuss it with Lloyd McRumen."

Shively didn't answer him immediately. When he did, his voice was quieter, under deliberate control. "I think you should understand, Joe," he said, "that so far as the president is concerned Pax is my sales assignment, to run as I see fit."

"And Montrose is my public relations project which I'll run as *I* see fit, unless Lloyd McRumen tells me otherwise."

Shively's smile was gone. "This is a Pax sales team, Logan, and you and Montrose are on it, like it or not. It's funny, the first squeak we hear from you is when we try to get our money's worth out of your little tin soldier. What's got into you anyway? Until now I thought you were a hundred percent behind our program."

Logan felt an anger running through him which he could neither completely understand nor direct. He dropped into a chair by the vice-president's desk. "Look, the whole success of this project means keeping Montrose divorced from any product endorsements. The only way he'll succeed for us is to keep him noncommercial. The minute he's linked *directly* to a hard-sell program his usefulness dwindles ninety-nine percent. People trust him, and because Raven is part of his legend, people will know and trust us. That kind of reputation can make your sales work a thousand times easier and even be reflected in your volume later on. But you can't have Horace slapping up a Pax concession every time Montrose opens his mouth."

"Well, I had expected from the beginning we'd bring Pax in eventually," Shively said. "After all, we're tying quite a bit of money up in that orator."

"You'll get your money back," Logan said patiently. "All I ask is that your sales people keep their hands off Montrose for a while. Then you'll see it was worth it."

"All right," Shively said. "But just don't forget who you're working for—Raven and Pax, not Montrose and his gook refugees."

The hearings in Washington which the pharmaceutical industry had been nervously awaiting for weeks opened with subpoenaed testimony from the president and other officials of Placebo Laboratories. Partly because the hearings came at a time when government investigations were at a minimum, and partly because the industry involved was one into which the public had never before had a good look, the sessions made for juicy copy.

"In the subcommittee hearing room," one columnist wrote, "a picture is being painted of irresponsibility toward the public in the matter of prices and profits which nearly obscures the luster of the drug industry's scientific accomplishments. The president of Placebo Laboratories, for example, attempted to justify a 600 percent profit markup on a patented life-saving antibiotic by explaining that his firm spent $4 million for 'medical education.' But under cross-examination it turned out that Placebo's 'education' was in fact nothing but sales promotion for doctors."

Others were more temperate: "It isn't all as bad as it looks. Senator Crain's investigation of price-fixing and flagrant profiteering is long overdue. But the list of miracle drugs turned out by some of these firms should not be overlooked or forgotten."

In spite of whatever hopes may have been entertained at the Raven company, nothing prevented Lloyd McRumen from receiving his invitation to appear before the Senate subcommittee. Al Shively and the company's legal counsel were also requested to testify.

At three o'clock on the day McRumen received the notice, Logan and Shively were seated in the president's office while the correspondence passed from one to the other. It specified that the Raven representatives were to appear before the committee the following week.

Logan handed them each copies of the material he had laboriously gathered or prepared, and, page by page, they went through it. Joe had furnished nearly four hundred questions, with the help of the legal department, which McRumen or the other Raven witnesses might be called upon to answer. After each was the suggested response. Some of the answers could be slightly embarrassing to the company, but Joe argued successfully that frankness would lend an air of sincere and complete coöperation which would be helpful to Raven in its relationship with the committee.

"An excellent and thorough job, Joe," McRumen said when he had gone through most of the material, "but what *else* can we do? That hearing is news and I would like to see us benefit to the fullest possible advantage."

"What about a drug donation to Bethesda or something?" Shively said.

"Sure, nobody'd be wise to that," Logan answered with sarcasm.

"It's too bad we have nothing else," McRumen said.

"I'm afraid that's the size of it," Joe said. "You know what we had to work with. If I had had a clearer idea of what the other companies were going to say, it would have helped."

"What about trying this for size?" Shively offered. "Lloyd brought up the fact that the hearing is primarily a news story. We need all the gimmicks we can enlist. Right?"

The other two men did not speak and he answered himself. "Right! Now, consider, gentlemen. What do we already have, ready made, right off the shelf, that's the best gimmick possible?"

He looked searchingly at one, then the other, and again no one answered him.

"Captain Montrose!" he announced triumphantly. "What better defense do we have than that?"

Logan said, "What do you mean—Montrose?"

"I mean," Shively explained patiently, "that Montrose is sensational with people. We've had plenty of occasion to learn that. Why wouldn't he go over well in those hearings too? And with the man in Milwaukee, our customer, who's reading about the investigation in his newspaper?"

"Sure," Logan said, "but what the hell does Montrose know about all this?"

"What does he have to know?" Shively answered. "He knows what we did for him when he was overseas. I've seen people bawl over that."

Helplessly, Logan lifted his hands in the air. "I wish I could follow you, Al. What makes you think he'd go to bat for us with a Senate committee? That's not what he's being paid for."

"Joe," Shively said, impatience thinning his voice, "why is it that you must always try to make the obvious sound significant? Of course that's not what he's being paid for. Columbus wasn't paid to discover America, either. We'd have to sell him on doing this bit. I know that. And I'd say you're the man to do it."

"Sure," Logan said, "but you wouldn't say how."

"At the moment, no. I don't know how."

Lloyd McRumen cleared his throat. "Perhaps there is a way to persuade him, Joe. Montrose on the stand in our defense telling the splendid story of our partnership when he was overseas, would do us immeasurable good, I think."

"You said you knew a way, Lloyd," Shively said.

McRumen took an envelope from his desk. "This came today," he said. "I intended to show it to you later, Joe, and ask you to prepare an answer. I think perhaps it has more pertinence now than I realized."

He handed the letter to Joe. Logan unfolded it, and Shively looked over his shoulder. It was from the director of the International Aid Commission.

It explained that Senator Crain had suggested to the IAC that Bedford Montrose would be a good man to head a special relief team which the commission desired to send to Southeast Asia. The team would dispense food, clothing and medicine in the hills of Malaya as part of a larger program carried on by IAC. The letter went on to remind Raven of what everyone sitting in the room was acutely aware—the chain of circumstances that had linked together the commission, the company and the captain once before.

"We are indeed eager to send teams over," the letter said. "Our problem, however, is one of supplies. We have already accounted for most of our budget for the next year. What we should like to propose to you . . ."

The proposal was quite simple. If Raven could see fit to supply Montrose with the drugs to take with him, and assume certain other portions of the expense, IAC would outfit him with the equipment and volunteers he would need to take the civil assistance unit into an area where American private aid was so desperately needed.

The letter made it clear that of course the assignment would not begin until Montrose's current speaking tour with the Raven company was satisfactorily completed.

Logan read the letter through and then looked up. "Well, good for Buddy," he said. "This is just what he's been looking for."

"I know," McRumen said.

"We'll do it, won't we?" Logan asked. "Best thing in the world for us."

McRumen pursed his lips. "Does anything else occur to you about it, Joe?"

Perplexity creased Logan's forehead. "I don't see . . ."

"Of course!" Shively cut in. "Lloyd, it's perfect, beautiful."

McRumen shifted uneasily. He ignored Shively's observation and kept his eyes on Logan.

Joe shifted his gaze to the vice-president.

"Look." Shively leaned forward excitedly in his chair. "Joe, suppose you use this as bait. Tell Captain Video that we'll see to it that he gets that assignment back there, with our drugs, if he'll sing for us. No testimony, no assignment." He looked at McRumen. "That's the way you had it sized up, isn't it, Lloyd?"

McRumen pointedly ignored the question. The last thing he wished was to find himself linked in common agreement with Shively on any matter. But, if the president's unresponsiveness had any effect on Shively, the vice-president failed to show it. He turned back to Logan.

"We don't want to put it to him crudely," Shively said, "but you can handle the icing."

"Are you sure you want to do this, sir?" Logan asked McRumen.

"What's the matter, Joe? Does it bother you?"

"Don't you think it would be a good idea to have him talk on our side in that committee room?" Shively asked.

"From our point of view, of course," Logan replied. "But he's a decent kid and I hate to see him get wrapped up in something that's none of his affair."

Shively's words were quick and incisive when he answered. "Joe," he said, "are you trying to coddle this guy? You've already spent a lot of time looking out for his welfare. Think about ours for a change. He'll buy this, one way or another. You take our offer and you hit him with it. If he resists, you offer him whatever else it takes. And I don't think it will take much. I haven't seen him send any checks back so far. Like anybody else, he's got a price and because he's just an over-age boy scout, his price can't be high."

"I don't think he'll do it," Logan said. "You don't know this boy."

"I knew him a thousand years ago," Shively said. "Everybody has some kind of price, Joe. You know that." He glanced at Lloyd McRumen.

"Maybe Montrose has higher standards than the rest of us," Logan said.

"That hardly seems a loyal thing to say," Shively said.

"You're no one to speak of loyalty," McRumen snapped. He looked benignly at his public relations director. "I don't think the captain will mind a bit," he said. "It's more personal publicity for him, for that matter, which can't hurt him. We can put the subject up to him, anyway."

"All right," Logan said slowly. "But there's still another big point here. What makes us think that committee is going to ring in an outsider like Montrose? They've got no reason to call him up."

Shively rubbed the palms of his hands together smoothly. "Maybe the idea wouldn't *occur* to them," he said, "but if it were *put* to them, by somebody who had personal influence . . ." He let the sentence hang unfinished and looked directly at Joe.

"I don't . . ." Joe said. "Oh, of course. So that's it."

"I see we're together now." Shively smiled broadly. "You know Senator Crain, and he's the chairman of the committee. Figure a good way to put it to him."

"All I seem to be doing this afternoon is protesting," Logan observed, "but I'm not sure the senator would be very favorably impressed if I cashed in on our brief acquaintance to make a pitch like this."

"You're entirely right, Joe," McRumen said, intending his agreement only as a rebuke to Shively. "Steam-roller tactics aren't the only ones. But I think you could make it reasonable. The senator is not inimical to us. I think you might very well suggest to him that the fair thing would be to get all sides of the picture. They *say* that's what they want to do; this will give them a chance to show it. Montrose's association with us is sufficient credential, I think. The committee *might* not be willing, but it's worth trying."

"They'll be willing," Shively said. "Those senators know the value of a headline attraction."

"I don't know," Logan said. "I hate to see him dragged into this."

"If it's good enough for the rest of us," Shively said, "it shouldn't bother him. We all know who pays our salaries." Unconsciously, Lloyd McRumen nodded gravely.

When the meeting was over, Shively asked Joe to step with him into his office for a few seconds. Once there, he closed the door and with a conspiratorial air turned to Logan.

"What I'm going to tell you, Joe, is confidential," he said. "You'll understand why."

Logan nodded.

"As long as we have to go through with this hearing, you might as well have everything you can use. You said it would help you if you knew what the other companies are doing about this investigation."

Joe frowned. "Yeah?"

"Well, I think there might be a way for you to get just that."

Still puzzled, Logan waited for him to continue.

"We've got tapes of all their top executive phone conversations recently," Shively said gravely. "It'll be a hell of a lot to wade through, but it might be worth it."

Logan dropped weakly into a chair. "What are you telling me, Al? How do we have tapes?"

Impatiently, Shively said, "That shouldn't be too hard to figure out."

"Wire tap?" The words sounded incredulous to Logan even as he said them. Shively nodded.

"I'll be damned. We actually have had somebody tapping their wires?"

"You already asked that. I told you. Yes."

"Why, Al? *Why*, for God's sake?"

"We had to, Joe. For the Pax program. We had to know if any of them was about to come up with anything else close to it."

"I still don't understand it," Logan said. "God damn, what a story to leak out. Old American-way Raven, the friendly, ethical drug house, tapping the competition's wires."

"There's not going to be any leak," Shively explained severely. "That kind of thing would wind up in a dozen dead-end streets before it ever could come back to Raven."

Logan sat in stunned silence, trying to let the enormity of the disclosure settle in his mind.

"We're not in here to discuss business practices anyway," Shively said. "I'm telling you what's available. I'll give you the name of the man to see and you can do whatever you want about it."

Logan stood up. "I'll talk to you about it later. I've got to digest this." He opened the door and then closed it again and looked at Shively. "This was your personal contribution to the Pax program, I suppose. Anyone else around Raven in on it, or am I it?"

"Never mind the questions," Shively said. "You can use it or not."

"I see." Logan closed the door behind him and walked slowly along

the hall. It was a hell of a way to make a living, he thought bitterly as
he turned into his own office.

15

GARIBALDI WAS half an hour late but Dr. Thatch turned his apologies
aside. "It doesn't matter a bit, Ambrose. I didn't make the lunch reserva-
tion until one-thirty. We'll still have time to go over some of these reports."

Garibaldi sat in a large uncomfortable consultation chair in Dr.
Thatch's office. Thatch was one of Raven's clinicians but he was also an
old personal friend of Garibaldi's. The two had been graduated from
medical school together and over a twenty-year period they had held on
to an association solidly bound with affection and mutual professional
respect.

Garibaldi surveyed the stack of patient histories on Thatch's desk and
said, "You're working too hard, Nate. When are you going to smarten
up and take a little time off?"

"Not this year," Thatch said. "Too damned busy. I hardly even get a
Wednesday afternoon off any more."

"Take some youngster in with you—to handle the patients while you
devote your leisure hours to the hypochondriacs."

Thatch examined Garibaldi seriously. "As a matter of fact, I was going
to bring that up again today at lunch. My patients being what they are,
though, Ambrose, I'd much prefer an older man with a wealth of experience. I know it's become a perennial joke but my offer still holds. When
are you going to get some sense and give up that executive routine? You
ought to be back in medicine and you know it."

Garibaldi smiled and raised his palm. "I should have kept my mouth
shut."

"You want to stay where you are?"

Garibaldi shrugged. "One of these days, Nate, I'll make the move
back. Give me time."

"It'll be here when you're ready," Dr. Thatch said, "if I don't drop
dead with a coronary beforehand." The two friends met each other's

gaze for an instant before Thatch said, "Well, we might as well get five minutes' worth of work done before I buy you that lunch."

Dr. Thatch drew a folder of papers from his desk and opened it just as his nurse thrust her head into the office.

"Excuse me, Doctor," she said. "Mrs. Abernathy is outside and she insists on seeing you."

Thatch looked at her in irritation. "Tell her office hours begin at three o'clock," he said sternly. Then he considered and said, "Well, wait a moment." He turned to Garibaldi. "As long as this woman's here, maybe you'd like to see her. She's one of our Pax cases. You can see what the drug has done for her. Four weeks ago she was all ganglia. Now she hasn't got a neurosis she can call her own."

Garibaldi nodded slowly and Thatch said to the nurse, "Send her in."

"Her son is with her," the nurse cautioned.

"Well, leave him outside," Dr. Thatch said, and then quickly amended it. "No, don't. I'd rather have him where I can see him."

An attractive portly woman flounced smilingly through the door. Garibaldi noticed an expensive dress set off by a soft and pretty face that wasn't too carefully made up, and a hairdo that failed to include two or three wispy locks. She was followed by a leering figure in corduroy pants and striped jersey. Dr. Thatch introduced Garibaldi as a colleague and the woman smiled appreciatively.

"I'm dreadfully sorry I couldn't get in during office hours but I'm in desperate need of more medicine," she said to Dr. Thatch. "I took the last pill this morning and—now, Gerald. Say hello to Dr. Thatch, dear. Dr. Thatch brought you into the world, so say hello."

With a sinister weaving gait, Gerald circled around the other end of the physician's desk.

"Honestly, Doctor," Mrs. Abernathy said, "you have no idea what those wonderful pills have done for me. I'm a *new woman*. I've told all my friends."

"Yes," Dr. Thatch said noncommittally.

"Gerald had become such a care, Doctor," the woman said. "And now I hardly have any difficulty at all, do I? He's really so well behaved. Dear, I wouldn't play with those nice tools of Dr. Thatch's. They're not for little boys to play with. Put them back and put the towel over them where it belongs."

Garibaldi watched as the child tossed what had been sterile instruments back into what had been a sterile tray. Although Thatch tried to appear unconcerned, he was frantically pressing the buzzer on the edge of his desk to summon his office nurse.

As Gerald made obscene gestures with his chubby hands, Garibaldi asked, "Have you—ah—been *completely* relaxed since you started your course of therapy, Mrs. Abernathy?"

"Oh, dear, yes. I simply don't worry about a thing now," she said.

Thatch sighed audibly as the nurse came into the room. "Excuse me," he said before Mrs. Abernathy could continue, "but would you take care of that instrument tray, Miss Williams? Run them through the sterilizer?"

"But they're ster—" she began. Gerald's smug leer caught her glance.

Mrs. Abernathy resumed her report as the physicians studied her and Miss Williams gathered up the instruments. The little boy edged toward the nurse.

"I've had some trouble convincing my husband about your little pills, Doctor," Mrs. Abernathy was saying, "but he's coming around." The woman sat placidly as she spoke, a beatific smile playing over her lips.

Garibaldi frowned. Quite probably, he thought, she was closer to comfort and some strange kind of untroubled normality than at any time in her life. But the woman's equanimity was almost more exasperating than the conduct of her offensive offspring.

With his eyes on Mrs. Abernathy, Dr. Garibaldi heard a sudden scream from the nurse, followed by the reverberating crash of a trayful of instruments.

Both doctors jumped to their feet in alarm. "What happened?" Thatch asked.

Miss Williams looked at him wildly. "That little monster pinched me."

Garibaldi took a sip from his martini, consciously trying to steady his hands.

"You see—it works, Ambrose," Thatch said. "She never used to be that calm."

"Did I understand her to say you delivered that child, Nate?" Garibaldi asked. "In a hospital?"

"That's the only way they ever would have let him in," Thatch said.

"He should have been whelped in a jungle."

"Pax seems to do the trick though, doesn't it?" Thatch asked. "It gives her what she needs to protect herself against him. She used to be a mess."

Garibaldi reflected on his glass for a few seconds before answering. "She's still a mess," he said. "And with that kindergarten satyr for an offspring, she'll probably end her days under the wheels of his tricycle." He was staring beyond Dr. Thatch and his eyes had a distant and troubled look. "My considered professional opinion is that she should stay untranquilized. She'd be faster on her feet that way."

That night the lights in both Logan's and Garibaldi's offices stayed on long past their usual time.

Logan was the first to leave, and seeing that the doctor still sat behind his desk, he stopped.

"What are you doing here so late?" the doctor asked. "Counting up your latest raise?"

Logan shut the door behind him and slid into a chair by the desk. "Delaying," he said, "to keep from leaving and tackling a job I hate to do." The doctor looked at him curiously and Joe said, "Montrose. I've got to make a pitch to him." He told Garibaldi of the meeting that day in McRumen's office.

"Ah, yes," Garibaldi said. "As I always suspected, the Raven team mascot will be a sacrificial goat."

Logan thought briefly of telling Garibaldi about Shively's wire-tapping, but he dismissed the idea. He was well aware of the change that was slowly coming over the doctor, the damp weight of futility and frustration, the overriding conviction that for the first time in his career with Raven things around the company were no longer under reasonable control. He decided it would be wise not to mention either Shively or Pax.

Garibaldi, however, brought them both up, together. "I have a most interesting document on my desk here somewhere," he said. "I wonder if you have seen it. It's a suggestion Shively has for mixing Pax into a raspberry-flavored liqueur for after-dinner relaxation."

Logan smiled. "I've seen it," he said. "I've also heard that he's talking about putting it into suppositories. For peace of ass, I suppose."

"You know about the Pax animal formula? When the preliminary vet reports came in, Horace was driveling around about chicken-Pax and cow-Pax for two days." The doctor laughed suddenly. "They're going to call one of them Poultry Paxy Cakes."

"It'll sell, Doc. Shively could have it vacuum-packed in oil drums and still move it."

"And everyone will call him a genius," Garibaldi said as a frown crossed his face. "The directors will vote him a block of stock and the public will think it owes him a debt of gratitude for serving up the Pax miracle drug."

Logan laughed uneasily. "He's really no fool."

"Your judgment is tragically precise," Garibaldi said. He stood up and turned his back to Logan, looking absently at the covers of the bound medical journals which lined the rear wall of his office. "And it seems that it's shared by Lloyd McRumen. Ten years I've known the president and never seen him when he wasn't sure of himself. Now Lloyd sits there like the three monkeys with all his senses shut off. 'I'm sure Al knows what he's doing, Ambrose,' he tells me. And of *course* Al knows what he's doing. He's getting ready to make a killing and he'll probably succeed. I haven't the faintest doubt he'll get his liqueur." He turned around to look at Logan again. "You know what I wish? I wish he'd put this whole program in a suppository."

"Well . . ." Logan started to rise from his chair.

"Oh, no, you don't," Garibaldi said. "You inveigled me into conversation, so you'll damn well sit there until the conversation is over. I want to tell you a little story about something I saw today." He related his encounter with Mrs. Abernathy in Dr. Thatch's office.

Puzzled, Joe said, "What's the point?"

"It's a very complicated one," Garibaldi admitted, "but it's important. I've been doing a lot of objecting to the sales plans for this drug. First of all, I objected to its going to the doctors with a lot of circus promotion before it was sufficiently proved. Recently I've been making as much racket as I know how about this over-the-counter madness. But it's all been theoretical objection. Now I've been exposed to my first average honest-to-God Pax eater, and I tell you it's a hell of an experience."

Logan smiled. "I see it was," he said.

"It's given me pause to consider this twentieth-century commodity in a new light. If very many people behave as this patient did after a steady diet of our great you-and-me drug, the future is a dismal one indeed. It's an eviscerating chemical, Joe, that leaves only a jelly mold where a personality used to be. The clinical cases tell the story, but you've got to see one in the flesh to understand the significance of it."

"You think it's a menace, eh?" Logan was smiling.

"Come in with Horace some time and look through these cases with the same devotion he brings to the task; perhaps the point will make itself clear." Garibaldi opened the folder on his desk and extracted a report. "Here is a teacher in Newark. His job didn't pay him much and he was planning to get married. Typical little everyday man with everyday worries —impending marriage, thoughts about his future, whether or not his wife would have to work. A week before the wedding he was all nerves. One of our investigators put him on Pax. He needed Pax like I need water skis. But the doctor had been asked by us to administer Pax to just this type of patient."

"And—his worries dissolved?"

"Precisely. He failed to show at the church. The girl wanted to sue the doctor."

"You can't really blame that on the drug, can you?" Logan protested. "Did you see the girl?"

Garibaldi laughed quickly, but there was no humor in it.

"Do you have many cases like that?" Logan asked.

"Most of them don't have these consequences," Garibaldi said, "but far too many follow the same pattern of social deterioration."

"But God damn it," Logan said, "*somebody* needs it."

"Sometimes I wonder," Garibaldi said. "No, I'll stick to honesty. This drug is useful for borderline psychotics and specified cases of extreme tension under the *careful* supervision of a physician." He punctuated his sentence with an expressive sigh. "But for the average person—well, I've come slowly and all around the barn to this belief, and it's a subversive one from Raven's point of view, but unavoidable after so many of these cases. This kind of medication can sometimes provide a superficial confidence for many people that they're better off without. It's like one drink too many. With an absence of the smallest anxiety goes a proportional lack of responsibility."

"Those are strong words," Logan said.

"I know they are. But the sad truth, which the profession has to come to recognize, is that a man can be only so relaxed." His face was doleful. "Peace of mind," he said, "may well become the plague of our time."

16

BUDDY MONTROSE poured a drink from the bottle standing on the polished writing desk in his hotel room and carried the glass with him over to the window. For a moment he studied his reflection, tall and straight and pleasing. He snapped off the light and continued to stand where he was, watching the shadowy outlines of the buildings in the city's glow, and the million points of light that winked enticingly below.

Over the past two months, many people had written things about Captain Bedford Montrose. Vivid words had been used to characterize him, and many small truths about the spirit locked inside him had been caught in isolated phrases. But no reporter had known, and no biographer ever would be likely to report, that Bedford Montrose came closest to feeling his own greatness when he found himself part of the massive, wild charm of the city.

Captain Montrose was a man of action standing twenty stories tall—a man of vigor briefly still, savoring in fact all the pleasures of his wildest boyhood fancies.

He was standing there when Logan knocked.

"Come in."

Logan opened the door. "Hey, it's dark in here. Mind if I turn on a light?"

"Hello, Joe. It's there by the door."

Logan flicked the wall switch, then walked over to the desk and started to pour a drink. "I didn't mean to interrupt vespers," he said.

"Just a little wool-gathering," Buddy answered. "My first night off since I can remember and I'm not quite in the mood to do anything with it."

"No date?"

"Later. I'm to pick Patty up in an hour."

Joe offered the bottle and Montrose shook his head. "You're too gloomy. I don't think city life agrees with you."

Montrose sat on the end of the bed. "I'm always gloomy when I think."

"Seeing faces again?" Logan asked.

Montrose smiled. "They keep popping up. Even up here."

Logan had been watching him carefully. "Buddy," he said, "I've got some good news. Something that might scatter that depression in a flash, boy." He saw the interest in Buddy's expression. "I've also got a problem." He raised the glass in Montrose's direction and took a sip. "Which do you want to hear first?"

Montrose looked at him closely. "Start with the problem, I guess."

Carefully, Logan explained to him McRumen's and Shively's hope that Montrose would agree to put in an appearance before the Senate sub-committee.

Buddy listened attentively, saying nothing. No reaction of any kind showed on his face, and Logan, when he had finished, did not wait for one. "Now for the good news." He told him in detail about the letter from the IAC, omitting only the part Senator Crain had had in the offer.

At the end of Logan's recital, Montrose's face was still impassive and the two men stood silently. Finally Buddy said, "I see. So it's a proposition."

Logan smiled suddenly. "You've been around us too long," he said. "You can see through the tricks. Shively and McRumen wanted me to pretty it up so it didn't sound like one. But I'll level with you. It *is* a deal. If you'll do this favor for them, they'll go along and see that you get that spot on the team, with the necessary financial backing."

Montrose rose and slowly walked to the window. He stood looking out for a long time. Finally he said, "It would cost Raven a lot of money to do it right, Joe."

"They figure it's worth it."

"They'd have to get a couple of doctors, interpreters, drivers, equipment."

"The IAC says no problem. All we worry about is the dough."

Buddy continued to stand where he was. "You say they want me to head it up?"

"You'd be in full charge."

Logan waited another minute. Then Buddy turned and said, "I'm sorry, Joe. That other thing. I'm really sorry but I just don't think I should do it. I hate to let you down. You people have been awfully decent to me. And you know how hard it is for me to pass up an IAC offer. But this Senate committee stuff . . ." He shook his head slowly. "I just don't think that's right."

Logan stood up. "I really didn't think you would," he said. "I told them that. And between you and me, I'd have been a little disappointed if you *had* agreed."

"Thanks, Joe," Montrose said.

"Look, Buddy. They wanted to make a bargain out of this, but I can talk them out of it. I'll take a stand on it. Senate testimony or no Senate testimony, we'll still get you this team assignment. By God, I'll see that we do." He smiled broadly. "Okay?"

Montrose broke the look between them and walked over to pour a drink. With his back to Logan he said, "I don't want you to stick your neck out for me, Joe."

"It's not going to be stuck out far," Logan said. "Wouldn't make any difference anyway."

"Sure it does," Buddy said. "You've got a job to do, Joe. You've got to look out for yourself."

Slightly bewildered, Logan said, "I just told you. I *want* to do this." Montrose didn't answer and after a few seconds Logan said, "You want me to, don't you?"

"Sure." Montrose carried his drink over to the spot by the window where he had been standing. "If everything worked out the right way. But there probably are too many things to prevent it. We've still got a lot of towns to hit on this speaking tour."

"Hell, man, the letter says *after* the tour." An uneasiness was beginning to crawl through Logan's mind.

"Well, yes," Buddy said, "but there are always a lot of things to wrap up in a situation like this. You know. The people, the details, the money."

A silence settled over the room then, and grew. At some indeterminable point it had lasted too long and it changed subtly into an awkward and uncomfortable void.

"Yeah," Logan said quietly. "I guess I do know, at that. But let's nail it down. You *don't* want to go. Is that it?"

"Wait a minute, Joe, now . . ."

"Yes or no. Do you or don't you?"

"Well, to tell you the truth, Joe," Montrose said, "I don't see how I could."

A suspicion of something he did not understand brought a hardness to Joe's eyes. "Maybe you'd better tell me about it," he said.

"Well . . ." Buddy's thoughts were swarming in a tormented jumble in his mind and desperately he picked his way through them. When he reached a moment of clarity he knew he had to use the truth; he had no choice. "This isn't the way I had planned to tell you, but—I've been wondering if maybe I couldn't do more good some other way."

Logan watched him quietly. "What other way?" he asked.

"I don't know," Buddy said. "I've been thinking a little about politics maybe."

"Politics," Logan said. He let the word settle before he spoke again. "I see. What about the 'hungry ones'?"

"It's just a thought," Montrose said. "I'm not really sure what I'm going to do."

"Who knows about this idea?" Logan said.

"Nobody, Joe. You're the only one I've mentioned it to. And I'd appreciate it if you wouldn't say anything. I don't . . ."

"Don't worry," Logan said. "It's not something I want to talk about."

"It might be the best way for me to do what I want to do, Joe. The biggest . . ."

Logan stood listening to him but he hardly heard him. Forcing its way to the front of his mind was another scene, with a man Logan thought he had seen a lifetime ago, talking with sincere emotion about man's faith in himself. *If you believe in something,* that man's urgent voice was saying, *you have to live it and act on it.*

"I'd really like to, Joe. I'd give my . . ."

"Okay, cut it, Buddy," Logan said. "It's none of my business. Have it however you want it. But it's time now to take that crap out of your speeches about how your big heart aches to get back . . ."

"Now wait . . ."

". . . because if there's one thing I can't take, it's a phony."

Montrose's face clouded with anger. "Who the hell are you to talk to me like that?"

"I think I'm on Shively's side for a while. I think you'd better sing before that committee."

"You go to hell, Logan."

"Don't push your luck, Buddy."

In a sudden rage Montrose threw his glass against the wall. The sound of its shattering sounded loudly in the room. "Phony!" he cried. *"Phony! What a goddamned laugh. You've got a colossal nerve, Logan, coming in here and talking to me about phoniness."

"Watch your language, sonny."

"Screw you. I don't need you to tell me what to do. I don't need you at all. I'll walk out on this tour and you can sell your damned pills by yourself."

"I don't think you will," Logan said. "You're not walking out on anything unless you want me to smash your political career before it ever has a chance to get off the ground. I'm just the guy who can do it. You're like every other two-bit idealist with something to sell, and like any whore you'll sell it to whoever's got the price. Now let's get down to business."

Montrose, his face white, started to speak but Logan cut him off. "Building you up wasn't easy. Tearing you apart would be a cinch. We leave it at that. I'll write a letter getting you out of this. I'll put the blame on us. But let's get this clear. You're willing to go before that Senate committee and do a nice job for Raven." He looked at his hands which he had unconsciously doubled into fists, and slowly relaxed them. "And that's not all I want," he said. The words came slowly and with deliberation. "I want something else. I want to know just how important this is to you. I want to hear you *ask* me to get you out of this spot."

"What do you mean?"

"What I said. Ask me, you son of a bitch."

For an instant Montrose appeared as if he were going to lunge at Logan, but only the muscles in his face moved. He didn't speak.

"I said 'Ask me.' "

The two men looked at each other with naked eyes in total understanding, the terrible silence holding their anger.

"God damn you," Montrose said, his voice hoarse with hatred. "I'll ask it, but not for the reason you think. I'm not . . ."

"I know what you are," Logan said as he turned and walked out of the room. He felt a strange and alien substance in his throat like the tightness that used to come with the hot tears of anger he had known as a child. Beneath the anger he had been shaken to his roots. Deep in him a malignant agony grew. Joe Logan, who had no gods at all, had come to believe at least a little in the myth of Buddy Montrose. And for men who have no gods, even little faiths die hard.

But this was not the worst of the agony. As Logan lay sleepless on his bed, staring into the darkness, he knew that not all the blame was Buddy's. Much of it belonged to Logan himself. He had used Montrose, and in the process he had helped to corrupt him.

It was a hard truth to face in the dark hours of the night.

17

TWO ISLANDS of consideration stood revealed in Logan's mind after the first dark flood of disillusionment had passed on through him: Pat Crain and Raven. He felt what he believed—or told himself he believed—was a responsibility to share with both of them his unwelcome knowledge.

He was in his office half an hour before Emily arrived. It was just as well, he thought. He spent the time typing his memo to McRumen, which he would not have wanted to entrust to her anyway. When she came, it was sealed, and he asked her to deliver it to McRumen's secretary with the request that McRumen read it as soon as possible.

Logan was certain the president would call when he had read the message. Short and succinct, it advised McRumen that because of newly acquired information, Logan felt it would be distinctly to the company's advantage to discontinue Montrose's services.

While he waited for McRumen's call, he tipped back in his chair and closed his eyes, resisting the temptation to telephone Pat. Spelling out the painful details in his message to McRumen, he had come to realize it was not really obligation he felt where Pat was concerned. With Raven, yes. With Pat, he understood, it was more a desire to use his knowledge to secure an advantage, and he determined to resist that temptation, strong as it was. He himself was freed now from any restriction Montrose's influence had imposed on him. He accepted that freedom willingly; it was the only good thing to emerge from this miasma. But he could exploit it only with care. His perception, although it had not, he thought wryly, been doing too well for him recently, told him now that he could never gain Pat by trying to alienate her from Montrose; indeed, there would be no surer way to lose her.

When McRumen called, he said, "I've read your memo, Joe. You'd better come on over here."

"All right," Joe said. "Maybe Al Shively should be in on this."

The telephone on the president's end was silent for a moment, and then McRumen said, "I'll tell him to be here."

Logan did not go to the president's office right away. He gave Shively time to arrive and read the memo, and then he went over.

The strident bark of the vice-president's angry voice could be heard outside McRumen's office, in spite of the closed door and above the staccato clacking of the secretary's electric typewriter. "Who the hell does he think he is, anyway?" Joe heard Shively demand. "The chairman of the board?"

Logan opened the door and walked in. Looking up, Shively said, "All right, start explaining, God damn it."

"That's what I'm here for," Joe said.

"You say in this memo to Lloyd that you don't think we ought to use this guy."

"That's my suggestion," Joe said, looking toward McRumen. The president seemed satisfied to let Shively do the talking for the moment.

"Is that right?" Shively's voice was heavy with scorn.

"That's right."

"You've been giving him the kid-glove treatment ever since you got hold of him and now you're telling us it was all a big mistake, we ought to kiss him off. What changed your mind?"

"Give me a chance," Joe said. "I laid the whole thing out for him last night—the deal, everything. He didn't take us up on our offer to help *him*, but he agreed to testify for us." He watched his listeners closely. "Do you know why?"

"No, I don't know why, and I don't see what difference it makes," Shively said, "as long as he's going to do it."

"Wait a minute," McRumen said. He looked at Logan with an unsmiling face. "Go ahead."

"He's going to testify for Raven because he's afraid I'll tell what I've found out about him—that he doesn't want this IAC offer or any like it."

Shively's voice, breaking through the silence that followed, was not so much angry as puzzled. "That's your big discovery?"

"That's it."

"What the hell difference does that make except to save us some dough?"

"I think it makes a lot," Joe said. "You see, for all his big talk, for all his passionate wishes to return and squat down on his hunkies, he doesn't want to go after all. He says he does. He says it night after night but when the flag is down, he doesn't want to go."

The president ran his fingers over his chin. "You mean Montrose *said* he didn't want to go back? Why, I thought . . ."

"That's what I thought, too," Logan said. "But it's not true. Not any longer. When he talks now, he's talking strictly for the galleries."

"But what's all this about cutting him loose?" asked Shively.

"That's my suggestion, Al. The guy's a phony. I don't think we want him around."

Alonzo Shively snorted. "For Christ's sake—a phony! I've been telling you all along he gets gas on his stomach the same way the rest of us do. What's so goddamned earth-shaking now that you've caught on? The only thing that's important is that he'll be the best man in the world for us to have up in front of that committee. That's *all.*"

"He's also a liar," Joe said, "and his lies might get mixed up."

"No one's asking him to lie now," Shively said. "All he has to do is tell the truth in our favor; talk about public service and all the rest of it. You've already said he agreed to do it."

"Sure, but only because I threatened him," Joe said. "He'll go along, if we save his neck and save his face."

"What did you tell him about the Aid Commission?"

"I told him we'd write a letter stalling them."

"Good." Shively nodded. "Tell them not right now. Maybe in another two months we'll talk about it."

McRumen turned thoughtfully to Joe. "I find what you've said impossible to believe. There must be some good reason why he's changed his mind. How do you know it isn't because of his girl? Maybe his physical condition isn't up to it?"

"I'd like to let you believe that, Mr. McRumen, but it just isn't true. He's got bigger plans."

"Look, let's forget whether he measures up to your system honor-wise," Shively said. "I don't think it's very damned important to us."

"We built him," Joe said, "but we don't own him."

"I think perhaps you've been too close to this project, Joe," McRumen said thoughtfully. "You're not seeing things as clearly as you usually do. I'm sure that boy—that boy's sincerity is above question." The older man's eyes gazed steadily at Logan and there was a challenge in them and a trace of anger. Logan's words had offended him as he sat remembering the lean young emissary who had so deeply impressed him. Enough of his world seemed to be coming undone and he would not let this part collapse.

He got up from his desk and stood looking out the window, his back to them. "I don't think it's your fault, Joe," he said. "You've been working very hard on this. I think you had better follow through as Al suggested." From the slow, level sound of the president's words, Joe Logan knew that the man's mind was set. He looked at McRumen and at Shively. The vice-president returned his stare, silently and unchanging, allied with McRumen in opposition to Logan.

An hour later, Joe finished his letter of explanation to the director of the International Aid Commission. It ran four full single-spaced paragraphs, each one soggy with corporate regret.

Joe tried several times to call Gladys Constable at her studio office before he finally heard her voice on the wire. Her greeting had a saccharine huskiness, unlike the forceful even tone she used before the television camera.

"So sweet of you to call, darling," she told him.

"It's not just social," he said. "I'm begging."

"Dear boy. And you've been so good till now. You want my lovely white body, don't you?"

"Hungrily. But I have something more prosaic in mind right now."

She sighed. "Men are such swine, honest to Christ. All right, lamb, what's your problem?"

Joe phrased his request carefully. Gladys sounded both cautious and puzzled. "That's all?"

"That's all."

"That's no trouble, baby. My listeners are all newspaper readers."

"Atta girl. Now isn't there some small favor I can do for you?"

"Not at the moment, darling." Silence on the phone. Then: "Mmm, Joe, dear?"

"Yes?"

"This boy of yours—is he really as—well, you know—tender-looking as he seems in those pictures?"

"Forks go right through him," Joe said.

"Aren't we graphic. Well . . ."

"Gladys?"

"Yes, baby?"

"Shall I see to it that he's uncommitted for Sunday night?"

"You're sweet, lamb. Now I've got to run."

Joe put the receiver down with satisfaction. Gobble him up, mama. Don't leave any scraps.

He turned himself with reluctant deliberation to the task of composing a telegram to the counsel for Senator Barton Crain's subcommittee. By monumental force of will he was able to keep his mind free of other distractions and to operate only as a Raven agent. And as an efficient agent he had decided that this course would be more successful than a direct request to Senator Crain, as Shively had proposed.

The wire, which he gave to Emily to send out, read:

SUGGEST YOU INCLUDE CAPTAIN BEDFORD MONTROSE AMONG WITNESSES FOR RAVEN COMPANY BECAUSE HE REPRESENTS IMPORTANT ASPECT OF AMERICAN INDUSTRY EFFORT TOWARD HELPING FREE WORLD ALLIES. FEEL HIS STORY OF VALUE TO ALL WHO HEAR IT EVERYWHERE PARTICULARLY IN VIEW OF YOUR CURRENT HEARINGS ON DRUG INDUSTRY OPERATIONS. MONTROSE APPEARS SUNDAY MAY 12 AT 7 PM EASTERN STANDARD TIME ON GLADYS CONSTABLE TELEVISION NEWS INTERVIEW SHOW WASHINGTON CHANNEL 8. WILL APPRECIATE YOUR APPRISING SUBCOMMITTEE MEMBERS.

LLOYD MCRUMEN
PRESIDENT RAVEN PHARMACEUTICALS INC.

It was late in the afternoon when he called Pat. "When can I see you?" he asked her.

"Oh, Joe," she said. "We agreed . . ."

"The hell we did. I didn't agree to anything. When can I see you?"

"Is—is anything the matter?"

"Nothing's the matter. I just want to be with you. How about dinner?"

"I'm afraid not, Joe. What are you doing with yourself these days?"

"Selling my soul to the devil, bits at a time."

"Has anything happened to Buddy?"

"How did his name get into this?" Joe asked. "Why would something have happened to him?"

"I haven't heard from him today. I just wondered if you had sent him off on another trip through the Congo."

"I haven't seen him. But, since you ask, I've been preparing him for his debut." He told her about the arrangements for the Gladys Constable program.

"Isn't that lovely? Will he be wearing a sweater with *Raven* on it?"

"He's going to be buck naked. It's the only way they'd take him. When can I see you?"

"Well—when did you say that television program is?"

"Sunday night. Why?"

"Do you want to come over here and watch it with me? Or will you have to be at the studio, pulling the strings?"

"No, but does it have to be *that* that brings us together?"

"I think it would be fun," Pat said. "The last time was in Meadow Hills, wasn't it? Remember, we sat together then, and . . ."

"I remember," Joe said. "All right. You asked for it. I'll bring a drum to drown it out, but I'll be there."

Gladys Constable's guests were not always the biggest names; sometimes they were barely known outside the coteries they traveled in. But she managed to probe the news-making zones in all of them so that even when her ratings were down her headlines were consistently up.

She usually had two guests on each show, interviewed separately. That represented another secret of her success: no one individual's personality should be exposed long enough to tempt boredom. Buddy Montrose shared his program with the official executioner of a state prison. Buddy appeared last. Watching him unveil his message before the small flickering screen in Pat's apartment, Logan acknowledged that Gladys was doing a masterful job. She quickly managed to find and explore the essence of the public Bedford Montrose. An audience estimated in the millions heard the story of Baopneng and its lesson to the world. Stripped of its nonessentials and beamed on cathode ray, it was still as vibrant as it had ever been.

"You breathe fire when you speak, Captain," Gladys said. "Obviously your experience was a meaningful one to you."

"Yes, I guess it was," Buddy said. He smiled his familiar disarming smile. "Maybe I should say I'm afraid it was."

"There's a curious combination of hope and hostility in what you have to say. Which do you believe is the more clearly felt in you?"

Montrose considered it. "That's hard to answer, Miss Constable. Hope is an easy reaction. You can feel it whenever you see a man fight hunger or withstand torture or hold to his beliefs under the most severe kind of pressure. But in a way I think hope is a self-indulgence. You use the word hostility. I'm not sure that would be the one I would choose. I'd say, rather, determination in the face of evil. But whatever it is, I think it's probably the more important."

"Well, let's stick to my word, if you don't mind," Gladys said sweetly.

"Hostility. Now, who are you mad at and what about, Captain? Is it just communism itself? Its effect on people? What is it?"

"It's all of that," Montrose replied, "and more. I think we in America should be a race of determined men—or, even hostile men, if you prefer the term—as long as the threat of communism exists on this globe."

"I know," Gladys said, "and I agree with you. Or I think I do. But if you'll forgive me, Captain, you're being vague. What can hostility itself accomplish in a world whose very existence depends on thoughtful, careful, painstaking progress through the most exacting problems of diplomacy?"

Montrose interrupted. "If *you'll* forgive *me*, Miss Constable," he said. His face was taut and he spoke with the measured tones of one who controlled himself only with effort. "I think you're the one who might be vague, at least in your conception of communism. You're speaking from the viewpoint of one who has not seen what can happen, who has never had the first-hand knowledge of the price we pay for 'progress,' as you call it. Perhaps if you had experienced Communist torture yourself . . ."

"Well, Captain, maybe we should both be more specific, then. What more than we're already doing do you think we *should* do? You speak of 'fighting' the menace as if we were not already doing everything we can. How else would you propose to fight it? With guns?"

"I say it is our duty not to relax for even a second. We have to meet it headlong. . . ."

"But that's what I'm trying to determine. What is *headlong?* Do you mean war?"

"I'll tell you what I mean, Miss Constable. You asked me a minute ago about my hope. Well, I do have hope. I have reason to have it. I've seen how brave men can stand and resist this monster even when it storms over them and threatens to destroy them. There are brave men throughout this world, prepared to resist whenever the evil threatens them, if only they are given the strength and encouragement to do so."

"Yes, the strength and encouragement. Do you mean, perhaps, that we should arm anti-Communists, wherever they are, in whatever . . ."

"I'm not in the government, Miss Constable. I'm forced to leave to the experts the job of deciding exactly what must be done—assuming they are willing and able to recognize the job at hand. I only say, and I say this with as much conviction as it is possible for me to muster"—Montrose looked directly into the camera, his eyes soft and sincere—"that we are being given now our last chance at greatness as a nation. What we believe in—*everything* we believe in, no less—is at stake. We can have glory, or we can have shame. The choice is ours."

Gladys watched him silently for a split second, and then she said, "I'm sorry we haven't time to continue this, Captain Montrose. There are many other questions I should like to ask you. But unfortunately our time is drawing to a close. I have a moment only to say that I understand you have made yourself available to appear before the Senate subcommittee investigating the drug industry, as a witness for the pharmaceutical firm which sent you supplies while you were in Baopneng."

Atta baby, Logan said to himself. *Now he's all yours.*

Montrose's face showed his surprise, but he recovered quickly. "Well," he said, "I haven't been asked by the committee to testify. . . ."

"That investigation, of course, is much in the news these days, and we'll all be watching the developments closely. Thank you very much, Captain Bedford Montrose, for being with us . . ."

Pat Crain snapped the television set off. She lit a cigarette and said to Joe, "That business about the hearings was clever. I take it you get credit for that."

"I do," Joe said. "Full credit. But not for anything else. The rest of it was all his."

Pat smiled. "Do you really think it makes a difference after all this time, Joe, whose words they were?"

Joe sat staring moodily at the still and empty screen. "I don't suppose it does," he said finally. Watching Buddy had been more painful by far than he had been prepared for. Stripped of the protective gauze of sincerity through which Joe had once seen him, the image was harsher, more exaggerated, less believable. And—what else? Was there a new dimension to the hero which he had not been aware of before? Now that the filter had changed in the retina of his mind, shapes and shadows were different, and it was difficult to know clearly which were distortions and which realities. Was there a dimension now of—danger?

Nonsense. So the guy doesn't believe half of what he says. You've been had, but so what? You don't have to look for danger in it.

Joe recognized that there was always danger, perhaps, in the birth of a hero. It was one of the occupational hazards of life. But something more disturbing had emerged from that torturous adventure on the television screen, with Buddy Montrose stripped of sincerity, draped in the incontestable issue of the day, dodging artfully every demand for honesty.

Many men had discovered they could gain attention, and sometimes power, by doing no more than declaring themselves against sin. Was that in itself a danger? Was the exploitation, for personal advantage, of the pressing fears and the haunting hungers of an anxious time in men's lives, itself a thing of danger?

Was it? Logan passed a hand over his eyes and closed them. The harvest of words can be a bitter one. *Let's get a little communism in this thing, Buddy.*

A dishonest way to gain an advantage if you don't have anything more than that to offer. Joe heard the voice of the hero in another day before he learned from the experts. Now the voice was the same but the message was different:

We must fight this evil wherever it appears.

What do you suggest?

I have no suggestions. I have no beliefs.

What do you want?

I want your allegiance.

How had that poem in the Midwest City paper put it? "Americans you have no choice. . . . Listen to the Hero's voice."

Finding implications of danger in the heroic image of Buddy Montrose was not a new experience for Senator Barton Crain. It was no easier to encounter a second time, however. It stayed in the senator's mind, troubling him, long after he had turned his attention from the television program to other matters. He had received a day or two before a copy of the letter sent by the director of the International Aid Commission to the Raven company, in answer to the senator's suggestion that Buddy be given a team assignment, and he hoped fervently that that would settle the problem—if it *was* a problem. It all depended on that company. They were a tricky outfit, by God. The engineering involved in the plan to get Montrose before the senator's committee was, Crain acknowledged, a smart bit of planning. He shook his head in a gesture which conveyed at once wonder and bewilderment. Perhaps, he reflected, he should give serious consideration to retirement when his term was up. Sometimes he had the sense of being more confused by the furies which swirled around his life than he used to be.

Emily Klinger had never been so thrilled in her life. Nor had she ever been so sure of what she had to do. It was now or never. Buddy himself had said we should all have determination. He had also talked about hope. Emily had both. Her hands were actually shaking as she sat at the small writing desk in her cramped apartment and composed her letter. "Dearest Buddy," it ran, "I know this might not be the proper thing, writing you like this, but we haven't seen much of you recently and I wanted to let you know right away how wonderful I thought you were on the TV tonight. You're a wonderful person, Buddy, and I think a great man, and I want you to know that for me it's an honor to know you. I've missed seeing you and I want you to know if there's anything I can do for you, anything at all, I want you to just let me know. Tonight with you on the TV screen it was almost like having you in my apartment and I almost opened the bottle of 'joy juice' I've been saving for an occasion. Well, it will be nice to see you again. Love, Emily K."

"I'm sorry, sir," the operator told Alden Root, "they report that Miss Constable has already left the studio, and Captain Montrose must have left too. He isn't there."

"All right, all right," Root said. "He's staying at the Dorwick Arms Hotel. Try him there in half an hour. Keep trying until you get him." He hung up and lit a fresh cigar, peering intently through the smoke at the silent telephone. Probably never get him tonight, damn it. That broad'll have him tied up. He let the cigar ash build and fall as he explored his scalp with a grubby fingernail. Everything was going good, too, real good, until that shocker at the end came along. The boy had done a damn good job, but by Jesus it was all going to be ruined if Alden Root didn't step in now and take the kind of action that had to be taken. He inhaled deeply on his cigar and glowered at the telephone, waiting with mounting irritation for it to ring.

"I'm going to stop this 'Captain Montrose' bit," Gladys Constable said. "I'll call you Buddy. You weren't really kosher with me tonight, Buddy."

"What do you mean, Miss Constable?"

"And you call me Gladys. Why don't you take off your coat and tie and get comfortable while I fix up some drinks. . . . I mean you were hedging with me on those answers. I wanted you to give out with something concrete."

"Well, I thought I tried . . ."

"Come on, lamb, don't try to fool your Aunt Gladys. Here, unzip me, will you? I'm going to slip into something easy. . . . It didn't really make any difference. The audience loved you, I'm sure of that. The hounds."

"You think it went all right?"

"Of course it went all right, pet. You know that as well as I do. I wouldn't trust you, but you went over like Ed Sullivan."

"You're mixing me up. I . . ."

"Nobody in this wide world's going to mix *you* up, baby. Now let's forget the program, huh? I want to relax. Goodness, you have cold fingers. Are you nervous?"

"I don't think so."

"Well, don't be. Come here. Bend down. I can't reach you that way. Hold me right here, will you? All right. Now kiss me. Hard."

18

THE TELEGRAM from Washington, addressed to Bedford Montrose c/o Raven Pharmaceuticals, Inc., came in early in the morning. At Logan's instruction, Emily tried to reach Buddy at his hotel, but she reported with a note of bewilderment in her voice that he wasn't in.

"Where in the world do you think he could be off to this early?" she asked.

Ten to one he could be reached by dialing Gladys Constable's private phone, Logan reflected. "Maybe he's decided to forsake us all," he said. "Give up cigarettes and civilization and women and do church work on the open road."

"He's a great man, Mr. Logan," Emily said. She said it with a solemnity that Logan thought both ludicrous and pathetic. "On the TV last night you could just feel the greatness coming through."

"Where did you feel it? Show me the exact spot."

"Oh, Mr. Logan, honest to God. Shall I try the hotel again pretty soon?"

"Did you leave a message?" She nodded. "All right, wait an hour and then if we haven't heard, call back. Anything else on the docket?"

"Mr. Blivet was in the first thing this morning. He said he would be back."

"Now, there's another great man," Logan said. "Don't you think so?"

"No I do not," Emily said evenly, "but he's polite and that's more than can be said for some people around here."

Joe was on his second cup of coffee when Horace Blivet returned, puffing a little after the long flight of stairs.

"Glad you're here," Blivet said, waving a sheaf of papers. He bustled to a chair and dropped himself into it. "Copy for the commercials. Just got 'em from the agency. Wait 'til you see how they were able to jazz up some of those clinical cases."

"Look, Horace, if you don't mind . . ."

"Lemme describe the whole bit," Blivet said, moving his hands in the air. "It starts with a giant Pax tablet dancing across the stage . . ."

". . . in a ballet costume," Joe said.

Blivet looked at him in amazement. "You've seen it," he said.

"More times than I can count," Joe said. He looked at the doorway behind Blivet and raised his hand. "Come on in, Doc." Ambrose Garibaldi entered the office and sat down. He regarded Blivet with tolerance but said nothing. "Horace, if you don't mind," Logan said, "Doc and I have . . ."

"You *couldn't* have seen this one," Horace told him. "This is fresh and new, really a work of art." He set to his task of description joyfully: the shapely tablet would glide onto a magnificent mirrored stage and come into the foreground of the television screen, luxuriously relaxed. There would be violins in the background. Then a distinguished-looking man with gray hair and a white coat would materialize as the tablet faded out softly. The man would lean forward intimately and say, "Medical science has at last been able to do something about your frayed nerves—your knotted tensions. Now you can forget your cares. Put away your woes and worries. Pack up your troubles—or, rather"—here the man smiles the smile of one who has a secret to impart—"Pax up your troubles."

Caught up in the spirit of the thing, Blivet excitedly ran his finger over the script he held. "After some more of this—you can read it yourself and see how he explains peace of mind and how it's available at a price too absurd to mention—the doctor—he's the *family* doctor—he fades into a bookcase and the beautiful tablet slides in again just like the beginning. Only this time she sings. Now try to *visualize* it." Blivet began to sing. "Are you addled? Are you ta-axed? Are you saddled? You need Pa-ax! Are you rattled? Can't rela-ax . . ."

"Oh, for Christ's sake, stop that," Garibaldi said.

The startled Blivet had been beating time with his foot, and his open mouth was still formed for the next syllable when Garibaldi jumped up and took hold of him by the arm.

"Now just a goddamn minute," Blivet protested. "Joe wants to . . ."

"Joe's ecstatic, Horace," the physician said, forcefully guiding the bewildered man's elbow. "So am I. But we can take only so much ecstasy."

"You haven't heard the rest. . . ."

"Oh yes I have," Garibaldi said, closing the door against Blivet's bulk. He snapped the lock and, with a shiver, resumed his seat. "That Mongolian defective is all over this place," he said. "As for *you,* my friend, of all your distinctions, the one you should prize most is that you live in my mind as the man who started this idiocy."

"Are you going to throw me out, too? It's my office, remember."

"I'm going to ask you to remain behind your desk while I sing that abomination to you," Garibaldi said. "Over and over and over."

Logan smiled and stood up. "Not me," he said. "Idea men learn early not to get trapped in their ideas."

"I couldn't have stated civilization's chief trouble any better," Garibaldi said, "and I've tried many times."

After Garibaldi left Logan's office, his buzzer sounded and he picked up his phone to hear Emily announce that she had reached Captain Montrose.

"Your wire from the subcommittee came," Logan said into the mouthpiece to Montrose. "Now get out here because I'm going to spell out *exactly* what you'll say."

"I'll get out when I can," Montrose said.

"Right away, God damn it."

"Easy, Logan. Don't try to give me orders."

"Take it however you want it. But be here within an hour."

Logan hung up abruptly.

For the next twenty minutes he dictated to Emily and she retired to the outer office to type what he had given her: a twenty-point outline of what Montrose was to get over to the committee and the public. Emily had just finished when Montrose arrived.

She took the pages in to Logan and said breathlessly, "He's here. He's outside."

"Well, don't maul him," Logan said.

"*Real*-ly, Mr. Logan."

"He was injured in the war, Emily. He can't do anything for you."

Her face darkened and she said haughtily, "Shall I show him in?"

Logan nodded. "Dally with him for a couple of minutes at your desk, while I read this over. Then show him in." She left the room stormily.

In the outer office, Buddy stood by her desk. He was holding the telegram from Washington. "He wants you to wait here with me for a few minutes, Buddy," Emily said. "If you don't mind," she added sweetly, her pique evaporating as her eyes boldly examined him.

"It's a pleasure," Montrose said in what Emily thought was a wonderfully courtly way. "How have you been?"

"Just nutty," she said. "Around this place you can't be anything else. You must be kind of tired after your television last night and all. Why don't you sit down?"

Montrose sat in the chair facing her desk.

"I don't suppose you got my letter," she said, straightening some papers on the desk. He looked at her curiously. "I only mailed it last night. It was silly, but after watching you on that TV show and not having seen you to talk to in a while and all, I just decided to write you a letter. You were the greatest, honest."

Montrose smiled directly at her and Emily felt herself go all weak. "You're sweet to say it. Maybe your letter will be in the afternoon mail."

"It's really not important," she said. "Just a billy dew. You look awfully handsome in that suit. This is the first time I guess I've seen you when you weren't in uniform."

The buzzer on her desk sounded sharply and Montrose stood up.

"The great genius is ready," she said. "Don't forget to bow on your way in."

Montrose left her and entered Logan's office. The two men nodded curtly but there was no verbal greeting. "Well?" Buddy said. "Can we get this out of the way now? I've got more important things to do today."

Logan passed Montrose a stapled copy of the outline from the corner of his desk. Then, his eyes and his voice hard, he said, "Sit down and read it carefully. It's your *script*."

Montrose ran through the pages quickly and said, "You've got all the answers, Joe. Suppose you tell me what happens if the committee doesn't give me an opportunity to get this spiel out."

"Anything short of that won't do, Buddy. You don't need any stage directions. The only opportunity necessary is the one they've already given you—to sit there and talk for a half-hour. Make these points in your answers if you can, but make them." He read from the paper on his desk. "One. Condense your experience. Get the guts of your speech across in the first minute. Then leave it alone. Then get to the American Way and Raven as representative of the progressive force exerted upon humanity by American business—in particular, American drug business."

"Why don't you write it all out and I'll memorize it," Montrose said.

"I'm not playing, Buddy," Logan said harshly. "Just remember the only reason you're there is that you know how free American drugs saved lives because of Raven. Scratch the industry's back as much as you can and go easy on your fire-breathing anti-Red crapola. I don't want to confuse the issue."

"Anything else?" Montrose asked sarcastically.

"No," Logan said. "I'll call you if I want you."

Montrose put the carbon copy in his pocket as Logan's telephone started to ring.

"It's for Captain Montrose," Emily said from the doorway. "It's long distance." Logan picked up the telephone and passed it to Montrose.

"Yes? Yes? Oh, hello. Well, wait. Hold on a moment." Montrose put his hand over the mouthpiece. "This is a personal call, Logan. Do you mind?"

"Go right ahead," Logan said, getting up out of his seat. He scooped some correspondence from the desk and carried it out to Emily. "Get Mr. Shively on another line," he said.

She picked up the phone and pressed a button on the instrument. "Whoever that is talking from long distance," she said, "has a voice like a pushcart peddler. What *volume*. Mr. Shively? One moment, please. Mr. Logan on the wire." Joe took the phone.

"Al, Montrose got his summons this morning. He's here now. I gave him a copy of what we want him to say. He seemed satisfied." For several seconds Joe listened, nodding absently. "All right. I'm sending you over a copy. Right." He hung up and standing by Emily's desk began leafing through one of the morning papers he had started reading before Montrose arrived.

Emily told him Montrose's telephone conversation was finished and Logan returned to his office. Montrose looked glum and preoccupied as he prepared to leave.

"That was a nice plug Gladys gave us last night, don't you think?" Logan said. "Nice girl, Gladys."

"I'd rather not have anything about my appearance before that committee on the air or in the newspapers," Montrose said.

"Is that right!" Logan said.

Montrose started to reply, then shrugged and walked out the door, closing it sharply behind him.

Logan stared at the closed door for several seconds, until the anger that had been building during his encounter with Montrose faded, leaving only a strong sensation of distaste.

The sensation did not disappear when Logan turned to his next project of the day. He unlocked his top desk drawer and took out the card Shively had given him. "Abner Murphy, Confidential Investigator." Grimly, he dialed the number.

Murphy's voice was cautious. "Shively told me you'd be calling," he said.

"You know what I want, then?"

"More or less," the man said. "When are you going to come by?"

Fingering the card idly, Logan saw that his address was in an upper West Side Manhattan neighborhood, near Columbia, and his sagging spirits began to revive when he remembered that this was one of the three afternoons a week Pat spent in the University library. "I'll try to make it later in the day," he said. "If something comes up I'll call you."

Early in the afternoon he picked up a company car in the Raven lot, and an hour later he found Pat deep in a volume of Alfred North Whitehead. His whispered greeting startled her. She removed her glasses, closed the book and followed him out of the reading room.

"What a hell of a coincidence," he told her, "finding you here."

"It's not fair," she said, "sneaking around people's lives like that. What on earth are you doing in a *library*, of all places?"

"Actually I'm here on a special research project, trying to find out how many women in this moldy palace would knock off work long enough to spend a reckless hour having a drink somewhere."

"And how many are there, Dr. Kinsey?"

"So far none, but I just arrived."

She smiled at him. "Thanks, but it's still early and I . . ."

"Coffee?"

"Did you know I'd be here from something I once told you? It's dreadful for people ever to give you information. You can always use it against them."

"Orange juice? Seven-Up?"

She looked at her watch. "A martini maybe, but only to help in your research."

As they sat across from each other in the afternoon quiet of a dim bar on upper Broadway, Joe said, "Pat—have dinner with me tonight."

"I can't, Joe. I'm going to see Buddy."

"Then tomorrow."

"Joe . . ."

"Please, Pat. Just dinner."

"Joe, I'd love to, but try to understand." She looked down at the table top between them. "I can't."

"That's not much of an answer."

"It's the only answer I can give. My life is so terribly muddled right now; I've got to let it get straightened out."

"But this isn't straightening it out," Logan protested.

"Yes it is. Joe, I *am* engaged to Buddy, you know."

"You don't have to tell me that."

"I'm afraid I do. Buddy and I *are* going to be married. We're going through a rough time right now, but it will work out. It has to. And I'm not going to add any more complications to it if I can help it."

Joe lit a cigarette for each of them. "You're bound to come across complications, Pat," he said. "I won't try to mess up your life—I promise you that. But look at us. You can't deny what you know exists. Can't we just relax and see what happens?"

"It wouldn't work," she said.

"Why not? Try it, anyway. One dinner."

She sat silently for a moment and then she smiled at him.

"You talk too much," she said.

"I'm a born salesman," Logan said. "Dinner then, once?"

"All right. Once."

"Tonight?"

"Now, Joe," she said warningly, "I told you . . ."

"Oh, yeah. Montrose. Tomorrow, then."

They did not mention the subject again while Logan was taking her home. But it stayed at the top of his mind, even after he dropped her off, and it almost made him forget to place his telephone call to Abner Murphy to leave the information that he would be in the next day to listen to the tapes.

19

WHEN BUDDY ARRIVED, Pat kept him waiting in the tiny living room while she sat at the dressing table in her bedroom, ostensibly choosing the costume jewelry to wear with her black velvet dinner dress. She handled each piece absently, picking it up, putting it down, picking it up again. She looked at herself in the mirror, trying earnestly to bring control to her disordered thoughts. *I've been through all this,* she said to herself with vigorous seriousness. She framed the words silently, moving her mouth with deliberate emphasis: *I—have—al-ready de-ci-ded.* She met her eyes in the mirror, held them levelly. *Now damn you, Joe Logan, get out of here.* She put a smile on her lips and went out to meet Buddy.

Half the evening later, sitting across from him in a Chinatown restaurant, she felt like someone at the end of a vague dream, not believing in it completely but feeling that she should.

"I know we'd planned to wait a while yet, darling," Buddy was saying, "but there's no reason we can't change our minds." He squeezed her hand, and the boyish concern in his face became a smile. "Is there?"

Pat did not answer him immediately, and he repeated it. "Is there?"

"No," she said slowly, "but I wish I knew why you've decided this, Buddy."

"It's bad for both of us, sweetheart, to wait this long. If we were married right away, everything would work out for us. This way . . ." He shrugged his shoulders helplessly and his face was drawn once more in lines of concern.

Pat looked into his eyes directly and finished the thought for him. "This way is impossible."

"Then you *do* think I'm right," Buddy said.

She looked away from him and her voice was a whisper. "Yes," she said, "I do."

Oh, do I? Do I really? She smiled quickly to banish this intruding thought.

From the beginning, the evening had gone well. There had been no dissensions. Buddy had been attentive and eager to please her. His entire manner had lightened and become more personal, as if he had released himself—or been released—from the preoccupations which had imprisoned him, and was able to look once more without distraction at himself and at her, and at them together.

Pat, unprepared for the change, expecting only a repetition of the empty frustrations and helpless irritations which had filled so many of their meetings recently, welcomed this new development with relief and gratitude.

Throughout dinner in the aromatic dining room, surrounded by platters of exotic vegetables and sauces, Buddy had talked of many things—the food, the city in the spring, the people they knew back home. Not once had Raven been mentioned, or the speaking tour, or the hungry people of Asia. The relief was so great, once Pat had realized that the evening was going to be different—the kind that she had been hoping for for weeks—that she hardly knew when the conversation had slipped into talk of an early wedding.

None of the surprises before, welcome as they were, had prepared her for this, and the complicated structure of her reaction confused her. Mixed in with her happy reception was a flow of reluctance she could not understand.

For this, of course, she told herself, was what she had wanted since the very beginning of the adventure that had carried Buddy so far away from her. And now as Buddy talked with animation about them and their future, she felt the conviction: of *course* this was what she wanted. She listened with gratitude while he drew her back to him with intimate eloquence, back over the gulf that had opened and spread.

Later, when she felt his arms close about her and his lips seek out her response, she felt again the small cold wind brush her mind and she struggled to rid herself of it. For release, she pressed herself tight against him, seeking to know in silence what words would never tell her.

"Love me, Buddy," she said once in a swift rush of panic, and Bedford Montrose replied, "I do. Oh, I do."

What appeared in Garibaldi's medical progress reports as "satisfactory" became in the Raven sales jargon "sensational." Again and again Garibaldi helplessly watched the adrenalin supplied by the sales and promotion staff pumped into the clinical corpus he was building. He resisted, but his defenses were futile. Peace of mind, release from tension, freedom from anxiety were not for him.

The contest between Shively and the medical research director was becoming sharper and the incidents which punctuated it more frequent. In each encounter, Shively would concede a momentary verbal victory, only to ignore and overlook the cautious views the physician advanced, or insidiously subvert his clinical results with the force of the hard-sell school and the promise of Pax profits.

When a copy of a letter which had been sent out by the American Psychiatric Society to its member doctors arrived on Garibaldi's desk, he took it in to the vice-president's office. The letter acknowledged the great contribution to psychiatry being made by some of the more potent tranquilizers in mental hospitals. It also, however, took serious exception to indiscriminate use for the relief of everyday tensions. "Casual employment of the drugs is medically unsound and constitutes a public danger," the letter read. "The tranquilizing drugs have not been in use long enough to determine the full range, duration and medical significance of their side effects. . . . Classification of many of them is still questionable."

Shively perused the letter thoughtfully and said, "What's this got to do with us?"

Garibaldi shrugged. "It was mailed to nine thousand, three hundred and fifty-three members of the society," he said, "and we're about to market a tranquilizer. It reflects an even larger area of professional opinion, which I believe deserves some passing attention from us."

A sweet and understanding smile crossed the sales vice-president's face. "But ours is for peace of mind, Ambrose," he said patiently. "They're talking about powerful drugs for psychos, not normal people."

Garibaldi said nothing.

"You say this went out to nine thousand doctors?" Shively asked.

"That's right."

"You don't think this could hurt *our* sales any, do you?"

"I have no idea," Garibaldi said. "You're the sales expert."

"After we market Pax," Shively said thoughtfully, "maybe you ought to write them a letter, explaining peace of mind—just to play it safe."

"That's ridiculous," Garibaldi answered him. "These men are psychiatrists."

"We're not *calling* Pax a tranquilizer, you know," Shively said archly. "We don't say that anywhere in our advertising."

"We can call it anything we wish," Garibaldi said. "That won't make a particle of difference."

"Well, it *will* make a difference," Shively said. "We just ride over things like that letter with the positive plus features of Pax. What the hell do you think we're spending all that dough on promotion for? I don't want to hear Pax called a tranquilizer again."

"Medicine will call it a tranquilizer whether we like it or not."

"The hell with medicine," Shively said. "We don't need the doctors to sell this product."

"We've got to keep some sense of proportion," Garibaldi said angrily. "Medicine isn't a fad, it's a natural science. We're a drug company. The favorable verdict of medical doctors is necessary to our existence."

"Verdict, schmerdict," Shively said with disdain. "Just who are you *for* anyway? Raven or the AMA?"

Outraged, Garibaldi stared at him without answering.

The vice-president smiled. "You're not sure, are you? You don't like what I say about the high priesthood, do you? Well, listen carefully." He leaned forward and waved the letter at Garibaldi. "Our drug is the *newest* and the *best* peace pill that anyone ever saw. It's *different* from any other. It's going to sell and sell and *sell*. And there isn't any room around here any more for people who don't believe that. So you had better make up your mind to get behind this thing, and soon. Or . . ."

"Or what?" the physician said.

Shively paused confidentially, the smile frozen on his face.
"Or we find someone else to be the company's conscience, *Doctor*."

Lloyd McRumen felt confident, but uneasily so, that Raven would
emerge from the Senate hearings with most of its reputation intact. His
worries centered only about his own scheduled appearance and he wished
fervently that it would all be over quickly, without the discomfort of
embarrassing questions. He was encouraged by the assurances of Raven's
legal counsel that even if the senators thought Raven drugs were ex-
orbitantly priced, nothing could or would be done about it unless there
was evidence of intercompany agreement to fix and hold false prices.
And Raven was as clean as most in that respect; there were few agree-
ments, no coöperative arrangements, and not many reciprocal deals—at
least there were none on paper. The company was strong and free and
independently competitive.

There was nothing to worry about. Raven had not broken any laws.
The company management had not done anything wrong.

Alonzo Shively enthusiastically backed up counsel's assurances; indeed,
he hopefully believed and insistently maintained that Raven had potentially much more to gain now than to lose from its Senate appearance,
with Montrose scheduled as a witness. The Senate, in fact, could have
chosen no more fortunate time to summon Raven than this period just
before the introduction of Pax. Anyone who hadn't heard of the Raven
company would certainly hear of it now. In spite of all the noise in the
papers, Raven was going to walk right on through with character. If there
was one thing Montrose's story would give them it was character.

The offices of Abner Murphy, one-time city policeman, licensed private detective, and extralegal wire-tapper, were sparsely furnished. They
wore an impersonal, unrevealing look. Even Murphy himself had the
nondescript appearance of a man who could be seen anywhere and seldom noticed.

Logan learned from Murphy that it would be more difficult than he
had expected to get what he wanted from the tapes. "The stuff from other
companies is all mixed in with the tapes we got on Raven's wires. Very
little of it is written out," Murphy told him.

"*Raven's* wires?" Logan asked in astonishment. "You mean Shively
had you tap our own telephones, too?"

The man shrugged. "We had quite a few of them bugged. He said he
wanted to make sure there weren't any leaks out of the company."

Logan was unprepared for this development, and he considered it for a few seconds. "All right, let's get on with it," he said finally. "All I'm interested in doing is taking a spot check through what you have, to see if we can turn up anything useful. Shively tells me he hasn't heard half of it himself."

"That's right," Murphy said, unsmiling. "We've sent him transcripts on any of the subjects he asked us to check for. But all the other stuff is just there. You can listen to as much as you want."

The tape recordings were not at Murphy's office, Joe discovered, because the man could not afford unnecessary chances. In the detective's car they drove to the Bronx. After winding through endless blocks of two-family houses all built of the same red and yellow brick, Abner Murphy finally stopped and motioned Joe to get out. They were less than a ten-minute ride from the Raven plant. Dodging a group of scrambling children on the sidewalk, Murphy led the way into one of the houses and into the first-floor apartment.

For three undisturbed hours Joe listened tirelessly to the voices of Abner Murphy's record collection. He learned a hundred things about the personal and business affairs of people he knew and people he didn't know. All of what he heard made him uncomfortable, and much of it filled him with a deep personal shame.

As he sat listening to these voices, the thought was born and thundered through him: *what am I doing here?* In it was the fearful presentiment that he had only to break through a tissue-thick wall and he would find answers to dismay and discredit him.

He had been alarmed, and then he had been outraged, when he learned about Raven's invasion into the private world of others. Yet here he sat, probing into the spoils the invasion had brought, as if no objection had ever risen to torture him. He had made his peace with an action he despised, and however uneasy a peace it was, it was the latest in a series of unworthy compromises he had made the last few months.

He felt heavily the responsibility of this knowledge and he saw no way to relieve it. It's all part of the fun, an easy voice offered, but there was no comfort in it, for Logan knew too well the boundaries of satisfaction. He had staked them out himself.

Like a hurricane hunter seeking out the eye of destruction, Logan had forced his way to the midst of the American business legend. It was here that he found his challenge. What he created for his listeners and his readers, they believed. The executives who mouthed his speeches and the scientists whose names were signed to the articles he contrived had faith in him and appreciated him, because he held before them a mirror that reflected a palatable blend of truth and the creations of their wish-

ful egos. Logan could recognize and delight in this for the private joke
it was, and still believe in it. For corporations were not held together
by their own weight like Gothic arches—they were great harnessed beasts
which somebody had to feed and drive. And it was here, precisely here,
that Logan found his challenge, and his home.

What, then, had gone wrong? Why was he sitting here in a shabby room
barred against the sunlight, alone with a monstrous ally whose voice
droned on in an endless recitation of offensiveness? The question was
only a beginning; it led to others.

The voice of Buddy Montrose cut sharply through Logan's reverie and
he looked up, almost expecting the voice to materialize into something
firm. It was a routine call Montrose had made to the plant. Logan wasn't
in his office, Emily coyly informed the captain.

"Well," Montrose's voice said, "will you tell him I called?"

"Sure," Emily said. "Oh—Captain Montrose—uh . . ." Silence.

"Yes?"

"I hope"—Emily's voice came almost in a breathless whisper—"I hope
you didn't think I was too *forward* in your room that day."

Logan was at first startled; then, remembering the instance in which he
had sent Emily to Montrose's hotel with some papers, he smiled.

"Of course not," Montrose said. There was a small silence and then
his voice continued, a bit smoother now, Logan thought: "Perhaps we can
get together again sometime soon. Maybe for dinner. Would you like
that?"

"Dinner!" Emily said. "That would be *won*derful."

"All right, then. I'll get in touch with you."

"I'll be looking forward to it." There was a click and then a sigh and
then another click.

Logan was half-amused and half-irritated. Emily, he thought, with that
ill-concealed desire to rub up against the hero, may live to regret it.

Long after the conversation had stopped and others were following in
depressing succession, the nagging memory of Montrose's intrusion remained to give force and direction to Logan's troubled pursuit. What had
happened? *What had happened?* How could his list of adventures have
swelled so far as to include the exploitation of a man whose life had
brushed against his? He was stuck now with the responsibility—at least
a measure of it—for what Montrose had become. And the unavoidable
truth remained that the process of integration had begun with Raven's—
and Logan's—willingness to exploit.

Something had gone wrong with the elaborate vigilance that went into
the operation of Raven. Somewhere, a long way back, some small part

of the company got out of hand and remained uncontrolled. And as a result the proud old organization had forfeited an unreclaimable portion of its pride and jeopardized its reputation. Many men were responsible for this demeaning, but Logan felt the blame riding heaviest on him. Perception, his special weapon, might have prevented this, and he had failed to use it.

He had seen the process start, clearly enough, with the decision to go after a fat share of the tranquilizer market with every means possible, fair or foul. Well, that was business. He had seen it start and he had watched it grow, ignoring it, telling himself it would grow around him and leave him free. He had heard, and he could hear now, so clearly that it outweighed the rasping voices on the machine, the resolute warning of Ambrose Garibaldi that a man ignores the evil around him at his peril. The plans for Pax and the plans for Montrose had a single source and each had fed the other. Alone, Garibaldi had been able to take no effective stand against the Shively-directed juggernaut. Alone, Logan probably could have done nothing. But if he had joined Garibaldi, perhaps, just perhaps, they could together have given Lloyd McRumen the strength he needed.

What, now, could a man do whose conscience told him that something should be done? Logan sat alone in the constricting room, his eye on the evil machine before him, and he told himself there was nothing he could do.

Like a man lost at the controls in the very eye of destruction, he was helpless.

He found next to nothing which he considered of any value in arming McRumen for the hearings. By early afternoon he had sampled all but twenty spools of tape, and Murphy gave him permission to take them home for use overnight.

20

LOGAN STILL had a couple of hours before meeting Pat for their dinner date and he planned to listen to as many tapes as he could. In his disordered apartment, he plugged in Murphy's recorder, arranged the first tape for playback, and settled down with a large pad of yellow note paper in his lap and his feet propped shoeless on a coffee table from which the varnish was peeling.

The tapes were undistinguished from those he had heard that afternoon. There were conversations involving competitors, producers and suppliers, Raven salesmen and admen and promotion men, and physicians who were testing Pax. More than once, Logan was surprised to hear his own voice on the line, usually in a routine conversation with some newspaper or magazine editor. Ploughing doggedly through it all, he recorded what few points of special interest there were.

At five o'clock he had three spools left to go. Pouring a bottle of beer from his unevenly stocked refrigerator, he decided that three more was about as far as his tortured conscience would travel, anyway.

Carrying the beer with him, he put on the next tape and settled down once more. An operator's voice began the next conversation by announcing: "Midwest City calling Captain Bedford Montrose, please." Then after a moment Emily's voice, "Public Relations, Mr. Logan's office," and the Raven operator's response, "I have a long-distance call for Captain Montrose. Is he around there?" "Wait a minute," Emily's voice said, "and I'll go in and get him."

A silence followed, and Logan, eyeing the machine with sudden interest, came back into the living room and stood over it. He remembered the circumstance well—it was only yesterday morning, when Montrose came out to get the outline of remarks Logan had prepared for him.

There was the click of a receiver being picked up and after another pause, Montrose's voice: "Yes?"

A bluff hearty voice that Logan recognized at once came on. "Captain Montrose? This is Root."

A flash of surprise—and with it, excitement—spread with electrical quickness through Logan.

"Oh, hello," Montrose said. He seemed cautious.

"Can you talk freely?"

"Well, wait. Hold on a moment."

There followed a short silence in which, Joe knew, Montrose was clapping his hand over the mouthpiece to tell Logan it was a personal call. Logan waited, tense and impatient, for the conversation to continue. Then:

MONTROSE: All right, Mr. Root.

ROOT: Where are you?

MONTROSE: Logan's office. He's out now, though.

ROOT: All right. Look, I been trying to get you since last night. From now on leave word where you can be reached. Now what was that on the television about you goin' before Crain's committee . . .

MONTROSE: Well . . .

ROOT: . . . to testify.

MONTROSE: Well, that's right, but . . .

ROOT: What the hell's it all about?

MONTROSE: It's nothing very serious. They just want me to tell my story all over again.

ROOT: Serious! *Who* wants you to tell it?

MONTROSE: The Raven people.

ROOT: It didn't have to be on the TV all over Indiana. What the hell kind of a sucker are you?

MONTROSE: Well, really, I didn't know. . . .

ROOT: How did they get you and the committee tied up?

MONTROSE: Logan saw Crain, I guess, or talked to him, and got him to agree to call me. They think it'll make their appearance a success.

ROOT: You damn betcha they think so. But how did they get *you* to agree? They must of asked you.

MONTROSE: Well, I don't know, Mr. Root. They asked me, and the way they put it it seemed the thing to do.

Standing by the machine, immobilized by a gripping curiosity, Logan grinned suddenly to himself. That's right, Buddy boy, he thought. The way it was put to you there wasn't much else you *could* do.

Realizing that part of the conversation had raced on ahead of him, he stopped the machine and spun the tape back a couple of revolutions, then started it again.

ROOT: . . . did they get *you* to agree? They must of asked you.

MONTROSE: Well, I don't know, Mr. Root. They asked me, and the way they put it it seemed the thing to do.

ROOT: Now listen here. It was a damn fool thing for you to do. You should of told 'em to pound sand.

MONTROSE: I don't see . . .

ROOT: You don't have to see. Just take my word for it. You know what the public's attitude is toward this drug hearing? I'll tell you what it is. They want to see those drug people crucified. Everybody who pays two bucks for a bottle of cough syrup wants to see it.

MONTROSE: But . . .

ROOT: There ain't any buts. I'm talking about the people and I *know* what the people think. This is going to put you in a bad spot—and more than that, it's going to put Crain in a good one.

A moment of silence. Then Montrose, guardedly: "Crain? You mean Senator Crain?"

ROOT: I don't mean his grandpa.

MONTROSE: But what's he got to do with . . . I—I don't understand. . . .

ROOT: Now look, sonny, you wasn't born yesterday. Use your goddamn head. What do you think he's got to do with it?

MONTROSE: But I thought . . . I thought the senator and I were going to be working together soon.

ROOT: Well, you thought wrong.

MONTROSE: But you said . . .

ROOT: Forget what I said! You're not a soldier boy now, passing aspirin around to the Chinee. You're big enough so you don't have to be coddled or kidded. All this crap about saving Crain's face was all right as long as we was moving the right way. But what you're getting into with that hearing gives it another color and you got to face facts. And those facts are that Senator Bart Crain ain't going to like your coming out against his man one goddamn bit and he's going to oppose us as much as he can, daughter or no daughter. Now this hearing is going to give him just what he needs to fight with. He's going to come out of this a hero, and you're going to look like a turkey's ass.

There was another silence, a long one, and then Root said, "You there?"

"I'm listening," Montrose said.

ROOT: All right, now I want you to listen some more. The boys out here are sold on you. You've got that congressman's hat right at the end of your nose *if you play ball with us.* But no more hanky-panky.

MONTROSE: I want to coöperate, Mr. Root, but this thing with Senator

Crain's got me worried. We're going to be related and I just can't . . .

ROOT: You better make it goddamn soon then, boy, because when he catches on we'll have a fight on our hands. It won't do no harm if you're married to her. Might even slow him down a little, but that's your business. This other thing's a hell of a lot more important right now. . . .

In the new stillness that followed this declaration, while the tape spooled away, Joe found himself leaning forward tensely, not breathing, waiting for the sound of the captain's voice. And when it came he did breathe, deeply, knowing sickness in the core of his stomach. "All right," said Bedford Montrose, "what should I do, Mr. Root?"

ROOT: You'll have to get yourself out of it the best way you can. Tell your war stories, but *get yourself out from under that drug company*. Pick out something *bad* they did to you. Then tell the committee about it.

Another silence. Then Root's voice again: "Got that?"

MONTROSE: It's pretty big. . . .

ROOT: Big! What we're after is big! If the stakes don't seem important enough to you, maybe you're getting into the wrong game.

MONTROSE: I don't mean that, Mr. Root. . . .

ROOT: I think if we don't understand each other, we'd better get it straightened out damn quick. I didn't bring you out here and talk you up with the organization just to drop the whole thing before we started, but I'm ready to do just that if you can't hold up your end.

MONTROSE: I said I'd do whatever you think best.

ROOT: All right, see that you do.

MONTROSE: Good-bye.

Logan switched the machine off and sank heavily into one of the leather chairs. With trembling fingers he lit a cigarette and drank deep from his glass of beer, trying to sort efficiently the jumbled thoughts that crowded his mind. On one level of his consciousness he was once again thinking for Raven; he knew he should come up with something quickly that would block whatever effort Montrose intended to make to sabotage Raven at the hearings. But he was powerless. His puny threats would never work again; he was certain of that. Montrose was so deeply committed he would never be intimidated by anything Logan could do.

The element of ruthlessness added a terrifying aspect to the man Montrose was, or at least the man he had become. Logan had already seen, with an insight that chilled him still when he recalled it, the face of deception that stood behind the other face Montrose so successfully showed the world. But tonight, he thought, had presented in unrelieved outline the pristine ugliness of Buddy's ambition.

When had the whisper first been turned loose in his mind: *I am greater*

than I knew? When had it taken on this monstrous shape? That it was
a congressional seat instead of love or wealth to give the whisper force
in Buddy added nothing fundamental to the knowledge of what had happened to him. But it gave a substance which demanded consideration.
Staring darkly into the room around him, Logan felt the insistence of the
demand, and he knew with cold and awful certainty that the anger and
contempt he had felt for Montrose before tonight were not enough. He
felt something else now crawl along his mind and he acknowledged it
with reluctance. It was fear.

Logan did not know how long he sat there, contemplating the frightening words that shook through his mind, but when the telephone rang
it startled him as if he had been alone with his troubled thoughts for half
a day.

It was Pat, a hesitant and apologetic Pat.

"I really am most terribly sorry, Joe," she said. "I . . ."

She broke off, but Logan knew what she was going to say and he felt
a useless anger. He didn't speak, but waited for her to continue.

"I'm afraid I'm going to have to call off our dinner date, Joe. I tried
to reach you at your office earlier but you weren't there."

Still he didn't speak.

"Joe?"

"I'm here. I heard you."

"I *am* sorry, really."

"Sure."

"Do you want me to tell you why?"

"I know why."

"I don't think so," she said. "If you did you'd understand."

"All right," he said stiffly, "let's don't labor it."

"Please. I can't tell you about it on the phone. I'm going to come by."

"When? Now?"

"Yes, just for a few minutes. Don't you go away, Joe Logan."

She hung up before he could answer and he was left with the silent
instrument in his hand and the anger in his throat. There was no place
to put the anger. But the telephone could be slammed down with violence.

It was half an hour before Pat rang the buzzer outside Logan's apartment and in that time he switched from beer to something stronger. He
carried his drink with him while he moved some of the debris from the
living room.

When the buzzer rang, he jumped, not because he had not been expecting it but because he had—and realizing this made him even angrier

than he had been before. Every nerve inside him had been wound tight, waiting for this sound to release him.

She was dressed as if she had changed her mind but Logan knew she hadn't.

"I'm here," she said. "May I come in?"

"Why not?" he said. "Will you have a drink?"

"I'd love one."

He poured a Scotch and handed it to her wordlessly, then sat in the leather chair opposite the one she had taken.

"Sorry the place looks so rough," he said. "It's time for the cleaning woman."

"It looks quite comfortable," she said. "I had no idea." She took a sip of the drink Joe had given her, then looked at him with quiet seriousness. "The reason I can't keep our date tonight is that I'm having dinner with Buddy."

"So I figured."

"We worked everything out last night."

"I'll bet you did."

"We're going to get married right away."

"And everything's going to be fine from here on."

"Is that all you're going to say?"

"I could say more. Is that what you want?"

"Of *course* it's what I want." She ground out her cigarette deliberately and stood up. "After all that's happened, why should you ask that?"

"Maybe *because* of all that's happened."

"Well, it is. Everything's just as it was, and that's the way I want it."

"Sure, sweetheart. Everything's just as it was, and that's the way you want it. Did he tell you why he's in such a hurry to get married?"

"That comes badly from you, Joe. I thought you'd be glad . . ."

"You already said that, baby, and I told you. I'm glad. I'm delighted. Christ, I'm delirious."

She set her drink down and picked up her bag. "I didn't come here to fight."

"Of course not, you came here to explain. By the way, where's Buddy boy?"

"I left a note for him to pick me up here," she said carefully.

"Well, you'd better run down to meet him. He doesn't like to have people keep him waiting."

"Good Lord, you can be nasty."

"I can be nastier than that."

She was at the door, with her hand on the knob, but she released it and turned and faced him angrily.

"I *know* what you can be," she said, "and I don't want any more demonstration. I had hoped at least that this could be pleasant, that things could work out decently if we talked. Well, I was wrong and I'm deeply sorry I disturbed you."

"Wrong? Baby, you don't know how wrong. What the hell ever gave you the idea that you could wrap up my feelings for me in five minutes? Why the special favor? Would you feel better if I kept my mouth shut and accepted your gratuitous little call in the proper spirit? Damn right you would. But I want it to be just a little painful for you, too. Stick around. I've got a surprise for you."

"Thank you, no," she said. "I find all this a little more than I can bear."

Logan's anger drove him relentlessly. "Do you know what these are?" he asked, pointing to the tapes piled on the floor. He didn't wait for her to answer, or even to acknowledge the question, but he went on to explain precisely what they were in blunt detail.

Pat's face was shocked and dismayed. "You can't be serious," she said.

"I'm serious, all right."

"Where *do* you draw the line?" she cried.

"Let's leave me out of it."

"Oh, certainly. Leave you out of it. You've done a lot of cheap things but this is disgusting."

"You've got something to face up to, too," Joe said evenly, trying to control his voice. "I'm going to play one of these tapes for you."

"Don't even suggest it," she said.

Logan walked over to the door and closed it firmly. Then he went to the machine, where the tape of the conversation between Montrose and Root was still in place. He found the spot where the long-distance operator announced the Midwest City call, and flicked the switch to start the tape rolling.

At the operator's mention of Buddy's name, Pat looked at Logan sharply, fury in her eyes. "I don't know what you think you're going to do," she said, "but I don't intend to let you . . ."

Logan grasped her roughly by the arm and forced her into a chair. "You'll listen," he said. "If you want to talk about cynicism you might as well know what you're talking about."

Captain Montrose? This is Root. The harsh voice filled the room, and the silence that followed was like the uneasy stillness that thunder brings. The exchange between the two men began, one voice hesitant and cautious, the other insistent.

Joe watched Pat carefully while the machine played out its grim revelations. He saw the fury die in her eyes, replaced by the vacuum of shock and a reluctance to believe. She was slumped in the chair, and she might have appeared relaxed but for the tenseness with which one hand clutched an arm of the chair.

She stared straight ahead of her while the tape spilled its ugly conversation into the air.

Listening to the voices for the second time that night, knowing what was coming so that surprise was no longer a factor in his reaction, Logan felt nonetheless the strength of the surprise which had assaulted him when he first heard this exchange.

You've got that congressman's hat right at the end of your nose . . .

In the silence that followed that declaration, Logan knew again the reluctant but exciting thrill of uneasy fear. While the faceless Root's voice then spelled out the instructions of betrayal guised in the rules of practical politics, and Montrose in his responses pinned on himself the identification badge that he would forever after wear, Logan began for the first time to experience a sense of shame for forcing Pat to hear this. The enormity of Buddy's deception was overwhelming.

I said I'd do whatever you think best.

All right, see that you do.

Good-bye.

Logan found suddenly that he could not look at Pat. The last syllable of the story he had to tell her was spoken, and he himself was humiliated. He walked over to the machine to flick it off.

"Pat . . ."

"Don't," she said, turning her head as if to dodge a blow.

"Pat, I can't believe I did that. It was a lousy thing."

The tape on the machine now was turning soundlessly, and Logan snapped it off.

Pat opened her eyes and looked at him. She stood up slowly and gathered her bag and gloves. "Well," she said, "thank you for the drink."

"Pat, please."

The doorbell sounded, suddenly and sharply. Logan ignored it for several seconds, looking at Pat beseechingly.

When it rang again he moved slowly toward the door and opened it to face Buddy Montrose.

Montrose looked quickly at Logan, then beyond him to where Pat stood.

"What's holding you, Patty?" he asked, his voice weighted with anxious concern.

She didn't answer him, and he said, "Sweetheart, we're going to be late."

"You go on, Buddy," she said.

"What do you mean? What's the matter?"

"Stop it!" She put the back of her hand to her mouth as if she were trying to suppress a cry. "Leave me alone!"

"Patty, what's the matter?" Montrose repeated, his voice alarmed now. "What's he been doing?"

"I think," Logan said quietly, "that you'd better leave, Buddy."

"I don't care what *you* think," Buddy said. "I want to know what's been going on here."

Pat brushed by them both quickly, and ran into the hall and down the stairs. Montrose looked after her and then abruptly started to follow. Logan caught him by the arm. "Leave her alone," he said.

"You son of a bitch," Montrose said. "Let go of me. What the hell have you been telling her?"

Logan barely let him finish the words before his fist drove at Montrose's face, crumpling him in the open doorway.

21

LOGAN WAS in no mood for the three Pax television commercials Shively insisted on showing early the next morning. He arrived in the vice-president's office as late as possible and settled himself dejectedly in a chair. His mind was too full of the pained image of Pat Crain to muster any interest in what was going on about him.

Garibaldi walked in a few minutes later, obviously not happy to be there. While Blivet fumbled with the movie projector, Shively addressed the group.

"Glad you both could make it," he said. "Ambrose, I know you're anxious to see these prints. Horace only got them from the agency yesterday."

Garibaldi was genuinely and disagreeably surprised. "Is *that* what this meeting was called for?"

"I know you didn't like the scripts, Doc," Blivet said, "but you'll love the finished product."

"We've changed them a little," Shively said.

"That's right," Blivet said. "We wind up with the family doctor actually *giving* Pax to a patient. It's a regular closet drama with him arriving on the scene at the end in time to give this guy his Pax and tell the audience how much the doctors like it."

"All right, can the narration," Shively said, "and let's get this thing on the road."

When the commercials were successfully run off, Shively asked for comment.

"Lloyd McRumen wants to see these films, fellows, as soon as he's free this afternoon. But I'd like to have the full benefit of your opinions first. What do you think, Ambrose?"

"You certainly don't want my opinion," Garibaldi said.

"I'm very much interested in your opinion. Do you think the family doctor comes through? Does it look convincing? I want to know."

"Everyone in this room knows precisely what I think," Garibaldi said.

Blivet watched the medical research director nervously. Logan studied Shively's eyes, narrowed by the smile that had fixed itself on his face.

"I think you overestimate us," Shively said. "I'd really like to hear what you have to say."

Logan shifted uncomfortably in his chair without taking his eyes from Shively. He didn't want to look at Garibaldi. Something had entered the tone of Shively's voice—something that carried an ominous challenge.

"I made myself perfectly clear, Al," Garibaldi said, "when we went over the copy before your films were made. I really don't have anything further to say." The doctor stood up.

Logan, watching, suddenly was acutely aware of Shively's intent. The vice-president was building to a showdown, preconceived and about to be elaborately staged. Shively didn't really care what Logan had to say about the television commercials and he *knew* what Blivet's feelings were. Shively asked only one last acknowledgment of his own victory now, and that from Garibaldi.

"What we have here, Ambrose," Shively said, "is the combined total of all our efforts—yours, Horace's, Joe's, and mine—a reflection of our fellowship. You may not have been in full sympathy with the way it was handled, but you *are* part of the Raven Team. They're your clinical cases. I don't see how you can still sit back and carp."

A flush of anger passed over Garibaldi's expression as he met the vice-president's eyes. He rose from his chair and walked to the door. "Don't leave, Doctor," Shively said. "I'd like to see us reach some decision opinion-wise before these go to the president. After today it's too late to change anything. Now's your last chance to *criticize*, Doctor. Take it."

Garibaldi opened the door and turned toward Shively. Joe thought the physician's face seemed calm and expressionless, but his eyes were alive with anger.

"Don't you have anything to say, Ambrose?"

"Opinion-wise," Garibaldi said with the faintest trace of an ironic smile, "I'm otherwise."

Logan left Shively's office a few minutes later. He went directly to Garibaldi's office and found the doctor standing pensively, his eyes fixed on some point far beyond the Raven plant outside his window.

"Doc . . ." Logan began and Garibaldi raised a hand.

"There wasn't a damn thing you could have done," the physician said. "You know it and I know it. It's early, but I'm ready for a drink."

"I'll buy," Joe said as he followed Garibaldi out of the office. "We can go across the street."

The two men found themselves alone in the forenoon quiet of the shadowy bar.

"Here's to Al Shively," Garibaldi said, raising a Scotch-and-water to his lips. "That was his scene this morning and he played it well. For the first time in our association he spoke the indisputable truth."

Joe drank with the doctor and then returned his glass to the bar empty. "Doc, this comes late, but—well, I apologize. I can't say it any fancier."

Garibaldi looked at him carefully. "For what?" he asked.

"For being such a goddamn fathead in all this. You were right—and I was awfully wrong. It's easy to see it now."

"Better now than never," said Garibaldi. "Welcome aboard the train of the loyal opposition."

Logan smiled ruefully. "Not so loyal. I'm going to quit."

Garibaldi took a long silent pull on his drink. Then he said, "I suppose there's no point in asking you why."

"I'm not going to be articulate about it, if that's what you mean." The bartender poured another drink. "Make it a double," Joe said, pointing to both glasses. Then he told Garibaldi, "It's an animal reaction, I guess. No gripe, but it's time for me to get out."

Garibaldi peered at him. "By God, Logan," he said, "you're a moralist."

"Don't cloud the issue. I just don't fit any more."

Garibaldi's face became serious. "I'm not so sure about that. But I'm not the one to talk you out of it." He looked down at his drink. When he looked up at Joe, he said, "It looks as if I'll be leaving, too."

"*You?* What the hell?"

"The regrettable thing is that I didn't make a decision earlier. This company doesn't want a doctor any more. As part of the façade, Raven may need a man with a medical degree, but it doesn't need me." Garibaldi paused and nodded sadly. "Any more than I need it," he said.

Logan watched the doctor closely. He understood only dimly, and only in part, how meaningful this decision was to Garibaldi, but he sensed that in it was an act of courage, the burden of which Garibaldi was still reluctant to shoulder. He summoned the bartender again.

"The point is," the doctor said, as if he were talking to himself, "I've decided I don't want the job. A helpless physician isn't much good to anyone, including himself."

Joe drew deeply on a cigarette and let the smoke come slowly out of his mouth as he spoke. "Where would this outfit be if you hadn't been around? You've got that to think of."

"Baloney," Garibaldi said. "The immediate future of the Raven company is a great testimonial to my effectiveness. Shively wanted his tranquilizer over the counter and it looks, by God, as if he's going to get it there—until either the government or the medical profession catches up with him. This company's riding for a fall, Joe, and when it comes they'll all need Pax."

Joe finished the drink the bartender had just poured and motioned him back again. "It's a shame," he said. "You shouldn't have to back off like this." He was beginning to feel the effects of the Scotch in his finger tips.

"I always thought I believed that medicine was something more than a profession," Garibaldi said, resting his gaze on the row of bottles behind the bar. "But my performance in recent months hasn't indicated it. A physician—has to have the skill of a diamond cutter and—the prescience of—a divine gypsy if he lays any claim to medical competence. And most of all, he's got to believe in what he does." Garibaldi drew a long breath and shifted his weight on the stool. "I used to be capable of a competent medical performance," he said. "Nearly twenty years of runny noses and athlete's foot. In the Army I lost my touch and I came here to mark time, Joe. Finally at Raven the job almost seemed worth doing. It was comfortable and easy. But that's all gone now—and who can say I'm not better off because of it."

"What *are* you going to do?" Logan asked him.

"Go back to runny noses," Garibaldi said, "so I can sleep nights."

Logan raised his glass. "Scotch relaxes," he said.

"I've had enough peace of mind."

"Are you addled? Are you ta-axed?" Joe began to sing.

"Indeed," Garibaldi said. "My thoughts of Al Shively are almost civilized again. I'll miss his hairtrigger brain and generous spirit . . ."

"And his wit and his verve," Logan said.

"And most of all I'll miss being on his team," the doctor said. "And the fellowship. I'll really miss the fellowship."

"We'll all miss the goddamn fellowship," Logan said. "Here's to that."

"To fellowship!" Garibaldi said. He took a large swallow and set his glass down on the bar. Then he raised his finger and shushed Joe. "Ever hear the Raven sales song?"

Joe nodded gravely.

"Writ by hand by Alonzo Shively," the doctor said. Then softly he began to sing the sales vice-president's creation to the tune of "Maryland, My Maryland." Before he was halfway through, Joe joined him:

> "Raven's drugs with doctors rate,
> Patients' ills evaporate,
> Larvae migrans runs away,
> Raven anthelmintics stay,
> Nematodes curl up and die,
> When the Raven man drops by.
> Winter, summer, spring and fall,
> Raven slays 'em one and all-l-l-ll."

As they walked back to the plant a silence settled over the two men. Garibaldi broke it by saying, "The trouble is—*how* will I sleep nights? How do you relinquish responsibility? I've still got a stake in seeing how all this turns out, a professional stake."

Logan nodded gravely. "I'm glad I'm not a professional."

Garibaldi belched. "I should write my letter of resignation right now," he said. "I'll spell out the particulars. Who knows? It might do some good."

They walked in silence for a few paces and then Garibaldi suddenly stopped.

"What's the matter?"

"Horace will be in my office. If there's one thing I can count on this afternoon, it's that Horace will be with me. How can I state the case for justice with Horace peeking under my desk blotter for case histories?"

"No problem," Logan said. "Use my office."

Garibaldi considered the suggestion and then started walking again. "What will you do?"

"Walk around. I don't know. I don't want to go back there."

When they arrived at Logan's office Emily was just returning from lunch. "I'm going to be out," Joe told her. "Dr. Garibaldi is going to use my office. He'll need your help. Give it to him unstintingly and, if possible, enthusiastically." He hiccuped loudly.

She looked at him with distaste.

"Don't you worry about a thing," Garibaldi said. "Go sit somewhere and think about the eternal things."

Logan saluted sharply, almost succeeded in executing an about-face, and left.

He walked through the crowded streets that surrounded the plant for almost an hour. Slowly, as he knew it would, the protective effect of the liquor wore off, leaving him with a faintly throbbing headache and a deep reluctance to face the task ahead.

Montrose stared at the wall of his hotel room, as he had been doing through most of the day, alternately surrendering himself to a tumult of thoughts and trying strenuously to discipline them so he could pick just a few that might be of assistance.

The need for discipline had never been so great in his life, and he reached desperately for it, through the constricting, almost paralyzing bonds of anger that wrapped around him. Nothing had changed. He had to impress it on himself over and over: nothing had really changed, and it wouldn't, if he could just manage to keep himself free of useless emotional rages. The big prize, the one he had been walking toward for so long, had not moved; it was still there; it was waiting. He had only to keep walking and not get helplessly caught in a welter of passions that could only weaken and diminish his effectiveness.

He had lost Patty, at least temporarily. He didn't know what had happened in Logan's apartment last night, and the one time he had talked to Pat on the telephone today she had refused to discuss it with him. She hadn't seemed upset, as she was last night; worse, she had been cool and polite so that her words had carried a finality they never would have under stormier conditions. Whatever had happened, it had driven her away from him, and he resented and regretted it with a fury that burned deep. He had planned to have Pat safely married to him before the lid blew off the kettle in Indiana. Now, it seemed, that was highly unlikely.

If he could work on it, devote all his time to finding the cause of her disaffection and removing it . . .

But he didn't have the time. The goddamned hearings were only two days away and he had no idea how he was going to do what Root had told him he *had* to do.

Later, when there was time—time for the luxury of personal indulgences—he would turn to the problem of Pat. However discouraging the prospect of getting her back seemed now, he had never before failed in his efforts to hold her. It would work again—later, when there was time. As a realist—and nobody knew better than Buddy Montrose just how much of a realist he was—he saw that whereas he would probably have another chance at Pat, the opportunity that Root was presenting would stand enticingly before him only once, only now.

He *had* to find a way.

He got up and started pacing slowly across the room, and back, and across again. The few ideas he had come up with were all right, as far as they went. But they were not enough. Not enough. He needed something that was direct and clear and dramatic.

Raven was vulnerable, he was certain of that. Probably it was vulnerable in a dozen different areas, if he could know where they were and explore them. When he found such a weakness he would not hesitate a moment to use it to the advantage he needed. He felt not the slightest loyalty to Raven, certainly not after last night. Once again the angry bitterness which he wished to keep under control began to swim through him as he remembered the pain and humiliation he had suffered at Logan's hands. Oh, he would sink that company. He would rejoice in doing it, for he would not only be protecting himself, by God; he would be hitting back at Logan in the only way that would really hurt.

He began to walk faster, his hands trembling and doubling into fists at his sides. He considered what sheer pleasure it would be, even at the risk of endangering everything, to pick up the telephone, call Logan and tell him precisely what was in store for him and his fine company. That would put fear into him. Giving himself over to the enormous satisfaction of the idea, Buddy began to regard it as a real project. The only problem, of course, would be getting to talk to Logan. The son of a bitch would tell his secretary he didn't want to talk to Montrose at all. He would have to be able to get around that obstacle. He could pour the charm on that ripe secretary of Logan's, of course, but that wouldn't work if . . .

Montrose stood suddenly still in the middle of the room. His hands relaxed; he brought one up and rubbed it slowly across the back of his neck. Now think it through, think it through carefully, a voice of caution was urging. But excitement was building swiftly all through his mind. It was just possible—by God, it *was* possible. It was certainly better than no idea at all.

He walked quickly to the telephone and dialed. When the Raven operator answered he asked for Logan, and waited impatiently until he heard Emily's voice.

"Public Relations. Mr. Logan's office."

"Hi," he said easily. "This is Buddy Montrose."

"Well, *hi,*" she said. "Where have you been hiding?"

"I saw you a couple of days ago," Buddy said.

"Well, sure, but you know, we like to see our celebrities oftener than *that.*" She giggled.

"Well, I got your letter and I wanted to say thanks. That was sweet of you, Emily."

"I guess it was a silly impulse—but I did mean what I said, Buddy. You were just great."

"You're my best booster," he said. "Are you busy?"

"*I'll* say. Did you want to talk to Mr. Logan?" she asked reluctantly. "He's not in this afternoon."

"As a matter of fact, I was calling you. Are you game for dinner?"

"Well, *sure,*" she said. Then in a new, lower voice, one obviously intended to be seductive, she purred, "I'd love to."

"I mean tonight," he added.

"*Tonight?*" The temptress had disappeared and Emily Klinger was back on the phone. "Well, that's kind of sudden."

"I know, but can you make it?"

"Well, I have a date. I . . ."

He rushed in before she could commit herself irrevocably. "Is it something you could possibly break?" He made his voice both personal and persuasive. "I've got to leave for Washington, you know, for the hearings, and I really hoped we could get together before then." He hesitated. "I've had the feeling," he said softly, "that we've been avoiding each other."

"Oh-h." Silence. "Yeah, I see what you mean," said the temptress huskily. "I'll break it."

"Good. Suppose you meet me here at the hotel after you leave work. That'll be cozier."

"All right," she said. "Well then, Abyssinia."

"I'll be waiting," he said. He put the telephone back on its cradle. *Don't get too confident,* he told himself. It wasn't the biggest idea he had ever come up with, but any way he looked at it, it was the only thing that held any immediate hope.

Hunched behind his desk, the president looked smaller than he ever had before to Logan. His face was drawn and sunken.

"This is a hard thing for me to hear, Joe," he said.

Standing in front of the president's desk, Joe said softly, "It was a hard thing for me to have to tell you."

"You won't reconsider?"

"I'm afraid not. I'm willing, however, to stay until after the hearings."

"You have a better offer, I suppose." McRumen said it almost without hope, and Logan, realizing how easy it would be to give him this much, said nothing.

"Is that it, Joe?" McRumen persisted.

"No, sir. I just think my usefulness to the organization is over."

McRumen turned in his chair and stared absently out the window, as if he had not heard. But Logan knew well enough that he *had* heard.

"Do you want me to stay until after the hearings?" Joe asked.

McRumen did not answer him.

"I think," Logan said, picking his words carefully, trying to prepare this man who had been his friend for the new shocks to come, "that you might have more need of help than you realize, even as bad as you think things already are."

The president swiveled around to look at him again, and stared at him soberly. "I'd like to hear something good for a change."

"I'm sorry, Mr. McRumen. I think you ought to know this."

McRumen nodded hesitantly, and Joe sat in the chair beside his desk and began to talk. For a few seconds the president's eyes were on him, and then McRumen stood up and walked to the window and Logan saw only his short stocky back while he told him the story of Montrose's alliance with Alden Root, and the consequences it would have at the hearings.

After Logan had finished talking, McRumen continued to stand there, not moving. When, finally, he turned to face Joe his eyes were those of a very old and stricken man and he had trouble controlling the muscles of his mouth.

"It's too much," he said in a hoarse whisper.

"I wish it weren't all true," Joe said.

"It's too much," McRumen repeated. He walked slowly to his desk and sat down heavily, wounded and bewildered. "Are you sure? How do you know?"

"I know," Logan said. "I'd have no reason to report it if there was any doubt."

"That boy," McRumen said, "I can't believe it." And as he sat filling his mind with the young man who had walked into his life and become for a moment of time his son, a helpless baffled anger began to rise inside him.

"He's nothing! A nobody!" He slapped the desk with the flat of his hand. As he looked at Joe, his anger began to spill out of its channel. "I see now why you're running out. When the trouble begins, the summer weather boys leave."

"You know that's not fair," Joe said quietly.

"Fair! Fair!" McRumen shouted. "For God's sake I'd like to see some fairness sometime. Don't talk to me about fairness."

Logan stood up. "Well, if that's all, Mr. McRumen . . ."

"That's all, that's all," McRumen said. "That's right—go ahead."

"Look, sir . . ."

"I *am* looking, God damn it! I'm looking at things I never thought I'd see. You with your talk of Montrose. You're just like him, just like him."

Although he knew it was unreasonable, Logan began to feel his own anger work up through him. He knew he should leave the room at that moment, but he did not. Facing the president, he said, "There's one difference, Lloyd. You never tried to make a piece of merchandise out of me. I owe you a little. Montrose doesn't."

Logan could see the bitterness drain out of McRumen, crowded out by the complex of discouragement and guilt which had tortured him before. And seeing it, seeing again the pathetic figure of Lloyd McRumen without the defense of anger, Logan felt his own wrath crumble.

"That's not entirely fair, either," he said. "You didn't milk his reputation. I did it for you. We both made the same mistake."

"We did a lot for him," McRumen insisted.

"We made a hero," Logan said, "and we've found out you can't always give a hero all the right qualities. You take your chances. Particularly"—he tired to make his tone gentle but still the words themselves had the harsh ring of unwelcome truth—"when you create him for a selfish reason."

"But, my God, Joe," McRumen said desperately, "all those people that liked him—they're the ones that made him. We just gave him a chance."

"He's our responsibility," Logan said. "Whatever else we say, we can't get away from that."

"But look what he's trying to do to us!"

"He's turning against us now, and that's a hard thing to take. It's still not as hard as knowing that we're responsible for whatever he is. And neither one of us will ever be able to forget it." Logan walked to the door.

"Joe," the president called to him, "you say you'll stay until after the hearings?"

"If that's what you want."

McRumen nodded quickly. "Maybe," he said, "maybe there's something else you can do."

Joe waited by the door, quietly.

McRumen looked at the desk top, and not at Joe. "You know Senator Crain," he said. His words were barely audible. "If you tell him about this, maybe he would keep Montrose off the witness stand." He brought his eyes up then to meet Joe's. "It's the last thing I'll ask."

Logan felt a substance hard and unpleasant in his throat as he looked at him, a little man caught in the inescapable posture of defeat and despair.

"I'll think about it," Joe said. He closed the door and left him alone with his guilt.

Quickly and deftly Buddy Montrose undid the buttons at the top of Emily Klinger's blouse. He put his hand through the opening and ran it slowly over her full breasts. His other arm was around her neck and he drew her down, forcing his body against hers. He pressed his mouth against her cheek and waited for her to turn her head, meeting his open mouth with hers. When he heard her breath begin to come in moaning little gasps he finished the kiss and drew his hand from under the blouse. Adroitly disengaging himself, he stood up and walked over to the table where the bottle and the ice bucket stood. "I'll make another drink," he said.

Emily murmured and leaned back against the pillow, her eyes closed. He poured the drinks and carried them over to the bed. He put them both on the night stand and sat on the edge of the bed, close to her. He didn't touch her, however. Instead, he lit a cigarette, slowly and carefully.

"You're sure that's what it was about?" he said, keeping his voice still intimate.

"What?" She opened her eyes and looked at him.

"The letter from Dr. Garibaldi to Mr. McRumen," he said gently.

"Sure I'm sure. I told you, I typed it this afternoon. I haven't even given it back to him yet."

He took a drink and looked at her. "You're a very exciting woman," he told her.

She smiled wickedly. "Is that right?"

"That's right." He pulled her to him and kissed her again. She responded eagerly, and he felt her hand travel up his side, reaching under his arm. He put his lips to her throat and kept them there, silently, for a few minutes. Then he asked, "Do you have a key to the place?"

"A key? Well, sure . . ."

"Will you go out there with me and show it to me?"

"Now?" she asked in alarm. "You mean *now?*"

"Well, not this very instant, darling—of course," he said. He slid one hand under her skirt. With the other he reached over and turned out the light on the night stand.

In the darkness of the room he whispered with soft urgency to her and after the violent rhythm of their bodies ceased, he rolled on his side with his arm under her neck.

"Let's never move from here," she said.

"Never?"

"Never, never." Emily turned her head to brush her lips along his shoulder. "Do you think people can fall in love in one night?"

"What do you think?" he asked.

"Buddy?"

"Yes?"

"I've loved you from the beginning."

"That's my baby."

"Do you think you could learn to love me? A little, I mean?"

He kissed her and tilted her chin up with his hand. "What ever made you think I didn't?" he said.

Her eyes were sad and she did not look directly at him. "I know I'm not exactly what you might want in a wife. I mean I've never been to college or anything—and I—well, I know it." She looked at him then and her tone was pleading. "But I try to dress nice, and—I'm not the dumbest thing in the world. I mean . . ."

He closed her lips with another kiss. She clung to him desperately and after a moment Montrose was aware that she was crying softly. "I'm sorry," she said when she released her grip and sat up in the bed, "I didn't mean to blubber like that. I just never thought I could be so happy."

"Do you want another drink?" She shook her head.

"I haven't even touched the other one," she said. Then as the idea grasped her mind she added, "But I'll make you one." She flicked on the

light and jumped lightly from the bed. When her back was turned he
glanced at his watch on the bedstand.

"How late can you get into the office?" he asked her.

"Tonight?"

He sipped the drink and nodded.

"Honey, let's not go out to that lousy old place tonight? I can show
you what you want in the morning." She sat next to him on the bed and
he rested his hand on her thigh.

"Couldn't we get it tonight? Come on," he said. She looked at him
doubtfully and he pulled her toward him. "Then when we come
back . . ."

Emily stretched out on the back seat of the cab with her head in
Buddy's lap and did not sit up until they stopped at the Raven gate. The
guard recognized her and waved the vehicle through. Buddy told the
driver to wait when they got out. Inside the main office building Emily
groped for the light switches in the hall and led Buddy up the stairs and
into the Public Relations Department as the batteries of blue-white fluo-
rescent tubes flickered on.

"I could get into real hot water if Mr. Logan or Dr. Garibaldi ever
found out I showed this to you," she said when she handed Buddy the
carbon flimsy of Garibaldi's letter. "He marked it personal and confidential."

He pulled her to him with one arm as he held the letter up with the
other and started to scan it. "I'll keep your secret to the death," he told
her. She smiled and rested her head against his shoulder.

As Buddy ran his eyes over the paper, the tiny coals of hopeful expectation blazed alive. Phrases began to leap from the text and dance
gloriously in front of him.

"Let's hurry," Emily said. "I'm getting nervous being here." He made
no answer and she said, "Are you through with the letter, Buddy? I've
got to put it back."

"Let me keep it," he said. "Just for a little while. I'll give it back."

"Buddy, I *can't*. I'd get in trouble."

"Just for a while."

"Buddy, *please!* You don't want me to get in trouble, do you, honey?"

"Oh, Christ," he said. He jammed the letter in his inside jacket pocket
and shot for the stairway.

Bewildered, Emily looked after him. "Buddy? Buddy! What's the matter?" She followed him and started to run as she felt a sudden fear.
"Buddy!" Her voice had risen to a cry as she reached the top of the stair-

way and started down. "Wait!" She heard the heavy front door of the building swing shut and the sound of it turned her fear to panic. She tried to take the steps two at a time but her high narrow heel caught on the edge of one and pitched her forward. She struggled helplessly for the railing as she felt her skirt bind her knees and saw the lower stairs rising quickly toward her. The fall was not far, but for a moment she was blinded by pain as one knee crashed against the bottom step. Then she got to her feet, sobbing, and managed to open the door in time to see the taxi driving out through the Raven gate.

She screamed his name again, her pain and her desperation making it an anguished cry of terror against the night. "Don't leave me!" She tried to run and she fell again, sobbing, saying his name and saying it as the taxi became two vanishing red points of light in the darkness.

When the driver pulled out onto the brightly lighted boulevard that led to the city, Buddy withdrew the letter from his pocket. The cross currents that had bedeviled his mind subsided gradually as a magnificent calm took their place. He imagined a shocked and beaten Logan, and he saw the approving nod of Alden Root. Gradually he allowed himself to savor the first sweet taste of retribution. He began to read the letter once more, slowly and carefully, while the taxi carried him back to the lights of the city.

PERSONAL AND CONFIDENTIAL

Dear Lloyd:

Attached you will find my formal resignation from Raven, to become effective at your earliest convenience. What follows here will explain the reasons for my decision. In the ordinary course of my responsibility as Medical Research Director at Raven, I would consider the nature of this letter to be an overstepping of bounds on my part. As the course of my responsibility has in recent months become extraordinary, however, I take the liberty of writing my sentiments down for you to read.

We have been associates and friends for more than ten years. During most of that time, I believe the company has prospered as the direct result of careful management and honest, intelligent direction.

Unfortunately, this appears to be all in the past now. The company has embarked upon a course of action with regard to the phitherdimethyldine tranquilizer which I consider to be ill-advised at best and potentially disastrous at worst.

I first called for time to give the compound a thorough run in the clinics before being released ethically. This was denied in view of the company's desire to capitalize on the tranquilizer boom as quickly as possible. I could understand the commercial reasons behind this decision only insofar as they did not necessarily compromise our medical integrity. The clinical material was rushed and the most severe pressure was exerted upon our research people to straighten out the odor and taste obstacles to the marketability of the drug. We did our best only to find that the drug was being improved in order that it be sufficiently palatable for proprietary distribution and that the favorable clinical results were to be used in television and other phases of a high-pressure consumer promotion scheme. I understand that even the good offices of Captain Montrose are soon to be diverted to this program as well.

I submit that our conduct with this drug, if pursued as Mr. Shively plans to pursue it, is a calculated attempt on Raven's part to defraud the Food and Drug Administration, the medical profession and the public. Mr. Shively has argued that it is perfectly legal so long as the compound has not been reclassified by the government. I can only add that it is not and never has been a question of legality so far as I am concerned. It is a question of our professional responsibility to the people who use the drugs we produce, and hence it is a question of morality.

Many times in the past I have heard you discuss your hopes for the Raven company and over the years I have found your concern for the health of the people Raven serves to be a deep and genuine one. In all candor I say that your recent support of Raven's new proprietary venture reflects neither of these. I therefore ask you most urgently to reconsider your decision on this program in the hope that Raven not be compromised by an irresponsible drive for profits.

Although my plans are not yet fully defined, I shall be returning to private practice very shortly. If you have the time, on a brighter day than this, I might suggest a luncheon post-mortem.

Ambrose Garibaldi, M.D.

22

LOGAN WAS discomfortingly certain that Pat had written out of her life everyone connected with her unhappiness, including, specifically, Joe Logan. He told himself now that his only reason for telephoning her was that he felt a certain obligation to let her know his plans.

When he heard her voice on the phone he rushed quickly into his speech before she could make any objection that would cut the call short. "I'm taking the tape of Buddy's and Root's conversation to Washington," he said, "and I'm going to ask your father to listen to it."

There was a little silence and then Logan was startled to hear a quick amused laugh on the other end of the wire.

"What's so damned funny?" he demanded.

"You sound so—belligerent."

Embarrassed, Logan laughed himself. "I was scared," he said.

"Oh, dear." Her voice was lightly troubled. "This is all pretty awful."

There was a pause and he said, "I just thought I'd tell you what I'm going to do. Do you mind?"

"I don't really care any more, Joe, what happens."

"All right," he said, "I just thought I'd tell you."

"Joe?"

"Yeah?"

Her voice seemed smaller suddenly, and timid. "I mean, too much has happened. But I've been wanting to call you—to apologize."

"What for?"

"For being so presumptuous," she said. "I've still got a lot to learn about myself."

"We all have," Joe said. "I'm the one who has apologies to make. I'd like to make them in person. Can I see you?"

"When?"

"Any time. Now, for instance."

"Would you—like to come for dinner?"

"You mean you cook?"

"With complete abandon."

"That's the dinner for me," Logan said. "I'll be there in half an hour."

He took along a bottle of wine and a spirit decidedly lighter than the one he had worn for days.

Pat sat in a chair facing his sofa and for a few minutes neither of them found anything to say.

"This is ridiculous," Pat said finally. "I'll make us a drink."

"I'll make the drinks," Logan said. "You show me where."

She got ice and liquor out for him. When he had handed her her glass, he lifted his in salute. "To—what?" he asked.

She smiled sadly. "I don't know," she said. "To some decent way out of all this."

"To the pillories, then," Logan said. "That's the only way out for sinners."

She sat on the divan beside Joe. He asked, "Are you ready for apologies now?"

"We could just dispense with them," Pat said.

"I want to tell you," Joe said. "You were right. We never should have used Buddy the way we did."

She took a sip from her cocktail and put the glass on the table in front of her and then leaned back with her head against the divan. "But I was wrong too," she said. "How could I have been so wrong about him, Joe?"

"Maybe you weren't always wrong," Joe said.

"But a person doesn't really change like that. That part of him must have been there all the time." She dropped her voice so low that he could hardly hear her. "Maybe I could have done more for him and it wouldn't have happened."

"This would have happened if none of us had touched his life," Joe said.

"Do you believe that?"

"I have to believe it."

"Yes," she said wearily. "We believe what we have to believe."

"That doesn't mean it isn't true," Joe said. "A lot of people have helped him along, people who don't know how much they have paid for the privilege."

"It's not that simple, Joe."

"I think it is. We're all responsible for Buddy."

"I used to think he'd be an important man some day." Pat smiled sadly. "He might be, at that."

"Maybe so." Joe lit a cigarette for her. "Well, it's all done now, Pat. We can begin to forget about it."

"I hope so," she said. She looked at him and there was a tenderness in her voice and he felt it. "I'm sorry, Joe."

"I'm not sorry," Joe said. "Now you're free of him."

She looked away from him, quickly.

"Maybe now you'll be able to hear the plaintive voice of J. Logan."

She kept her eyes away from him and reached down to get her drink. Joe caught her hand.

"Pat . . ."

"Joe, please."

"Have you known how I've felt?"

She didn't answer him. "I'm in love with you, Pat," he said. "I have been for a long time."

Joe kept her hand in his for a few moments and then he let it go. "Well? . . . What the hell's wrong with that?"

She stood up, tears forming in her eyes. "Not a thing. I—I'm going to get the dinner ready."

"I'll help you," Joe said. "I can cook, too." He walked behind her into the tiny kitchen. "What do we do—light a match to everything in sight?"

"Not everything," she said. "Not the wine." She brushed her eyes quickly, and turned.

"Joe," she said, quietly, and went to him.

23

LOGAN WENT to Washington in the afternoon of D-Day Minus One for Raven, after a telephone call to Senator Crain elicited from the senator an agreement to see him.

Once he had decided to make his request of Senator Crain, Logan had selected carefully the facts he would present as the background—those least damaging to Raven and yet sufficiently forceful to explain satisfactorily how the recording of the Montrose-Root conversation came into his possession. As he outlined the situation in the senator's office, the company had for the last several months been preparing for the introduction of a new product, a tranquilizing drug, and as part of the effort—a misdirected part, but there it was—to keep the news secret, it had had recording devices placed on several of the telephones inside the company. He took care to avoid giving any suggestion that the wire tapping had been any more extensive than that.

"Well, that's the story, Senator," he said. "The first chapter of it, anyway. Now comes the tough part."

Crain looked at him curiously.

"I have come across one of those conversations which I should like to ask you to listen to," Logan continued.

"Indeed." Crain's expression became more sober. "Do you think there is a good reason why I should?" The window blinds in the senator's office had been slanted against the late afternoon sun. Now the sun had passed but the shades had not been adjusted nor had any light been turned on, so the room was growing dark.

"Yes, sir, I do," Logan said. "I know there is something distasteful about the request, and I assure you I wouldn't make it if I didn't think you would find it pertinent. I'd like to warn you first, though, that the most distasteful part of it all is that you are directly involved in this conversation. If you listen to it, you won't find it very pleasant."

The senator's eyes flickered with interest. "You make it pretty hard for me to refuse your request, Logan."

"I had hoped I would, sir."

The senator smiled. "Let's hear it."

Logan plugged in the portable tape recorder he had carried with him. He flicked the switch on the machine and returned to his seat.

For the next several minutes they sat alone in the darkening room, their eyes fixed on the tape as it moved slowly from one spindle to the other. Never once was Joe conscious of the senator stirring in his chair while the grim, unlovely story was told by the authors themselves.

When it was over, and Joe had turned off the machine and sat down again, there was only silence. The senator's face was grave and thoughtful, and Logan, watching him across half the length of the shadowed office, could read nothing in his expression.

Finally, after what seemed an unbearable hour of agony to Logan, Senator Crain said, "All right, tell me. What did you hope to accomplish by having me hear this?"

Joe replied uneasily, "I'd hoped it might persuade you to withdraw the committee's invitation for Montrose to testify."

"I see." The senator smiled faintly. "Yes, I can see that you would hope that. It must be disheartening to know Buddy intends to do the opposite of what you want him to do." He turned in his chair slightly and stared beyond Joe for a long while, his eyes fixed and unmoving. "But there's nothing I can do about it," he said finally. "It would be impossible. You did such an excellent job of seeing to it that Buddy *did* get involved in this that it would raise serious questions if we dropped him now."

"Even though his deliberate intentions are clear, sir?"

"Frankly, Logan, your company's position doesn't emerge as a particularly virtuous one."

"I realize that," Joe said.

"I hope so," the senator said. "Since these hearings were started, I've learned a lot. And I don't mind telling you I've become just a little annoyed with people who try to use the Senate as an instrument of their own convenience. Montrose apparently plans to do just that if he can.

But you yourself have already tried twice now to put an active hand into the subcommittee's work in your company's behalf, once in influencing us to invite him, and again right now."

"Senator, I don't hold any brief for Raven or myself in this. It was a gamble bringing this information to you; I thought it was possible—just possible—that you would be so shocked by this discovery that you would be disposed to act favorably for us. I lost the gamble."

"I'm afraid you have," Crain said. "Who else in your company knows you brought this tape for me to hear?"

"No one, Senator. I made the decision entirely on my own. I never could have got sanction for this if I had tried to get it. Listening in on employees' conversations is not an operation a company would like to have widely known."

"I should think not," Crain said. "Does your president know about Montrose?"

Logan nodded. "Because I told him. But he doesn't know about the tape. He doesn't know anything about that operation of Shively's."

"He doesn't *know?*"

"That's right, Senator. Shively has managed to have things pretty much his own way. I feel sorry for Lloyd McRumen. He's going to pay heavily for his mistakes. Montrose will see to that."

The senator leaned back and studied Logan with eyes that were stern but not unfriendly.

"Let me make one thing abundantly clear," he said. "Understand that we are trying to gather information which we hope will become the basis for formulating future government policies on health and welfare. The committee—so long as I am its chairman—isn't interested in embarrassing anybody. We're not digging dirt—although, if we were, our experience has shown so far that we wouldn't have to go too deep to find it. But the Senate is not the Justice Department. Neither is it a producer of entertainment, except by accident or indirection. Quite frankly, I could see no reason for inviting Montrose to appear before the committee. But the other members of the committee were more susceptible to your company's persuasion. Now that he is going to appear, we will question him and listen to what he has to say *only* so long as it bears upon matters material to our investigation."

Logan nodded. "That sounds fair," he said.

"All right," the senator continued. "I want you to understand further that what I have learned from you today has hardly prejudiced me in favor of your company. Eavesdropping on employees smacks to me of shabby business ethics. But I shall endeavor not to let that influence me in the pursuit of the information I am trying to get in committee session."

"That's a generous attitude, Senator," Logan said. "Well, now that I've made a botch of all this, I suppose I might as well step back to survey the damage."

"The damage. Yes," Crain said. His voice dropped to a low, almost inaudible note. "You discovered quite a bit about Buddy Montrose with this record, didn't you?"

Joe nodded. "It wasn't all new to me, though." He told the senator about Montrose's reaction to the offer from the International Aid Commission.

The senator drummed the desk softly with his fingers. Finally he said, "I wondered what happened." He stood up and walked to the window and raised the blind. There was still some light outside, forming a rectangular patch against the gloomy room. Looking out the window, Crain said, "This tape of yours was a hard thing for me to hear."

"I know it was," Logan said quietly.

"It was best that I did learn about it, of course, but it was hard nonetheless. Politics is a strange business. There's a mixture of everything in it. The shoddiest along with the best that a man can give. Can you understand that?"

"I'm not sure," Logan said.

"I'm talking about myself more than anything else. It's a good deal my own fault that this has happened. Alden Root is an unprincipled man and I've known it for years."

He turned around and stood silently for a moment, his face drawn. "I've always told myself that kept under control Root was harmless. But of course he's not harmless at all. With a man like Buddy working for him he could become a very troublesome person indeed."

"It's not only Root," Logan offered hesitantly.

"No. It's not only Root." The senator's voice was sad. "Buddy's ambition seems to have fit in beautifully. It's not a pleasant thing to learn."

Out in the city the siren of a fire truck wailed. Together they listened to it build and recede before the senator spoke again.

"Ambition could make Buddy a dangerous man. He has a power over people to use wisely and well—or, if the ambition were great enough, to use dangerously. Men like him should never find their way into politics. They're too often shaped by expediency."

"It was not a pleasant thing for me to learn, either," Logan said.

"I gather not. Does Pat know all this?"

"Yes, sir. I . . . ."

"I'm glad she knows. That relieves me of a responsibility I'm not sure

I could handle. How about Montrose? Does he know about that tape?"

"No, sir."

The senator nodded. "I think that was wise." He looked at his watch. "May I drop you by your hotel?"

They walked into the hall, deserted now and dimly lighted. They made their way down a long corridor in silence for a while, and then Crain spoke again. "Don't ever forget this about Buddy, Joe. He's resilient, if nothing else—and incidentally he is a good deal else. He *did* a job in the Army. Do you know that?"

"I've never doubted it," Joe said.

"His record was a proud one and his honors were well deserved. I wish none of this had happened to him, and he had stayed there, or at least had gone back as he said he wanted to do. He could have brought credit to all of us as well as to himself."

They walked by the committee room where the hearings had been taking place. It was well lighted but empty, its floors waiting to be swept.

"There is the room that will be Raven's home for a while," the senator said.

Logan looked inside with interest. There was nothing much to see— the heavy furniture littered with the debris of folded newspapers and crumpled note papers, filled ash trays and half-empty water glasses. But out of the events of the afternoon, ebbed away now, with only this physical flotsam left behind, the newspapers had had another headline and the public had had another look into the machinery of the industry it both resented and invested with its hope. Tomorrow Raven would be sitting here while the headline built around it.

In the lobby of his hotel, Logan bought a newspaper. Flipping through the pages in the elevator, he saw that the story of that afternoon's hearing had got no further than page three. Tomorrow, he was certain, would be a page-one day.

When Horace Blivet had set up the first meeting for the expanded sales force that would blanket the nation with Pax, he certainly had not expected it to fall on the eve of Raven's testimony. His chief regret, as he had nervously explained to Al Shively, was that he knew the boys would be expecting a few words from Mr. McRumen.

Shively had personally felt that the conflict was a blessing; he was delighted that McRumen had left for Washington that morning—there was no reason at all to identify him with Pax in the minds of the sales force. He had not told Blivet this, of course. Instead he had looked at the hulking man sadly and observed, "Well, it's too late to make a change now,

Horace. I'll stay through the opening session anyway. You'll have to learn to think ahead in the future, though."

Now, Shively stood in the rear of a rented banquet hall listening to Horace get the meeting started by leading the men in a full-throated rendition of the Raven sales song. It was always a good spirit-booster at the beginning of any session.

The group stood as it sang in husky unison, each man wearing a boy's plastic football helmet—emblazoned across the front with "Pax." Brightly painted posters displayed around the hall carried the Pax campaign slogans, and large block letters strung out high above the stage screamed the simple theme of the meeting: *"Win with Pax."*

After the last note of the song had died, Blivet, dressed in the white linen plus fours and black-striped shirt of a referee, faced his audience silently and dramatically for a full half-minute before he sounded the whistle that dangled from a cord on his neck. Then, his resounding bass amplified by a public address system, he announced, "You fellows are the starting line-up in the greatest game this company has ever played—campaign-wise."

He paused again, permitting the full effect to sink in. He was enormously proud of himself this morning since everyone in the room knew that Shively had elevated him from assistant sales manager to director of advertising and promotion.

"In a moment," he continued, "I will give you the program which is going to bring peace of mind to people and children everywhere. But first, I want to introduce a man to whom everyone in this room has cause to be grateful. Al Shively has managed to squeeze ten minutes out to spend with us, and each and every one of us appreciates it. Fellows, our captain, a great guy, a real gen-u-ine person, a man who needs no introduction from me to you, a one-hundred-percent . . ." Shively had donned a helmet himself and came charging on the platform as the applause drowned any further words of Blivet's. He dashed to the center of the stage and straight-armed Blivet, nearly upsetting the new director's balloonlike bulk. The salesmen howled delightedly.

"Hiya fellows!" he shouted into the microphone.

"Hiya, Al!"

"You see this ball I'm carrying?"

"Yeah!"

"That's the ball you're going to stay on! That's the ball you can't afford to drop! That's the ball you're gonna carry for twenty million dollars' worth of Raven touchdowns!"

"*Yeah-ayyy!*"

"That ball's not easy to get! And just to prove it, the first man to carry it makes himself a thousand-dollar bill!"

"*Yeah-hooo!*"

With a vigorous heave, Shively sent the ball flying out over the field of outstretched arms. The ball leaped high and higher still until it touched the ceiling and hung there, buoyed up by the helium that filled it. A roar of disappointment went up from the men, followed by laughter.

"You gotta *reach,* boys!" Shively shouted into the microphone. The men laughed and settled back in their seats. "Keep reaching and you'll all be a hell of a lot richer!"

Then he treated them to a broad outline of the Pax sales plans and recited some of his own maxims. Before he left, he led them in a cheer he had just written himself:

PAX! PAX! PAX RELAXES!

PAX! PAX! PROPHYLAXIS!

24

WHAT HAD BEGUN as a matter of fiscal curiosity with Senator Barton Crain's investigating subcommittee was spiraling into a study of the lines that held together the health of the nation. Senator Crain himself, in an interview published in a news magazine, conceded that the investigations conducted thus far had convinced committee members that an examination of the entire public health situation in the country might well be in order. He envisioned the investigations as the beginning of a far-reaching study for the Congress, one which could result in a program geared to *anticipate* the country's health needs rather than one hitched to hindsight.

Did the senator think further regulation of the drug industry was in order?

"It would appear that the powers of the Food and Drug Administration are not broad enough, but not all the evidence is in. Perhaps all the pharmaceutical industry needs is more competition from itself."

Might that not cut down profits?

"I should think so."

Were drug profits, then, excessive?

"They are large, certainly."

The position of the pharmaceutical industry is that its risks are greater than most and consequently its profits have to be high.

"Let's say they should be *equitable*."

Returning to the question, then, *did* the senator consider drug profits to be excessive?

"That is one of the points our committee is attempting to determine."

The interview appeared the day executives from the Raven company were scheduled to begin their testimony.

A strobe light flashed and the searching eye of a television camera sought out Alonzo Shively as he sat, poised and articulate, his shell-rimmed glasses dangling in one hand, facing his inquisitors. Shively presented the perfect picture of the perfect industrial executive—knowledgeable and efficient, immaculate, self-assured and patiently understanding.

Senator Crain directed a few perfunctory questions, but it was the senator who sat to the right of Crain—the Eastern Seaboard's Johnsmeyer Rogers, a man of ponderous size and laborious mind—who emerged as the Raven vice-president's chief interrogator. He began with a number of general questions about the Raven organization which could have been answered with a careful reading of the company's annual report, and then he became more specific.

"Mr. Shively, how many new pharmaceuticals does your company market each year, on the average?"

Shively stroked his jaw lightly as if considering his answer.

"Perhaps three or four, Senator," Shively said. "But that's a very rough guess. It depends on the results of our research effort."

"Would you be able to tell us how you arrive at a price for each of these new products?"

"I can give you a general idea, Senator," Shively said. Rogers nodded for him to continue. "First we figure our costs for research and development which are usually very high. These are the most significant costs. Then we estimate, on the basis of anticipated sales volume and the production capacity of our equipment, how much our plant will turn out unit-wise. We figure our overhead, our sales and other expenses and add them in, arriving at a cost price per unit—that is, for each vial or tube.

Then we add our profit margin and come up with our manufacturer's list price."

"And how much is that profit margin?"

"It varies depending on the product, sir," Shively said. "Our over-all profits last year, I believe, were about seven or eight percent of sales. Something like that."

"Ten point eight percent after taxes, according to your auditor's statement," Senator Rogers said.

Shively smiled apologetically.

"Our information indicates that the particular markup on at least one of your products runs as high as ten times that amount. Why is this, Mr. Shively?"

"Well, I don't know of any offhand, sir, that run that high. We have some products we lose money on and there have to be compensations for that."

"By what system do you arrive at a hundred percent profit markup?"

"I don't know of any like that in our line, Senator. All of Raven's products are priced competitively. They have to be. Those we lose money on we carry as a service to the medical profession."

"Do you subscribe to the thinking that a fair price for a drug is anything the market will stand?"

"Not at all," Shively said emphatically. "A fair price is a fair price, always reasonable and always competitive."

Rogers studied a paper in front of him. "Let's pick an example," he said. "Let's take one of your vermifuges. What about this one—Pinflux. The government buys it in quantity for use in veterans' hospitals and armed forces establishments. I understand that this is the only drug of its kind, that you have the patent on it. A patient pays about thirty-five cents a capsule for it. Your company has been selling this for approximately four years. Your sales price is twenty cents. According to chemical analysis obtained by this committee, one of these capsules contains material worth about a fifth of a cent. If this is true, how do you arrive at a selling price such as you have?"

"I'm afraid that's erroneous information you have, Senator," Shively said. The slightest trace of irritation had come into his voice and much of the friendliness in his expression had disappeared. "As I mentioned, our research costs are very high and with a special drug like this we spent a good deal of money. I wish we *could* figure it only cost us a fifth of a cent." He smiled then, as if the idea were too absurd.

"But you purchased the formula for this particular drug from—from"—

the senator leafed through a sheaf of papers—"from a French company which discovered and developed it."

Shively examined Rogers darkly and then said, "We don't always get a return on our other pharmaceuticals, you know. We have lots of research costs to amortize for those that never reach the market."

"Mr. Shively, you are aware I'm sure that the drug industry has net total profits each year higher than any other industry in the United States."

Several members of the committee began to lean forward. Alonzo put on his glasses and carefully recrossed his legs.

"The industry also spends more than a hundred million dollars a year on research," Shively said. Belligerence had come into his voice.

"Do you actually enjoy a markup of sixty- or seventy-to-one on this particular product?"

"Which product is that?"

"The one I've been talking about."

"I don't know how we *could*. We don't have a clear markup like that on any product."

"What does it cost you to manufacture this little capsule?" Rogers held up the capsule between his fingers.

"I really don't know," Shively said.

"One cent? Ten cents? Fifteen cents apiece?"

"I am not a cost estimator, Senator. I said we have costs on our unmarketable products to pay for, you know. It gets very complicated."

"Apparently. And you ask the patient who buys this drug to pay for your mistakes?"

"Science isn't perfect," Shively said. "All our laboratory discoveries don't turn out and they all cost money."

"Will you explain some of these costs?"

"I did, Senator. I just finished . . ."

"Not to my satisfaction," Rogers said.

"Well, frankly, I don't know what you want. We set a competitive price on the basis of . . ."

"But this product has no competition. It is protected by the patent rights which you purchased. I want to know why this drug sells for as much as thirty-five cents a capsule to a sick person, and how this price is arrived at."

"The wholesaler and the druggist take about fifteen cents of that."

"Very well. How do you arrive at *your* sale price of twenty cents?"

"I don't have that information," Shively said.

"But you have just told us what your customary markup is and how you set a sale price for a unit. If it is fair to say your profit averages nineteen or twenty percent before taxes, then may we assume that after four or five years of production this tiny capsule costs you four-fifths of its price to make—or sixteen cents each?" He passed the capsule along the committee table for everyone to examine. "Come now, Mr. Shively, isn't that a little steep? Is your production so inefficient?"

"We have to make up our losses, and our overhead is steep," Shively said sharply.

Senator Rogers leaned forward and flipped through some papers in front of him. "Mr. Shively," Rogers began again, "does this product cost you sixteen cents a capsule to manufacture?"

"I have no idea about something that specific," Shively said.

"Can you tell me why you recently raised the price on this—Pinflux?"

Shively contemplated the clear-lacquered nails of one hand before he looked up at Senator Rogers. Good Christ, he thought, leave it to this dumb politician to pick out a half-assed product like Pinflux for an example. He remembered perfectly well when and why he had ordered a price rise on that particular vermifuge. It was a low-volume product and Raven wasn't clearing enough on it to satisfy him.

"I don't remember," Shively said.

"It was a substantial increase," Rogers said. "Four dollars a hundred capsules at the manufacturer's level. Certainly you have some idea? Please try to be a little more coöperative."

"Senator, I'm trying to be as coöperative as I can," Shively said. "You're asking me impossible questions. The only way we stay in business is to make a profit on what we sell."

"Are we to assume," Rogers asked, "that this is an arbitrary price— as much as the market will stand? You raise it whenever you think you can?"

"I can't help what you assume. I told you I can't be that specific."

"It's important that you try," Rogers said flatly. Anger flashed in his eyes as he watched Shively. The vice-president shook his head disgustedly and looked at his watch. "I warn you to consider your answers and your feelings," Rogers told him, "or you will have reason to regret your responses before us."

"I have told you what I can, sir," Shively said. "My company is a respectable, ethical business house and we keep very exact records for the government."

Senator Rogers, his voice tight with anger, said, "Mr. Chairman, this witness should be warned of the consequences if he persists in his conduct."

"Mr. Shively," Crain said solemnly, "I advise you that you may be cited for contempt if you are not able to keep your feelings under control in this room." Shively answered the senator with a silent glare as Crain began to spread some papers in front of him.

"You tell us you don't remember why that price was raised," Senator Rogers said. "Do you have a record of the situation? Any correspondence about it anywhere which would refresh your memory?"

"I don't think so. It was so insignificant we wouldn't have any record."

"We will give you time to check with your office if you wish," Rogers said.

"That's not necessary," Shively answered him. "Something like that would have been taken care of by telephone."

"By whom?"

"I have a half-dozen assistants who could have taken care of it. In the ordinary course of my day it would be a very petty matter."

"I consider it a rather important matter," Rogers said. "Now somewhere in your organization must be recorded a memo or a letter or something which would satisfy me as to *why* you would raise a price on something when it is *already* so far out of line. It would exist unless you or someone in your company took special pains to make certain it *didn't* exist! Must we have every one of your assistants down here under oath or can you tell us what we want to know?"

Shively looked around him with impatience. He ran his gaze the length of the committee table, examining each face quickly for some sign of agreement with his position. Certainly *all* of these people weren't as antagonistic as this Rogers, he felt. Those who returned his look, brief as it was, watched him with curious, unfriendly eyes. Crain, the only exception, studied him inscrutably. "Senator," Shively said, his voice edged with deliberate scorn, "every one of our records—those we normally keep —is available to anyone with a right to see it."

"But you have no record anywhere of why you increased the bulk price of one of your products?"

"I told you. It's not important enough to warrant a lot of memos. It would be a telephone matter, that's all."

Senator Crain broke in. "Mr. Shively, I am as interested as Senator Rogers in getting an answer. This was a telephone matter, you say."

"That's right, Senator."

"Would there perhaps be a record of the telephone conversation?"

"I'm afraid not, Senator," Shively replied. "We don't normally keep records of telephone conversations."

Crain's voice seemed to change, become lighter, more friendly. "Mr. Shively, I understand you are about to market a new tranquilizer."

When Shively spoke, the impatience had lifted from his voice and pride had begun to take its place. "You're talking about our new Pax, which is for peace of mind, Senator."

"Whatever you call it," Crain said. "Now the price increase for Pinflux, as I understand it, was a comparatively recent development. Perhaps it took place during the period you have been making marketing plans for your tranquilizer. Would you then perhaps have a record of the conversation?"

Shively frowned. "I—don't understand, sir."

"Consider your answer carefully, Mr. Shively. You are under oath. *Would* you have the records of telephone conversations made during that period?"

Bewilderment crowded Shively's expression as he tried to understand the implication of Crain's question. Could he . . . ? No! Jesus Christ, he *couldn't* know. Shively felt the blood drain from his face. "I—I don't know what you mean," he said weakly.

"Yes or no?" Crain demanded. Pain and confusion appeared to overwhelm Shively and he sat unable to speak.

At his elbow he heard the whisper of the Raven legal counsel. He turned in the direction of the voice as the lawyer rose and asked Crain's permission to confer with the witness. The senator granted him permission and everyone in the room appeared to talk at once. Lloyd Mc-Rumen, his face creased in bewilderment, waited tautly for Shively to resume. Crain sat expressionlessly.

The Raven lawyer bent close to Shively and said, "What's the matter with you, Al? You've *got* to answer his questions straightforwardly or they'll have you on a contempt charge. If you can't remember, offer him our entire accounting department—anything—but for God's sake coöperate. The whole committee is against you."

"I don't need you to tell me that," Shively said, fear sharpening his anger. "I *can't* answer those questions."

"Why not?"

"I can't go into it here."

"What do you *mean* you can't go into it here? You'd damn sure better go into it with me."

"Oh, Jesus." Shively felt perspiration rolling on his forehead. He took out his handkerchief and mopped his face. "All right. All right. It's wire tapping. That son of a bitch must know something about it."

The lawyer looked at him blankly for a second. "Wire tapping? Whose wire tapping?"

"Ours." Shively ran his handkerchief around the collar of his shirt.

"My God." The attorney sat dumbly.

"What do I do? What can I say?"

"Did you tap the wires of our competition too?"

"Yes."

"Jesus!"

The attorney collected himself, and then, his mouth close to Shively's ear, he spoke hastily, drumming a finger on Shively's arm for emphasis. "All right. Now do this. Say nothing that will incriminate you. He can't prosecute you, but you implicate yourself in anything like that at this hearing, and you may find yourself in a federal court on a criminal charge." He scribbled on a piece of yellow note paper and handed it to Shively. "Weigh the questions," he said. "If you can answer them noncommittally, do so. If you have any doubts, just read this."

Shively read the scrawl. "What do I need the Fifth Amendment for? That makes me look guilty as hell."

"*Looking* guilty won't send you to jail. The wrong answer to one of Crain's questions could. Do you understand that?"

Shively stared at the lawyer in stubborn contempt.

"I said *jail*," the attorney repeated. Then he rose once more and announced that the witness was ready. Crain called the room to order.

"Now, Mr. Shively," Crain said. "Do you have, or do you know of the existence of transcripts of telephone conversations made—which would help shed light on your reasons for raising that Pinflux price?"

Shively considered the question and then said, "I know of none."

"If a Pinflux telephone conversation took place during the period of time in which your company was making its marketing plans for the new tranquilizing drug, would it be likely that a record of that telephone conversation would exist?"

Shively fingered the piece of paper the lawyer had handed him. He read it silently and looked up. In a dry and breathless voice, he said, "I decline to answer that question on the grounds that it might tend to incriminate me."

A murmur rose slowly and spread around the room. It did not diminish until Senator Crain called for order. "Have you been advised by counsel that your answers could be used against you in the future, Mr. Shively?"

". . . Yes."

"How? Did counsel tell you that?"

Shively looked nervously at the Raven attorney and then back at Crain. "I decline to answer that question on the grounds that it might tend to incriminate me," he said.

Senator Rogers shook his head and pushed the papers in front of him to one side so that he could spread his elbows on the table. "It appears that you may have been mixed up in some highly unethical business for a representative of the *ethical* drug industry," he said.

Shively sat mute and tense. He crossed and recrossed his legs and twisted his perspiration-soaked handkerchief in his hands. Senator Crain regarded him gravely. Shively dropped his glasses and Crain waited while he recovered them from the floor before he addressed him. "Mr. Shively, I see no reason for you to avoid the questions put to you by this group unless you are concerned about the consequences. When I began to question you, I had reason to believe that you had been secretly making recordings of telephone conversations within the Raven company, but I had no idea that it extended any further. As you could be concerned over self-incrimination only if you feared you were in violation of the law, and as you could be in violation of the law if you carried your eavesdropping activities beyond your own company premises, I can only conclude that this is what you have done. Have you ordered wires outside of Raven tapped too? Competitors' wires perhaps?"

There was a long silence before Shively answered, in a low voice that could be heard through the room only because of the silence, "I decline to answer that question on the grounds that my answer might tend to incriminate me."

Only Shively knew as he sank deep into his chair how bilious was the taste of humiliating and ironic defeat. But Logan, having helplessly watched Shively design his own trap and spring it, could sense it almost as if it were his own experience. He could hardly bear to look at Lloyd McRumen, who sat staring out at the constricting world, his eyes glazed with outrage and disbelief.

There were other questions, but not one further fact issued from the mouth of Alonzo Shively. Once or twice he seemed to make some effort to regain his composure, but his inquisitors quickly reduced him to the monotony of his constitutional plea.

Before he was released, Shively heard Senator Crain tell him, "We have pursued the matter as far as possible in this hearing room. It is only fair to inform you that the record of your testimony today, together with what other information we have on your telephone tapping expenditures and activities, will be turned over to the Justice Department for study. It is certainly a moral matter whether it ever becomes a legal matter or not."

Alonzo Shively was a shaky caricature of his early-morning self by the time he stepped away from the witness chair. He followed quickly after Logan and Lloyd McRumen, who were making their way through the crowd into the hall. Shively caught McRumen's arm.

"Lloyd, let's get out of this place and get some lunch where we can talk," he said.

McRumen looked up at him and for a moment did not appear to see him. Then he turned to walk away.

"Lloyd, hold on," Shively persisted. Logan stepped between them, blocking Shively's path.

"Let him alone, Al. Things are tough enough," he said.

Shively stood uncertainly where he was and Joe followed the president. Two energetic wire-service reporters cornered Shively as the crowd flowed around them, obscuring Lloyd McRumen from his view.

Walking a few steps in front of the bellhop, his once-precise military bearing relaxed only by the soft lines of the blue flannel suit he wore, Bedford Montrose entered the main lobby of the Mayflower Hotel and crossed it to the registration desk. He signed in as a resident of Midwest City, Indiana.

Alone in his room, Montrose unpacked and changed into a fresh shirt. He called the operator for the correct time, reset his watch at five minutes before noon and flicked on the radio next to his bed. He opened his dispatch case in his lap and drew from it a note pad, Logan's outline, and the copy of Garibaldi's letter to Lloyd McRumen. Before he closed the case, he also removed a brown envelope, fat with unread fan mail forwarded to him by Gladys Constable's program staff.

The twelve o'clock news, with its thumbnail report of Shively's disaster, stopped him from reading any of them. After the first surprise, he began to consider what effect the news would have for him, and after several minutes he decided it couldn't be anything but good. He had counted on a sympathetic audience tomorrow and now, it seemed, he might even have an enthusiastic one. Maybe, he thought, it would be worth his time to sit in on the afternoon session, with Lloyd McRumen in the witness chair. It would give him an opportunity to gauge the temper of the committee, certainly. He pulled the knot in his tie up tightly and slipped on his coat.

When the taxi turned off Pennsylvania Avenue in front of the Capitol grounds, Buddy asked the driver to let him out. He walked slowly along the wide concrete approach to the Capitol steps. The building glistened chalk-white in the warm afternoon sun and he narrowed his eyes against its brightness. He looked to either side of him at the great wings of the Capitol building. Up the long broad stone steps and into the building he went, stopping only when he reached the sudden gloom of the rotunda.

This is where I will stand. Here I will draw my strength. Behind him he heard the questioning voices of some school children on tour and in front, bounding back from some dark unknowable crevice of the future, he heard his own voice articulating the wishes of the people. In the chamber of Buddy's mind, Congressman Bedford Montrose moved slowly through the halls of Congress. It would be a rich life, and productive. He would do justice to it. He stood in the gallery and looked down upon the deserted floor of the House and heard his voice speak on, as it moved the world to understand his importance.

Buddy stayed there a long time, his eyes focused on the future, the infinite future, which was his friend.

When he left the building finally, he knew it was too late to go to the hearings. He went down the long steps, not looking back until he had reached the bottom. The massive stonework now had a warm and gentle look, its color softened by the lowering sun. This would be his home. A place of honor in its halls would be his.

The price could be high, he knew, and there was depression in the knowledge. To get the down payment together had already involved the expenditure of past resources. He had regrets. There were things he would rather not remember, or at least not think about now. The path to destiny should be so clear that a man could ride with honor all the way.

But—life went otherwise. Later—later there would be opportunities to be completely the man he wanted to be. Now it was vital never to forget that the people wanted him and he owed them more than he owed to any single soul who pressed against his life.

Back in his hotel, he did not turn on the television set. The vision of himself was too comforting to disturb. He mixed an iceless drink from a bottle he had brought with him and held the glass in front of the mirror, toasting his splendid image, toasting the future.

McRumen was called by the committee as soon as the group had reassembled. His small presence contrasted with the self-assured and buoyant Shively who had started off the session that morning. Lloyd's expression was grave and the lines in his face were deepened with concern.

After Senator Crain opened the afternoon session, McRumen asked and received the chairman's permission to read a statement. He cleared his throat and unfolded the paper Joe had given him.

The statement was short, but listening to it, Joe Logan—who had written it—thought wryly that it probably was the best piece of prose he had ever composed. It had been put together in the course of the lunch hour, on a typewriter in the Senate press room. The statement was, in a few pages, a concise presentation of the pharmaceutical industry's position and defense. It described the medical revolution of the past two decades. It charted the swift descent, in less than a generation, of diseases which for centuries had held mankind in bondage and in fear. It held up for senatorial inspection the hope of health and life and well-being, which were the fruits of the revolution, and it invited attention to the drug industry's courageous and imaginative part in the promotion of that revolution. "Where we have erred," it concluded, "we welcome examination of the error. But we cannot relinquish our pride that even error reflects something of our zeal, however misapplied, and our dedication to the removal of physical suffering, the oldest problem of man."

When he had finished, Lloyd folded his hands on the table in front of him and looked at the senators. "Because it represents what I believe about our industry, I am glad to have that statement on the record," he said. "Now I should like, if I can ask your indulgence further, to comment about my own company before you begin your questions." He waited for Senator Crain's nod before continuing. "The information which emerged this morning was professionally distressing and personally painful to me. I knew nothing about it until I learned it, as you did, in this room at that time. But the point I wish to make is that it is my responsibility nonetheless. The reputation of Raven is my responsibility, and I accept it. The distressing and distasteful situation which faces us now could have been avoided had I been more careful of that responsibility—more involved in it, as I should have been."

The effect of his words upon the room was silence, as if there was a general sense that although he had addressed his remarks to the group he was speaking to himself, articulating the acknowledgment which for so long had been bound mute in the twisted shroud of intimidation and self-deceit.

The change in the attitude of the committee, which had been hardened into a glaze of unfriendliness by Shively's performance, was apparent. They treated the president with a conscious courtesy as he answered their questions gravely and as honestly as he could. Nowhere in the fifty-year record of the Raven company was there any evidence or suspicion, hidden or revealed, of collusion or price-fixing, to the best of McRumen's knowledge. Yes, the companies did agree occasionally to stabilize the price on a drug marketed by the parties concerned, but, in complete frankness, these prices seldom yielded anyone much gain.

In the matter of profits, he did not evade. Markups on some drugs were quite high. Very possibly they were too high—neither the company nor the industry was totally unresponsive to that criticism. But marshaled against the apparent high costs were facts with which the public was not acquainted: unlike most industries, the pharmaceutical industry was constantly threatened by obsolescence. The new products it was forever seeking in its laboratories were not only modifications of the ones that had gone before; they were, often as not, radical innovations which over-night could render useless—indeed, had, many times—millions of dollars of investment in equipment and facilities. This special risk was, for the protection of the financial foundation on which the industry rested, reflected in the price the consumer paid for his medicine. Like all reasons for special consideration, however, this one had its dangers: in too many instances, cynical advantage was taken of these facts to the victimization of the public and the discredit of the companies involved. The industry had not distinguished itself with a show of vigilance against such excesses, and as a result had only itself to blame for such attentions as this in-vestigating body was paying it now.

In all, his testimony lasted some two hours, and by the end of that time, when he stepped away from the table after the session was adjourned for the day, he had attracted at least the limited sympathy of his listeners. His public assumption of guilt and obligation rested on him heavily but it gave him also a quality he had not sought: a dimension of dignity which fitted his small frame well. The pharmaceutical industry had finally found as its spokesman the man who had always wanted the job.

The crowd rose and moved noisily toward the doors. Anyone watching Senator Crain would have seen his eyes follow the figure of Lloyd Mc-Rumen as it merged with the others in the room. Some of McRumen's words had reached particularly deep inside Crain. The two men were of a mold, the senator thought; brothers under their neatly pressed business suits, guilty of the same transgressions in different arenas, punished for the same sins of omission against different gods. McRumen's penance had stirred admiration but something more besides. It is rare that a man is able to turn his best side to the world's attention, and in a way, Crain envied the Raven president his defeat.

In McRumen's suite at the Willard an hour later, Logan uncapped a bottle of Scotch and poured two tumblers half full over ice. He handed one to Lloyd, sitting quietly against the faded flowers of an overstuffed couch. McRumen's silence had been unbroken from the moment they managed to escape from the crowd. Indeed, the two men had exchanged only the barest minimum of remarks all day. After Shively's testimony in the morning session, a shattered McRumen had indicated to Logan that he wished to be left alone during the midday recess. When they had reassembled, Joe had handed the president the statement he had worked out; McRumen had studied it silently and then looked at Logan gratefully and said, "Thank you, Joe. It's just right. I'll read it." Those were his last privately spoken words. After the hearings he had responded only with a nod when Logan congratulated him on his presentation.

Now he spoke for the first time, as Logan lifted his glass in salute and said, "Here's to tomorrow."

"Tomorrow," McRumen repeated with a wry smile. "Yes, there's still tomorrow, isn't there?"

"It may be worse than today," Logan said.

"Whatever it is, it can't be as bad as what Al Shively has done." Through the weariness in the president's voice, the tones of bitter hostility were unmistakable. "How could he have done what he did without my knowing it?"

Would it have made any difference? The question formed in Logan's mind but he dismissed it quickly. The climb up from the bottom was a tough one, but the little man seemed to be trying determinedly to make it, and what he needed now was confidence. Instead he said quietly, "*I* knew it, sir. I should have told you."

"*You* knew it?" McRumen's surprise was deep enough to preëmpt the darker forces which had dominated his attitude. He sat forward on the couch. "*You* did, Joe?"

Logan nodded. "My guilty knowledge goes a lot deeper than that." To an amazed McRumen he recounted the circumstances of his meeting with Senator Crain. "When I pull strings, I really pull," he said. "They may be the wrong strings, but they make a hell of a lot of noise."

"You know," McRumen said suddenly, "that's what I'm going to do from now on. Make a hell of a lot of noise."

Logan grinned. "You sure did today. We should have had you out on this speaking tour instead of Montrose. Just as effective and not nearly so much trouble."

"Trouble," McRumen said. "We always seem to come back to that word, don't we? Well"—he hunched his shoulders in a gesture Logan found both ludicrous and strangely poignant—"we'll take it as it comes."

"That's the spirit," Logan said. There would be a good deal to take, he knew, in the days ahead—the consequences of Shively's actions, the effect of Garibaldi's resignation, the still unknown nature of Montrose's assault, the steel-tipped questions that would come from a suddenly cautious and hostile board of directors. Maybe they were too many, or too big, and Lloyd would not get through them.

It occurred to Logan quite sharply as he stood at the table pouring a fresh drink that it would be a real shame if Lloyd were left to take trouble as it came, alone. He had not traveled a solitary path to reach the broken field he found himself in now. *The little son of a bitch is going to need help,* Logan thought.

Easy, now. Would building monuments on ruined ground be any better work than making heroes? Who could know? A man had to take his chances, keep his perception sharpened, and do the best he could; that's all there was.

The telephone rang and Logan answered it. Covering the mouthpiece with his hand he looked at McRumen. "It's Shively." McRumen shook his head. "Not tonight, Al," Logan said into the phone. "Make it Monday in the office." He hung up and walked over to hand McRumen the fresh drink.

"Monday is going to be a busy day," McRumen said.

"I wanted to speak to you about it," Logan said. "I thought I might drop around and talk about the future. I hear the pension benefits around Raven aren't too bad."

McRumen studied him seriously. "Do you mean that, Joe?"

"If I'm still employable."

McRumen smiled, weakly at first, and then with some conviction. "That holds for both of us," he said and emptied his glass.

When Logan left, the president walked with him to the door. "You know, Joe," he said, "I still have the feeling that maybe—maybe Montrose won't do anything to us tomorrow after all." Logan did not answer and he went on, "We *could* be wrong. There is that possibility."

In the elevator Logan suddenly changed his mind about going to his room and remained inside to be taken down. He hailed a cab on Pennsylvania Avenue and directed the driver to the Mayflower. He did not stop to call Montrose's room from the lobby. He got the number at the desk and went straight up. Buddy opened the door at his knock.

"What do *you* want?" he demanded.

"I want to talk to you." Logan passed into the room and turned to face Montrose, who was watching him with both irritation and curiosity. "I forced you once to ask me for help," Joe said. "Now I'm asking you."

"You'll get nothing from me," Montrose said.

"I don't know whether I will or not, but I'll try. . . . Look, Buddy." Joe spoke quietly, with deliberate control, trying to temper the hostility in his voice. "I know you plan to rub Raven's nose in shit tomorrow. I suppose you've collected enough dirty wash since you've been around us to make quite a display in that hearing room." Seeing Buddy's bewilderment, he explained, "You had a long-distance conversation with Root in my office. With the news that came out today you can see it wasn't as private as you thought."

Buddy's face went slack. *Holy Christ. That telephone call.* Not once through the day had this implication of the wire-tap mess occurred to him. Now his mind worked desperately to keep the facts in order, to think this through. Logan knew about it, but who else could find out about it? Consideration brought a measure of calm. It was too late for anything to come out before tomorrow morning, and after that it wouldn't matter anyway.

"What's on your mind?" he asked, his voice cautious and noncommittal.

"I'm not going to threaten you," Logan said wearily. "I couldn't if I wanted to." He met Buddy's eyes and held them evenly. "When you throw that spear tomorrow, aim at me."

"Get out of here," Montrose said.

"That's not a hell of a lot to ask, is it? All you want to do is keep yourself clean. You could do it this way as well as any other. I'm expendable."

"What makes you think I'd do *anything* for you?"

"You'd be doing it for Lloyd McRumen." Logan's voice grew soft. "You know what? He still believes in you."

Compassion stirred briefly in Buddy's mind. He heard Logan continue to talk, and one phrase found its way to the chamber of the inner man: "It would be a decent thing to do."

For a moment in time, in the relentless unfolding of circumstance shaping the outline of the road to destiny, Buddy Montrose hovered in balance. Out of the confidence which had grown during the afternoon, a wisp of good will emerged, interlaced with his hunger to reach greatness with dignity. Down the dusty road of gracious memory Captain Bedford Montrose rode slowly, returning with pride the salutes of people who had found and would forever honor decency in him.

But—what was the price? His story wouldn't be as strong if he surrendered the big item and used only Logan as his target. Suppose it wasn't strong enough. . . . Later there would be plenty of time for decent gestures, the impatient voice of the afternoon repeated. *Now* was important. *Now.* The warning rose almost to a scream inside him. There were people out there now who wanted him and they didn't care about some lousy drug company that was bilking them anyway.

"Get out," he said to Logan.

Logan walked to the door. In the doorway he turned. "McRumen still believes in you," he repeated.

So do a million other people, more important. Buddy closed the door slowly in Logan's face.

Only after it was shut did the realization strike Montrose with whip force that Patty probably knew about that recorded conversation, too. *That* was what was the matter with her. He sagged against the door and closed his eyes.

Later there would be time for all that. Later, later, later.

25

MONTROSE'S TESTIMONY began the following morning as soon as the hearings had reconvened. Senator Crain explained that he had been summoned, at Raven's request, as what might be described as a character witness for the industry, and why. Then the senator, his expression grave, announced that because his own relationship with the witness had been a personal one, he would turn over the chair to Senator Rogers.

Buddy took his place opposite the committee and sat with his elbows out, his hands folded calmly in his lap. Logan was not surprised at his appearance. In a handsomely cut tweed suit he commanded no less attention than he had in his bemedaled uniform. It would be tweed, Logan realized, and it would be magnificently tailored. The tweed to accentuate the casual boyish charm, and the tailoring to give it the unobtrusive distinction Montrose enjoyed. His hair was longer than when he had been in uniform, and just barely tousled. The proper touch, Logan thought. It gave him the appearance of the civilized rail-splitter, backwoods sophisticate—the twentieth-century All-American—self-made, hard-hitting, well-meaning, mother-loving, seven-faced son of a bitch. Watching Buddy now, he knew the sensation of uninsulated, slow-maturing revulsion. He had become that much involved.

At the gentle and deferential invitation of the senators, Montrose recounted, as if it were the first time he had ever told it, the story he had repeated in so many high school auditoriums and hotel banquet halls—

and for a while as he told it the general feeling of good will which had begun to build during McRumen's testimony was buttressed enormously. They were both heroes—the modest and courageous captain who had taken Americanism into a land of alien gods, and the generous American firm which had supplied him.

Logan waited, tense and impatient, for the jolt that inevitably was coming. He knew that McRumen and Crain, both watching the serious young speaker with faces intent and drawn, were waiting, too.

"That's a mighty impressive story, son," Senator Rogers said. "I can see why you wanted to come here and speak up for this company. You must be grateful to them."

It was a casual observation, and even the silence that followed it was unspectacular. But the silence remained until it dominated the room.

Montrose's eyes were directed toward the table. "Yes," he said finally. "I'm grateful to them, of course, for what they did for me while I was over there. Nothing can destroy that."

Senator Rogers' eyes were fixed on him. "Is there something else?"

Montrose looked up quickly, his face concerned. "I don't mean to suggest that, sir," he said.

"Never mind, now. I know you didn't mean to. But if there *is* anything, I want you to tell us."

"Well," Montrose said hesitantly, "there's nothing serious. I'm not really much of a businessman, and there are some things I don't understand very well."

"Go on."

"Well, you see, sir, I've found it necessary to cancel my association with Raven."

The stillness in the room was heavy. "Is that right?" the senator said.

"Yes, sir. My letter should be in Mr. McRumen's office now."

"Will you tell us why, please."

"Oh, Senator, I . . ."

"Tell us why."

Montrose looked carefully and hesitantly at the faces around him before responding, and when he began he spoke slowly. There was in his manner a characteristic which Logan remembered well. It belonged to the young officer of a few months ago, sitting in the hushed offices of Lloyd McRumen, presenting to his captured listeners the appealing face of shy and inarticulate boyishness; treading, it seemed, with caution and reluctance on emotional ground where men must exercise prudence in order to know what responses they can trust. But behind that deliberately constructed manner, Logan knew well, lay the disciplined and hard-formed words themselves, already constructed, ready to roll after just the right amount of halting quality had established beyond question the sincerity of the speaker.

"I—mentioned before, Senator," Montrose said, "that I'm not much of a businessman, and maybe these things are not so difficult to understand, but for me they were. I . . ." He paused and spread the fingers of his hands apart in a gesture of helplessness, as if hoping that the gesture itself would take the place of words. "We had a bargain, an agreement, which worked fine, I thought. But then things began to happen. It seemed as if—well, I wasn't sure at first—but it seemed as if I was being *used.*"

Once again, Logan felt the old familiar sense of admiration for the speaker's talents. He had wondered with almost a detached curiosity what device Buddy would use and now as he listened he realized that a better one could not have been selected. He had just enough hard fact to throw in—and under senatorial prodding he did, indeed, throw it in—to give credence to his words: Logan's revision of his speech, the Midwest City newspaper advertisement, and the Pax product display.

"These things," Montrose said slowly, "disturbed me a good deal. They caused me to lose faith in the company I was representing—because of course the people I've spoken to *do* connect me with Raven. But I kept on, hoping I was wrong. And then—well, the other day I learned something that convinced me that Raven wasn't the kind of company I could allow myself to be connected with any longer."

The silence in the room was enormous. Senator Rogers broke it by asking, "And what was that?"

Montrose drew from his pocket a folded paper. "This is a copy of a letter which Raven's medical research director wrote to Mr. McRumen. It's all explained in there." He handed the letter to the temporary chairman.

"I see," said Senator Rogers, "but suppose you tell us something about it in your own words. What exactly was it that caused your disaffection?" He passed the letter to the committee counsel without taking his eyes from Montrose.

"Well," Montrose said, "it's a little complicated, and I don't understand all of it, but essentially it's a plan to trick people. You see, the company has this new drug, a tranquilizing drug . . ." Briefly, concisely, making it not seem complicated at all, he told his listeners, whose faces grew sterner by the minute, the sales plans for Pax, based on the fact that it had once sold without prescription as another product.

When he had finished, one of the senators said, "That's a very grave charge, Captain."

"The facts are in that letter, sir," Montrose said.

"May I ask you, Captain," Rogers said, "how this letter came into your possession?"

"A young lady at Raven who has been sympathetic with the position I've been in, and who has shared my growing disillusionment, gave me that copy," Montrose said. "Perhaps some will think she was disloyal to her company, but she thinks—and I think, too—that there are higher loyalties than to a company getting ready to exploit the public."

There are some ladies, Logan ruminated grimly, *who do their thinking with their ovaries.* He looked at McRumen. The old man was studying Montrose with eyes that were enormously sad. *So it ends,* Logan thought. *Or, rather, here it begins.* The company deserved what it was getting, but that didn't make the job any easier. The task of building monuments on ruined ground was going to be a big one.

Certainly, thought Logan, *it will be the end of Shively's plan for Pax.* In defense of its own reputation for vigilance, the FDA would be in print before the day was over with its intention to reëxamine phitherdimethyldine and, if necessary, permit its sale on prescription only. And no doubt the Federal Trade Commission, in its eagerness not to be overlooked in the news picture, would volunteer the information that the Raven company would find itself in court at the first sign of fraudulent or misleading advertising.

Montrose met McRumen's stare and his own eyes were troubled, too. "I wish all this had not had to come out," he said quietly, looking at McRumen but speaking to the group. He tore his gaze from the president's and faced the subcommittee chairman. "It would be so much better not to have all this said. As I told you earlier, nothing can destroy in my mind the great things they did for me in the past."

"My boy," said Senator Rogers, "no one will want to destroy it. Remove that troubled idea now. You've done your duty with magnificent courage." Most of the other senators nodded their heads gravely in agreement, and Montrose's reply was hoarse. "Thank you, sir."

"Buddy—ah, Captain Montrose." Senator Crain's voice boomed in the still room and then stopped while he smiled apologetically at his colleagues. "Personal relationships are confusing in this room," he said. "Excuse me." He turned to Montrose again. "Young man," he said, his tone jovial and hearty, "it sounds to me as if you're trying to avoid giving us the big surprise about yourself. Everyone here is proud of what you've done and interested in you. I think you ought to tell us."

Montrose was mystified, and his face showed it. "I don't understand, Senator," he said.

"Now, come on, Buddy," Crain said. "According to the information I have received, you're going back to the Far East to finish the work you started there."

There was a rumble of approving and surprised noise from the senators, and the reporters in the room began scribbling on their pads.

With astonishment Logan looked from Senator Crain, whose face was strangely grim behind his smile, to Montrose, whose face was taut and white as it stared blankly back at Crain.

"The International Aid Commission people tell me they've offered you a team to take back over there, if some American firms will put up the money," Crain said. He paused thoughtfully for a moment. "And in view of your record and accomplishments, that should present no problem, certainly. Everybody here is proud of you, and interested in you—myself perhaps a little more than most."

"Well," Montrose said—and Logan knew his halting was real now— "it's—not all worked out yet. The details . . ." His voice trailed off.

"But you will be going back," Crain persisted.

"Well—yes—"

"When will you be leaving?" Senator Rogers asked. "Soon?"

Montrose nodded, his head moving slowly.

"Well, I can tell you for sure," Crain said—"and I think I speak for everyone in this room and a good many people over the country—we're going to be watching for those details. The fact that you've volunteered to go back is an inspiration to every American."

"*I* want to endorse what Senator Crain has said," Senator Rogers interposed. "This is a fine thing to hear."

One by one the committee members added their assents. Montrose sat silent and ashen through it all, a thin smile fastened to his face, his eyes clouded and confused.

Logan was stunned by the boldness of Crain's unexpected action. The senator's plan would work, at least to a point—Joe was sure of that. The reporters in this room, bending eagerly over their note pads, had been given a new and different kind of story to write. It was a story that would find circulation in newspapers across the country. Montrose was going back. The thrill of heroism would spread once more through every community Buddy had visited, and in new ones where his name was not yet even known.

The publicity would force Montrose to accept the IAC offer, Logan realized; his political future would certainly be imperiled if he refused.

What further effect it would have no one could be certain. Joe was sure Senator Crain hoped Buddy Montrose once again would become America's proud evangelist in foreign lands. Could he? It was all too possible that a bitter Montrose who had tasted defeat could never again be the young officer who had done his duty as he found it and in the process found a bit of greatness, too.

Or perhaps he could. Stripped of the trappings in which his gifts had grown grotesque, perhaps he would find again whatever valid splendor he had had. Circumstance had shifted the course of Buddy Montrose once before. Perhaps, just perhaps, it would again.

The chairman brought the session to an end with his gavel, and Logan stood up and walked silently with McRumen out to the hall. Neither of them spoke. Joe met Senator Crain's sober glance, but the senator gave only a perfunctory nod. He wore the mask of a lonely man whose solitude cannot be intruded upon, and Joe made no effort to approach him.

Ahead of Logan and McRumen, Senator Rogers walked toward the corridor with Buddy Montrose, his arm thrown heavily around the young man's shoulder.

"Captain," he was saying, his voice warm with interest, "have you ever considered politics as a career? You ought to think about it while you're over there—and when you get back . . ."

Logan didn't hear the rest of the senator's statement, nor did he hear Montrose's reply. He was blinded by a sudden explosion of light. It came from the flash bulbs of the photographers who were converging on Buddy Montrose.

TREASURY AGENT

THE INSIDE STORY

by

ANDREW TULLY

EDITOR'S NOTE

This is the story of Treasury agents in action—the world-famous T-men and their relentless war against crime.

The extraordinary events narrated here are drawn directly from the closed files of the United States Treasury—from the most exciting true crime dossiers of the century. These closed files were opened for Andrew Tully, White House reporter for the Scripps-Howard newspapers, who has written the story of Treasury Men matching wits with some of the worst hoodlums in history.

From Mr. Tully's exciting book we present the account of the rise and fall of the Capone empire; the trap set for Waxey Gordon; the adventures of a one-man narcotics squad; the Treasury's vital part in solving the Lindbergh kidnaping; and the grim history of the six men who killed, or tried to kill, Presidents of the United States.

Hoodlums, Inc.

A BUM NAMED CAPONE

IT IS A MEASURE of the intelligence and bad taste of the average hoodlum that a cheap little Brooklyn girl-peddler named Alphonse Capone should have risen to command a goodly part of the nation's underworld during Uncle Sam's unhappy experience with prohibition.

Al Capone was an upper-case bum. He started his career in Brooklyn as a neighborhood bully who frightened his female neighbors into prostitution so he could live off their earnings. He did his fighting with a baseball bat, usually accompanied by a small army of lesser bums lest the going get rough. But one day Al forgot and started playing rough in a dance hall at a moment when his boys were out stealing a car. Abruptly, an irritable dancer pulled a knife and carved a slash down the side of Al's face.

The resulting scar gave him the "Scarface" nickname he bore the rest of his bloody life—but it also gave him his big chance in the rackets. His family was worried about him and appealed to a Chicago relative named Johnny Torrio, who was known to boss a beer and rackets combine of considerable importance. Would Johnny take young Al under his wing?

Torrio met young Al at the station and took him over to a restaurant owned by a mobster named Big Jim Colisimo.

"Put him on as a bus boy," Torrio ordered, and Big Jim clawed at his topknot and obliged.

A week later Big Jim phoned Torrio.

"The kid's a slob," he told Johnny. "He ain't smart enough to be a bus boy."

Torrio sighed. Then he got an idea. "Give him a mop," he told Big Jim, "and tell him to keep the joint clean."

Al Capone did fine as a scrubman at $25 a week, but he was unhappy. He yearned to be a big shot. So one fine day he picked an argument with

Big Jim and so impressed Colisimo with his loud talk that Colisimo hired him as his bodyguard at $75 a week. A few months later, Bodyguard Capone shot Big Jim Colisimo to death in his own restaurant, walked out the door and joined Torrio's gang as a muscleman assigned to collecting tribute from Torrio's girl stores.

This, to Al Capone, was the social swim. He spent his salary and horse winnings on diamonds, flashy clothes and big cars. Occasionally, he favored one of the syndicate's girls with his company; he paid the fee by getting the girl the night off. For kicks he also committed an occasional murder.

It was this violent hobby that first brought Al Capone to the urgent attention of the police in 1924. Al learned that a mug named Joe Howard had beaten up an old brothel-keeper named Jack Guzik, who later became one of Al's top lieutenants. Al drove all over Chicago looking for Howard and finally found him in Hymie Jacobs' saloon on South Wabash Avenue.

Howard was talking to three men when Capone entered. "Hello, Al," he greeted him. Capone walked up and grabbed Howard by the front of his coat.

"What's the idea of picking on Guzik?" he snarled.

Howard laughed.

"Go back to your girls, Dago," he told Al.

Whereupon Capone, white with rage, shot three illegal holes in Howard's head.

The case was assigned to one William McSwiggin, a young state's attorney. He worked hard and got a couple of the saloon's hangers-on to admit they'd heard the "Hello, Al." But both claimed they hadn't recognized Capone. Hymie Jacobs, owner of the place, said sure he knew Capone but unfortunately he was busy opening his safe when the shots were fired. Eventually, after a few months in hiding, Capone surrendered to McSwiggin, but the young prosecutor had to let him go after a few hours of questioning. A year later, McSwiggin was killed by Capone gangsters.

Just about that time, Torrio left town for good and Al took over the mob. He brought in Frank Nitti, "The Enforcer," made him second in command and assigned him to arrange for all future killings made necessary by business conditions. Whenever anybody got out of line, Al would tell Nitti. Nitti then would hire out-of-town thugs to rub out the offending mobster; if the thugs failed Nitti would have them killed.

Not that Al had grown soft; it was just that a tycoon had to be careful. Capone now was boss of practically every illegal activity that flourished in

Chicago, with branches in other cities. He bossed the beer and alcohol racket, the whorehouses, the bookies and the gambling joints. In return for protection money, he also cut himself in on such legitimate businesses as dry-cleaning establishments, bakeries and trucking companies. He made an occasional quick grand out of blackmailing crooked road contractors.

So Al became what might be called a social killer. His favorite sport was to toss one of his mobsters a big banquet and then, after the guest of honor had said a few words of thanks, to beat the man's brains out with a baseball bat. "I like to hit people," he'd tell Frank Nitti, and Nitti would grin horribly and pat Al on the back.

In this cozy atmosphere of prosperity and adulation, Al Capone could not have known that his bell was tolling. Indeed, had he heard the notes he probably would have dismissed them as being none of his concern. Of course, brother Ralph had mentioned something about taxes, but who worried about a thing like that?

Yet, because Ralph—being a Capone—couldn't resist cheating even in little things, the spring of 1926 marked the beginning of the end for Alphonse Capone.

Ralph, Al's older brother, was cast in the same mold. He was a gambler, a loafer, a sometime bully, a kind of pensioner of Al's sprawling organization of crime. He had been picked up three times for toting a gun and once for "scaring a horse with his automobile" but had beaten all four raps. He fancied himself as a big race-horse owner.

In that spring of 1926, Capone ran into Eddie Waters of the Internal Revenue office in Chicago. Waters was a kind of missionary in Chicago's underworld. He used to prowl the dives trying to get Capone's mobsters to cough up some income taxes, and occasionally he was successful.

Eddie delivered the same spiel to Ralph Capone that he should pay up and keep out of trouble. Ralph was bored. "It takes too damn much time to fill out those blanks," he told Eddie. "I got business takes up all my time."

Eddie made it sound easy. "Just tell me what you made, Ralph, and I'll fill in the blanks for you and then all you have to do is sign."

Curiously, Ralph took him up. He furnished figures showing he'd earned a total of $55,000 during 1922, 1923, 1924 and 1925.

"Put down my business as gambler," he told Eddie. "I made it all on bets."

Back at his office, Eddie Waters figured out Ralph's tax—it came to $4,065.75. He brought the returns back to Ralph, and Ralph signed them. And promptly forgot them. He forgot them until January 1927, when the Collector of Internal Revenue lost his patience and had warrants of distraint issued. Ralph went to his lawyer, and the mouthpiece explained that it meant the government could seize his property.

"My God, they can't do that!" shrieked Ralph. "All those horses of mine are worth a helluva lot more than four grand."

Right there, Ralph Capone should have paid up, but the thought irritated him. "We gotta make a deal," he told his lawyer. So a few days later he went to the Collector's office wearing a mournful face. His lawyer explained that Ralph was broke, but that he'd borrow $1,000 if Uncle Sam would accept it as full payment.

Uncle Sam would not. The Internal Revenue office knew Ralph was not broke, and now the T-men set out to prove it. The assignment was given to Archie Martin, an agent with the Chicago office's Intelligence Unit, and Martin started making his rounds.

For more than a year, Martin made those rounds. He visited every horse parlor, brewery and gambling joint where he knew Ralph Capone was cutting in on the profits. He button-holed hundreds of startled hoods and tried to pump them for information. He got nowhere. There was no evidence Ralph was getting a dime.

In November 1929, Ralph Capone raised his offer to $2,500, and when Internal Revenue shook its head, he went whole hog and offered to pay the full amount owed, $4,065.75. But he said he was damned if he'd pay the $1,000 in interest and penalties.

"Get it from Mr. Astor or Mr. Vanderbilt," Ralph snarled.

Ralph would not have been so stubborn had he known what the T-men knew. Just before Ralph's last offer, local police had raided a gambling joint known as "The Subway." The books of the establishment were turned over to the Intelligence Unit, and Intelligence agents called in the owner, one Oliver Ellis, for a chat.

Confronted with some penciled figures that indicated he might go to jail for tax evasion, Ellis talked—a little. He admitted he had some "partners"—or protectors—but gave no names. He also acknowledged he had a bank account under an assumed name. Checking, Agent Martin discovered a $3,200 check drawn on that account to the order of one James Carroll.

At the bank, it was learned Carroll had closed out his account, and bank officials had no idea of his identity. Martin and Agent Nels Tessem, a kind of human, early-day Univac, started studying Carroll's account. It had started with the identical sum that had been the balance in the account closed by one James Carter, also unknown at the bank. Carter's account had been started with the exact amount that had been the balance in another account closed out by a mysterious James Costello, Jr. Further back, the closed accounts of Harry Roberts and Harry White told the same story.

Finally, there was the account which had been closed out October 27, 1925. It was in the name of Ralph Capone and its balance had been transferred intact to that of Harry White. Tessem gloated over the figures: the account, under various names, had accommodated $1,751,840.60 from 1924 to 1929.

There was no doubt, then, that Ralph Capone had lied when he said he was too broke to pay his income taxes. As a matter of fact, his account had a balance of $25,236.15 on October 4, 1927, the day Ralph promised to borrow $1,000 to settle his indebtedness to Uncle Sam.

Bank employees insisted Ralph Capone had not been inside the bank since his account—under his real name—was closed out in 1925. It seems the money was brought to the bank by a messenger boy—a messenger boy with a bodyguard named Dago.

Agent Martin felt a bulb glow in his mind. Off he went for a rogues' gallery picture of one Antonio Arresso, and showed it to the cashier.

"That's the man," said the cashier, shuddering.

Which was just splendid, because Antonio Arresso, known as Dago, was Ralph Capone's personal bodyguard.

Once the grand jury started listening to this tale—bolstered by the suddenly remembered stories of scores of little businessmen who had helped fatten Ralph's bank account—Ralph came somewhat clean. He admitted to a special assistant United States attorney named Dwight H. Green (later an Illinois governor) that the phony bank accounts were his. Swiftly, he went to trial and swiftly he was found guilty, sentenced to three years and ordered to pay a $10,000 fine.

Shortly, Al Capone threw a little party for his big brother, and delivered him a public lecture.

"You got caught because you wasn't smart," Al told Ralph. "You talked too much and you put too many things in writing. You gotta be smart, Ralph, and I hope you will be when you get out."

Presumably Al Capone was smarter than Ralph. For one thing he had never filed an income-tax return, and thus the government had nothing on him in writing. Secondly, his operations were so shrewdly anonymous and on such a strictly cash basis that there seemed no way even the smartest government agent could trace any part of his income. Anyway, nobody tattled on Scarface Al.

Fortunately for the honest taxpayer, however, there was a President in the White House who was determined to put Al Capone in jail. His name was Herbert Hoover, a man who has caught more brickbats than posies in his day, but who was destined to receive the ultimate compliment from the world's most notorious gangster.

"That bastard," said Al Capone years later. "That bastard got me."

Herbert Hoover probably disclaimed any such credit, but it is a fact that he figuratively breathed down the necks of Internal Revenue's Intelligence agents until they sent Al to jail. All through the Ralph Capone investigation and trial, Hoover kept the subject a must in his almost daily conversations with Secretary of the Treasury Andrew Mellon.

Mellon reminisced in later years about Hoover's so-called "Medicine Cabinet," a little knot of officials who used to toss the medicine ball around with the President every morning.

"Every morning when the exercising started, Mr. Hoover would bring up the subject," Mellon recalled. "He'd ask me, 'Have you got that fellow Al Capone yet?' And at the end of the session, he'd tell me, 'Remember now, I want that Capone in jail.'"

At any rate, with Ralph Capone salted away, the Treasury's Intelligence Unit started its pursuit of Al Capone in 1929. A committee of anonymous citizens called the "Secret Six" made available $75,000 in cash as a starter, and Elmer L. Irey, Chief of Intelligence, organized his forces. At that initial Chicago conference the key men were Irey, Arthur Madden, Intelligence Agent-in-Charge in Chicago, and two Intelligence agents from Washington named Frank Wilson and Pat O'Rourke.

Madden had made a hobby of collecting information on Al Capone. Wilson was a genius for detail, who later became head of the United States Secret Service. O'Rourke was an Irish undercover man who looked, at times of his choosing, like a Jew, an Italian, a Greek or any other nationality that was called for. A teetotaler and nonsmoker, he was an expert poker player who during more than ten years as a spy on the underworld had become acquainted with more hoodlums than any cop in the world.

Irey explained that they needed plenty of information on the Capone mob, from the inside. "How'll we get it?" he asked O'Rourke.

O'Rourke grinned. "I'll join the mob," he said.

So Irey gave O'Rourke a part of the $75,000 for his trousseau. He had to stock up on checked suits and loud overcoats, white hats and silk shirts of purple and green hues. Next he took a train for Philadelphia, where he looked up an old hoodlum friend named Max "Boo-Boo" Hoff, who was the Al Capone of the City of Brotherly Love.

O'Rourke, of course, was searching for an identity, and he naturally turned to Boo-Boo for help because Hoff and Capone had severed diplomatic relations as a result of Al's getting picked up in Philadelphia for carrying a gun. So for two nights Pat visited with Boo-Boo, soaking up Philadelphia gang lore. Then he was off for Brooklyn for a similar session with a mobster whose hangout was a few blocks from Ebbets Field.

Finally, O'Rourke took a train to Chicago and registered at the Lexington Hotel, headquarters of the Capone mob, as Michael Lepito.

Pat's routine was a relaxed one. He spent most of his time hanging around the Lexington lobby, reading the papers or shooting craps. He asked no questions and was asked none. After a few days he started writing himself letters and mailing them to friends in Philadelphia, who mailed them back to him. It was a pleasure to discover that somebody was opening his letters.

Al Capone and his aides lived in the Lexington on three floors—the sixth, seventh and eighth. Pat O'Rourke lived in Room 724, next door to Phil d'Andrea, who was Capone's chief bodyguard. In the lobby, in the elevators, in the barbershop, O'Rourke observed some of the biggest names in gangdom going about their meticulous business. Machine Gun Jack McGurn was about, and so were Frank "The Enforcer" Nitti and Tough Tony Capeizzo, Jack and Sam Guzik, Paul Ricca and Louis Campagnia, known as "Little New York."

Apparently these characters noticed Pat, too. Anyway, one afternoon Pat was accosted by a mug named Mike Kelly, y-clept Michael Speringa. "What's your line?" asked Kelly.

O'Rourke hesitated. "What's yours?" he drawled.

Kelley looked startled. "Oh," he said finally, "I work around here."

Pat grinned. "My line is keeping quiet. I'm from Brooklyn, but I came here from Philadelphia. It's hell sitting around here all the time, but I guess it's healthy."

In a few days, Kelly and Pat were having drinks together (ginger ale for Pat, because, he said, of an ulcer), and in a week's time Pat was sitting in on the gang's poker games. O'Rourke gossiped knowledgeably about the latest gang feuds and about which mobsters had acquired new mistresses. He reminisced fondly about the good old days in Brooklyn and Philadelphia, sprinkling his recollections with the names of approved gangsters.

Meanwhile, Frank Wilson was busy on his more tedious assignment, checking whatever financial records were available, as a result of raids on bookie joints and gambling houses. Chewing patiently on his cigar, Wilson spent eighteen hours a day poring over this vague evidence, and occasionally he came up with something. By early 1930, he reported to

Elmer Irey that he figured he had the goods on Frank Nitti and Jack Guzik, Al Capone's two top aides.

"I think we should get Nitti and Guzik first and then go for Al," said Wilson. "So far nobody wants to talk much about Al, but if we put a couple of his big shots away maybe people will be more co-operative. They don't have to be co-operative about Nitti and Guzik because those boys got careless."

Nitti, the one-time barber and alcohol-cooker, had made a tactical error. He had endorsed a check for $1,000, which Wilson knew was part of the receipts of a Cicero gambling house. Agent Nels Tessem went to work on it.

Tessem took the check to the Schiff Trust and Savings Bank, where it had been endorsed. Bank officials told him they'd never heard of Frank Nitti. Tessem found nothing in the deposit slips to indicate Nitti banked there under his or any name, and there was nothing on the paying-teller's sheets showing the check had been cashed at the bank. Suspicious, he set up his own books for the day the check had cleared—and found the books $1,000 short.

That tore it for bank president Bruno Schiff. The general ledger and the general-ledger tickets showed a long list of checks credited to Frank Nitti. Schiff admitted he'd entered into an agreement with Nitti to keep The Enforcer's name off the records. Legal, maybe, but unusual.

Nitti's financial hideaway crumbled. In March 1930, a grand jury handed down a secret indictment charging him with accumulating more than $700,000 in 1925, 1926 and 1927 without filing any tax return. Nitti promptly disappeared, thereby proving that some secret indictments are not that secret.

While Pat O'Rourke kept his eyes open for Nitti, Wilson went after Guzik. Jack also had signed a few checks and deposited them under a variety of aliases, then had withdrawn them in the form of cashier's checks. The deposits and withdrawals had been made by one Fred Ries, the cashier in one of the gambling houses from which Guzik drew tribute, but unhappily Ries had disappeared. Wilson went out to find him.

For more than a week, Wilson's search was fruitless. Then one night he ran into a hoodlum who was en route to St. Paul. The hood had private reasons for entering into honest negotiations with the Treasury agent. That night Wilson and Tessem left for St. Louis, and the next day they bagged Ries in his hotel room. Also in the room, the T-men found a letter from Louis Lipschultz, Guzik's brother-in-law. The letter enclosed money and advice: keep going, to California.

Ries wouldn't talk. Wilson knew he'd have to arraign his prisoner before a Federal judge, but he hated to do it in St. Louis because Al Capone had a branch office there and he knew Al's boys would bail Ries out and then, maybe, shut his mouth for good. So Wilson explained to Ries that he couldn't find a Federal judge in St. Louis and they'd have to go to Danville, Illinois. There, a Federal judge set Ries's bail at $15,000—an amount considerably in excess of the amount Wilson knew Ries had in his pocket.

Ries spent three days in jail, thinking. Between times, Wilson chatted with him about Capone's habit of bailing out his pals and then having them rubbed out lest they become gossipy. Ries talked.

That was on September 18, 1930. Guzik was arrested on September 30. On October 3 he was indicted and on November 19 he was convicted and shipped off to the pen for five years. Ries was given several thousand dollars from the Secret Six fund and told to tour the country so that he would be alive and friendly when his testimony was needed again.

Pat O'Rourke found and trapped Frank Nitti in his own imaginative way, and thus cleared the last obstacle to the prosecution of Al Capone. Pat was out in the suburb of Berwyn one day when he saw a pretty woman drive by. She looked a lot like Mrs. Frank Nitti. He looked around for a cab but none was in sight, so he hailed a passing car driven by a garage attendant, flashed a ten-dollar bill and told him to "Follow that car."

Pat and his chauffeur tailed the car into Cicero and promptly lost it in the traffic. But Pat figured she must be going shopping, so he made the rounds of grocery stores, looking for a car with a Wisconsin number plate. An hour later he found it, and within a few minutes the woman who looked like Frank Nitti's wife came out of a store and got into the car. With Pat following, she drove to a beauty shop, where she stayed three hours, while Pat fumed at female vanity.

Eventually the lady emerged from the *salon de beauté,* however, and drove off. Her woman's intuition must have been working, because she first took a long ride in the country, and then turned around and drove back to Cicero. Then, apparently satisfied she wasn't being followed, she drove to an apartment house on Clinton Avenue in South Berwyn, parked the car and disappeared inside.

Immediately the house was placed under twenty-four-hour surveillance. O'Rourke was sweating to find out which apartment the Nittis lived in, but he didn't dare ask around for fear of raising an alarm. So he acted with characteristic directness. One night he shoved the Nitti automobile in front of a fire hydrant and pulled the alarm. Fire apparatus roared up and disgorged some angry fire-fighters. Within minutes they had discovered the name of the car's owner. It was "Belmont," and he lived in Apartment 3D.

The surveillance went on for two more days, and then O'Rourke and his assistants were delighted to see Nitti sitting down to dinner in the apartment. Police were summoned, and the door to Apartment 3D quivered under the beefy knock of a husky sergeant.

Nitti's voice barked a "Who's there?"

"It's the police, Mister," hollered the sergeant. "Open this door or I'll break it down."

"There must be some mistake," yelled Nitti. "My name's Belmont. I'm the well-known Belmont." Then he added crisply, "You son of a bitch!"

The sergeant gave the door one shove with his shoulder, whereupon Nitti unlocked it and invited him in. The cops invited him out, while Pat O'Rourke quietly returned to the Lexington Hotel to resume his spying.

Nitti caused no trouble. He took a look at the evidence against him, spent a couple of days conferring with his lawyer, and then quietly pleaded guilty. He seemed relieved when the judge sentenced him to a year and a half in jail. As a colleague said the day of sentencing, "I figure The Enforcer is quitting when he's fifty years ahead of Uncle."

The stage was now set for getting the Big One—Alphonse Capone. The so-called little people with whom he dealt had learned a lesson from the convictions of Jack Guzik and Frank Nitti. It was, simply, that if Uncle Sam could get big shots like that he could get little shots like them. They were thinking it might not be too smart to refuse to co-operate with the T-men.

Moreover, Al Capone himself apparently was worried. Somebody must have explained to him about the Treasury Department. Anyway, in the summer of 1930 he and his lawyer came calling on Frank Wilson in the Chicago office of Internal Revenue. Al was most genial, and his lawyer, an import from Washington, said Mr. Capone wanted to help all he could and certainly he desired to pay Uncle Sam any money that was owed.

But all Wilson got when he asked questions like "Do you own 'The Subway,' Al?" was a large dose of double-talk. It seemed, as the lawyer explained it, that Al didn't want to furnish any information which might be used against him in criminal proceedings. When the conference ended, inconclusively, and Al and his lawyer got up to go, Al lingered a moment for a last word with Wilson.

"Be sure to take good care of yourself, Mr. Wilson," he said, smiling.

"Thanks, Al," replied Wilson. "I'm watching my diet these days."

Wilson, meanwhile, was digging up some information on Al. Among other things, he discovered Al had been the recipient of more than

$72,000 in Western Union money orders. He was spending $6,000 a year, in cash, for his hotel suite, $3,000 a year for telephone service. He paid cash for some property in Florida. His suits cost him $150 apiece, his shirts $35 and his underwear $15 a set. Clearly, Al had plenty of dough to throw around.

Shortly, too, it appeared that Al was getting more nervous about those T-men. After several visits with Wilson, Al's lawyer admitted that Capone *was* making a little money, but not much. Wilson suggested that the lawyer draw up a schedule of Al's earnings so Al could sign it and everything would be official. The lawyer obliged with a manuscript that would have been gobbled up by any soap-opera producer.

According to the script, Al was the sole support of his widowed mother. His house was mortgaged and he had to support a son and a sister. Unfortunately, his business organization kept no books, so it was hard to arrive at any accurate income figure, but he would say that he got one sixth of the profits. Unhappily, Al had never made more than $75 a week until 1926.

There was a kind of frankness from there in, however. The lawyer actually came up with an estimate of Al's income. "I am of the opinion," he said, "that his taxable income for the years 1926 and 1927 might fairly be fixed at not to exceed $26,000 and $40,000, respectively. For the years 1928 and 1929, it did not exceed $100,000 a year."

Wilson and his colleagues got belly laughs from this. Everybody knew Al spent more than $100,000 a year on his horses alone. But they still had a job ahead to prove it.

Frank Wilson's dedication to financial records provided the big break. Going through some seized books one night, he came across a ledger titled "Barracks, Burnham, Ill." He recognized the title as relating to a Capone house of assignation and he opened it up for a look.

Immediately, Wilson saw the title was a phony. The entries involved not a cheap little bagnio but a gambling joint selling horse bets, dice and other games. More important, on almost every page there were entries noting the payment of sizable sums to one "Al." One of them, for instance, read, "Frank paid $17,500 for Al." To Wilson, "Al" was Alphonse Capone, and he figured he could prove it if he found some people and talked to them.

Next morning he went to the police and they obliged. The joint in question was the Hawthorne Smoke Shop, a Capone outlet which had been raided on April 26, 1926, the day after the murder of young William McSwiggin, the Assistant State's Attorney who had quizzed Al about the Joe Howard murder. Some more prowling and some study by handwriting experts told Wilson that the Smoke Shop's cashier at the time was one Leslie Shumway. Wilson also discovered that Shumway had blown town. A friend with a police record and a grudge suggested that Wilson try Florida.

Wilson showed up several days later at the Hialeah racetrack, and there was Shumway, toiling at the two-dollar window. That night Wilson and a Miami agent named Charles Clarke followed Shumway to his apartment and talked with him about old times.

At first Shumway clammed up. But as in the case of Fred Ries, Wilson discussed with Shumway the facts of life. He cited the indictments of Nitti and Guzik and dwelt knowingly on other Capone wheels who were being investigated. Uncle Sam, he pointed out, could force Shumway to testify, and unco-operative witnesses seldom received favors from the prosecution. Finally, he suggested that Shumway give thought to what would happen to him if the government jailed him as a material witness and Al Capone bailed him out. Shumway folded.

In considerable detail, he figured out the Smoke Shop's profits. It had cleared $587,721.95 during the twenty-two months Shumway worked there, prior to the April 1926 raid. Capone's admitted one sixth of that total would come to $97,970.33 in a two-year period when he claimed his total income: (1) was never more than $75 a week; (2) did not exceed $26,000 for twelve months.

Gleefully, Wilson ushered Shumway back to Chicago and offered him as a witness before a grand jury. Shumway repeated his story, and on March 13, 1931, Capone was indicted for evading income taxes for 1924. The bill was returned just two days before the statute of limitations would have prevented the government from prosecuting Al for that year. This time the indictment was kept secret, and Shumway left for a vacation trip, accompanied by a Treasury agent. He'd be needed again, too.

Two months later Capone was again honored by the grand jury. It handed down twenty-two counts charging evasion for 1925–1929. The charge was that he owed more than $200,000 on a total income for those years, plus 1924, of just over $1,000,000. Al showed up, grinning, three hours later and gave himself up. He was free on $50,000 bail within thirty minutes.

Three days later, Wilson got a worried phone call from Pat O'Rourke, still living with the enemy at the Hotel Lexington. He reported that Capone had imported five hoods from New York whose assignment was to murder Wilson, Elmer Irey and Arthur Madden.

All Wilson could think of to ask was "Why?"

O'Rourke was impatient.

"Dammit, what does that matter? I suppose Al figures it'll scare the jury to death. I've seen 'em. They're riding around town in a car with New York plates."

Wilson, Irey and Madden took the news calmly, although Wilson and Irey did move to another hotel. They also drove around town looking for the New York car. Then, four days later, O'Rourke called back and said the signals had been changed.

"Somebody talked Al into calling 'em off," he said. "The hoods went back to New York."

Next on the program was attempted bribery. A young man who looked like an advertising account executive called on Joseph H. Callan, a businessman who had brought Irey into Internal Revenue years before when he, Callan, had been an assistant to Commissioner Daniel C. Roper.

"I'll be brief," said the stranger. "If Irey's boys let Capone off without a jail sentence I'll give you one and a half million dollars—in cash."

Callan kicked him out, literally.

Nevertheless, it began to look as if Capone would get off easy. From the Justice Department in Washington came word to U. S. District Attorney George E. Q. Johnson that if Al would plead guilty the government would compromise on a two-and-a-half-year jail sentence. There were, after all, the danger of hostile witnesses and the fear of a frightened jury.

Subsequently, on June 16, 1931, Al came into court and, before Judge James H. Wilkerson, pleaded guilty to everything—including 5,000 eleventh-hour Justice Department indictments for bootlegging. Al was smiling and gracious—a celebrity who waved to his fans from behind the cordon of police assigned to protect him from any rival mobster who might have violent ideas. The defense requested and received a two-week delay in sentencing so that Al could arrange his affairs.

That same day a Chicago newspaper ruined it all for Al. It broke the story that the government had compromised for two and a half years for Capone. Apparently, Judge Wilkerson hit the roof. After all, the prosecution can recommend a sentence, but the judge is under no obligation to honor that recommendation. Keeping his temper, Judge Wilkerson granted another delay and then, on July 30, he made his point.

He declared that it was "an unheard-of thing . . . that anybody, even the court itself, could bind the court as to the judgment which is to be made by the court. The court will listen to recommendations of the district attorney, but the defendant cannot think that the court is bound to enter judgment according to those recommendations."

Capone looked as if somebody had punched him in the nose. Hastily, his counsel withdrew the pleas of guilty, and Judge Wilkerson got down to business. He threw out every one of the 5,000 bootlegging indictments but ruled that Capone would have to face trial beginning October 6 on the income-tax charges.

But Uncle Sam was not out of the woods. Five days before the trial the ineffable Pat O'Rourke was on the phone to Irey.

"They got the jury list," he reported. "Al's boys are out interviewing the jury panel. They've got dough and they've got guns."

Pat was right again. Capone's gang somehow had gotten the names of the 100 citizens who would be called for jury duty in connection with Al's trial. The citizens were getting the full treatment.

Irey called on Judge Wilkerson. His face tightened as he heard the news, then he smiled faintly. "Now, Mr. Irey," he said, "I advise you not to worry. Everything will be all right."

The day before the trial, the special panel showed up for pre-trial questioning. Judge Wilkerson excused a few for legal cause, then told the rest to show up the next morning for the selection of the twelve-man jury. Nobody reported any threats, and the judge didn't ask about them. He seemed serene.

And no wonder. Next day, as the trial opened, the Treasury men got their reassurance. When the bailiff called the first prospective juror, Capone's attorney glanced at a paper on his desk. Then he gave it a closer look. Hastily, he checked a second paper. He went through this same routine when the second name was called. Finally he gave up and tossed the papers to one side.

Judge Wilkerson had outsmarted the Capone mob. Earlier that morning he had ordered that the regular panel of jurymen assigned to other cases be substituted for the hundred men Al's mugs had been intimidating.

The trial lasted eleven days. With the help of characters like Ries and Shumway, and a parade of butchers, hotel men, jewelers, haberdashery salesmen and real-estate agents, the government proved that Capone's income was much bigger than he claimed. His vassals testified that he made the money, the tradesmen that he spent it, and the Treasury men that he paid no taxes on it.

On the final day of the trial, Al lost his bodyguard. During the noon recess, Pat O'Rourke and Special Agent Jim Sullivan suddenly escorted Phil d'Andrea out of the courtroom and into a little anteroom. There they relieved him of a loaded revolver. Phil went to jail, and when Al's trial was over Judge Wilkerson sentenced him to six months additional for contempt.

After ten hours of deliberation, the jury returned its verdict shortly after

11 P.M. Al Capone was guilty of tax evasion for the years 1925, 1926 and 1927, and for failing to file returns for 1928 and 1929. Oddly, he was found innocent of tax-evasion charges for 1924, 1928 and 1929.

Some days later, Judge Wilkerson imposed sentence: eleven years in the penitentiary, a $50,000 fine and $30,000 costs. Al Capone, the pimp from Brooklyn, murderer, thief, showoff, had been knocked off by some guys in business suits who knew about something called a comptometer.

WAXEY GORDON, SALESMAN

LAUGHS OF THE HOLLOW VARITY echoed in various law-enforcement offices on a rainy day in 1940 when a thug named Waxey Gordon was released from Leavenworth Penitentiary. Gordon, having served seven years of a ten-year stretch hung on him for income-tax evasion by the then fighting young prosecutor, Tom Dewey, was quoted in newspaper reports as determined to go straight.

"Waxey Gordon is dead," he announced. "From now on it's Irving Wexler, salesman."

Gordon turned salesman all right—if a dope peddler can be graced with that title. And eleven years later, in New York City's General Sessions Court, he was sentenced to two terms of from twenty-five years to life, to be served concurrently, after he was caught delivering a $6,300 package of heroin to a Federal Narcotics Bureau undercover man.

Sanctimoniously, some of Waxey's underworld pals expressed surprise that such a big shot should have stooped to engage in a trade which is at the bottom of the criminal caste system. It should have surprised nobody. Irving Wexler, sixty-three at the time of his sentencing on the narcotics rap, had been a full-time hoodlum since the early 1900s. He was a convicted pickpocket in 1905—his nickname was a tribute to his smooth fingers. He had been in jail for petty and grand larceny and assault and battery. He had operated a whorehouse. And during the Prohibition Era he was one of the three or four top bootlegging barons, a notoriety which in 1930 earned him the title of New York's Public Enemy No. 1.

He looked like a little white grub—a dumpy man, only five feet six

inches tall with a few wisps of hair on his dome and a penchant for
loose-fitting, double-breasted suits. He had a fondness for the kind of
rich living that calls for opening-night seats at sexy musicals and the best
tables in the swank traps patronized by café society.

By 1920, Waxey was head of his own business, a close-knit mob of
pickpockets, pimps, girl-house operators and, narcotics agents suspected,
a little dope dealing on the side. He operated out of New York's Lower
East Side until 1923, when he took over the Fourth Avenue Hotel with
a St. Louis bum named Maxie Greenberg, whose record boasted forty
arrests. Waxey nimbly skirted trouble; in 1924 the Narcotics Bureau got
him indicted for shipping two trunkfuls of heroin to Duluth but couldn't
get a conviction. When the cops kept raiding the Fourth Avenue Hotel
as a bordello, Waxey and Maxie moved their headquarters to 1476
Broadway, from which respectable location he launched his bootlegging
empire.

Gordon did well. He backed an occasional Broadway show and sent
his son to the best schools. He paid $6,000 a year for his apartment.
But he had bigger ideas, involving three illicit and valuable breweries in
New Jersey controlled by some mugs named Frank Dunn, Jimmy "Bugs"
Donovan, Fred Werther and James Culhane. In one of the most striking
series of coincidences of modern times, Dunn and Donovan were assassinated and Werther was critically wounded—all within two years' time.
Culhane took the hint and moved to Yonkers, where he opened a modest
brewery. Whereupon, in March 1930, Waxey Gordon moved into the
Alexander Hamilton Hotel in Paterson, New Jersey, and hired Werther as
an "expert."

Waxey also hired another "expert." He was Murray Moll, another St.
Louis export, who was installed as vice-president in charge of discipline
—to wit, murdering people who bothered Waxey. Moll was a devotee of
the direct method. There was the day he was being held in St. Paul on a
murder charge (which he later beat) and a clerk from a Los Angeles
drugstore identified him as the man who had robbed his store of $23,000.

Moll was released on bond, to appear in Los Angeles. The day he
arrived the clerk was shot to death. Moll beat that one, too, because
nobody saw the clerk murdered, and the death of the clerk had eliminated
the witness to the drugstore holdup. It was inevitable that Moll should
die as he lived, and he did. Some of Dutch Schultz's boys filled him with
lead in the Bronx one night.

But aside from his murderous heart, Waxey Gordon was a shrewd
businessman with a flair for keeping the law off his neck by paying
protection money where it would do the most good. This was necessary

because a brewery cannot be operated under cover—it's too big. So Waxey paid well for protection out of a take estimated in the early thirties at $1,000,000 a year. He was ingenious, too. Since do-gooders were always complaining about all those trucks rumbling out of the illicit breweries, Waxey arranged with his political friends for his beer to be pumped through pressure hoses running through the sewer systems of Paterson, Union City and Elizabeth.

Meanwhile, however, Internal Revenue's Intelligence Division had taken note of Waxey's activities. In 1931 they were particularly interested to learn that Waxey had paid less than $100 in taxes in the past three years, although he lived like the Aga Khan.

"Don't bother me," Waxey told a T-man who came to call. "I don't keep any records and I never signed a check in my life. You'll never get me."

He was wrong. Intelligence agents tracked down a number of fat checks deposited for Gordon under phony names. They got a couple of malt salesmen who did business with Waxey to furnish figures on how much beer he made. The brewmaster got a nickel a barrel, so he was able to corroborate that Waxey brewed between 3,000 and 7,000 barrels a week.

The jury took only forty minutes to convict Waxey. For good measure, the judge added a $20,000 fine to the ten-year sentence.

Waxey Gordon was fifty-two when he got out of Leavenworth in 1940 and proclaimed himself an honest man. But obviously he was still bursting with energy, and still a man who couldn't resist a fast buck, no matter how dirty it was. Soon he was in the soft-drink business and soon he was in trouble again. A man who moved with the times, Waxey had gone into the black-market sugar racket when World War II's rationing was imposed, and he pleaded guilty to diverting ten thousand pounds to an illegal distillery. He got a year in jail for that.

When the jail door opened again for Waxey Gordon, there apparently was nowhere for him to go but into the narcotics racket. By 1947 the Narcotics Bureau had a bundle of information on him, but it wasn't wrapped up tightly enough to make a case. Then, in early 1950, Waxey made a 9,000-mile trip around the country that piqued the interest of Narcotics Commissioner Harry J. Anslinger. Wherever he went, he introduced a pal named Sam Kass to his underworld comrades—and Kass was down in the book as a big narcotics supplier. One day, too, somebody called Captain Peter Terranova of the New York Police Department's narcotics squad.

"If you want the big shot in the dope racket, look up Mr. W.," said the caller, and hung up.

Clearly, the time had come for Uncle Sam to make his move. From Washington, Harry Anslinger called James E. Ryan, head of the bureau's New York district. "Better turn our man loose," he told Ryan.

"Our man" was a thirty-seven-year-old ex-convict who had been picked up on a charge of bootlegging alcohol. His name was Morris Lipsius and he came from Waxey Gordon's own Lower East Side neighborhood. He had been released from prison in 1948 after having done twelve years for armed robbery, and he didn't want to go back to jail.

Ryan put the proposition to Lipsius bluntly. "Morris," he told him, "I would like to give you an opportunity to get killed." Specifically, the Narcotics Bureau wanted to use Morris as a plant, an undercover man who could work with Gordon, win his confidence, and then deliver him to the law. Morris Lipsius took the job.

That was in December 1950. For the next seven months Lipsius concentrated on the buildup. He hung around in bars and restaurants along lower Second Avenue, where Waxey could be seen and cultivated. It was Lipsius' own neighborhood, so the boys made him welcome. It didn't take him long to meet Waxey, and within a few months the two were cautious pals; Lipsius, playing the role of the young punk, sat at Waxey's feet while Waxey reminisced about the good old days of bootlegging.

But it wasn't until Saturday, July 14, 1951, that the law got down to business. On that day, under orders, Lipsius sought out Gordon to "make a buy." He sauntered into one of Waxey's saloon hangouts, but Waxey wasn't there. The pubkeeper suggested he try a warehouse on South Street, just off the East River waterfront. By that time it was too late to do much more, so the agents with whom Lipsius was working told him to postpone the call until the following Monday. That Monday morning, Lipsius was given $6,000 in $50 and $100 bills with which to try to buy a half kilo of heroin. (A kilo is 2.2 pounds.)

At the warehouse, Lipsius shot the breeze with Waxey for a while, and then Waxey asked him, "What's on your mind?"

"I'm in the market for some stuff, W.," said Lipsius. "An old customer is in town. He wants a half kilo of horse. I got the six grand with me."

Gordon seemed horrified. "I wouldn't touch that stuff for a million bucks," he told Lipsius. Then he launched into a lecture on the perils of pushing dope. Lipsius turned to go. "Okay, I'll try elsewhere," he said.

Waxey called him back. "Wait a minute," he said. "Maybe I can get it for you, but it would cost me six thousand. I gotta make at least five hundred on the deal. If you can get your customer to come up with $6,500 for the half kilo maybe we can do business."

Gordon assured Lipsius the heroin would be 50 per cent pure, and Lipsius said he'd see his customer and give him the score. He went back to a drugstore at Broadway and Barclay Street which had been turned into an informal headquarters for the agents working on the case. Agent Le Roy Morrison of the Narcotics Bureau gave him another $600, and Lipsius had an idea.

"Just to make it sound on the level, I should offer him only three hundred more," he told the agents. They agreed, and Lipsius took off to meet Gordon.

At a bar on Market Slip, Gordon had news for Lipsius. It seems he was getting 87 per cent pure heroin instead of 50 per cent. Lipsius said that was fine, but his customer wouldn't pay more than $6,300. Waxey agreed without argument, and Lipsius counted out the money. It was arranged that the two would meet at First Avenue and Twenty-sixth Street at 8:00 P.M. for the delivery.

Waxey met Lipsius as scheduled in front of a soda fountain named the Bellevue Inn. Two narcotics agents lurked near by. Waxey immediately hailed a cab and told the driver to go to the corner of York Avenue and Sixty-seventh Street. The agents followed in their own car, and here Morris Lipsius made a tactical error that was almost fatal.

Waxey asked Lipsius to keep looking out the back window. "I wanna know if we're being tailed," he explained. "See if anybody turns in behind us when we turn off First."

The cabbie turned off First at Sixty-sixth Street and headed toward York. Lipsius took a quick look and got another idea: he'd offer an explanation in case Waxey noticed the agents' car following them.

"It's okay," he told Waxey. "A car just turned in behind us, but he made a left turn off First. He came from the opposite direction from us."

Lipsius knew immediately he had blundered. First Avenue was a one-way street, northbound; a car could not turn left off First unless it had been moving south in violation of the one-way regulation. He shot a glance at Waxey, while his hands grew clammy. But Waxey hadn't noticed a thing.

When the cab pulled up at Sixty-seventh and York, they both got out and Waxey told Lipsius, "Wait here, I'll be back in a few minutes." Then he walked north to Sixty-eighth Street, where Agent Charles Ward was parked in his car. Shortly, as Ward watched, a sedan approached Waxey and stopped. The driver handed Waxey a package wrapped in a *New York Times* and drove away. Ward had no trouble recognizing the driver as Artie Repola, a young Harlem gambler, who had been in the narcotics book of suspects for some time.

Waxey strolled back to where Lipsius was standing and handed him the package. Then he hailed a cab, put Lipsius into it and waved good-bye. Lipsius was suspicious. The cab had seemed to drive up even before it was hailed; it looked like a plant. So, instead of telling the cabbie to drive him to the Cornish Arms Hotel, which was his rendezvous with the agents, he had him take him to the Commodore Hotel. At the Commodore, he walked into the lobby—followed by two agents—then took a cab to the Cornish Arms.

At the Cornish Arms, the heroin was handed over to the agents. Two days later word came from the Narcotics Bureau laboratory in Washington that Waxey Gordon had chiseled. Instead of being 87 per cent pure, the stuff was only 35 to 40 per cent pure. It was decided that Lipsius, to stay in character, should complain to Waxey the next time they met. Three days later, he did so, but Waxey insisted there was some mistake. "We tested it, and it came out at least eighty per cent," he told Lipsius. The undercover man accepted Waxey's defense.

The second buy was set for July 26, and when Lipsius met Waxey in a bar the hoodlum was jumpy.

"I got word I'm being set up for the Feds," he said.

Lipsius was startled but tried not to show it. With a great show of concern, he asked Waxey if he had any idea who was setting him up. Waxey said he didn't know, but that "the mob" wanted him to lay low.

"Listen, Irving," Lipsius told him. "You should listen to wiser heads. If the mob tells you to quit, I think you should quit. But, please, don't heat me up. I don't want to get sent up again."

"You should worry," replied Waxey. "If I get pinched it means life."

But Waxey was greedy, and Lipsius had $1,650 in his pocket as a down payment on a quarter of a kilo of heroin. So he took the $1,650 and set up a meeting at Lafayette and Fourth Streets at 7:30 that night for the delivery.

On that second buy, the waiting agents witnessed the appearance of a third member of the gang. When Lipsius arrived at the meeting place, he and Waxey got into a cab and were driven to Second Avenue and Forty-seventh Street, with the agents in discreet pursuit. Waxey left Lipsius at the corner and walked a block south to a restaurant.

Two agents followed Waxey into the restaurant. A few minutes later, in walked Sam Kass, the well-known dope supplier, the man Waxey had been introducing to his pals during that 9,000-mile trip the year before. Kass and Waxey exchanged a few words, and Kass walked out of the restaurant and over to his car, where he picked up a package. Then he delivered it to Waxey in the restaurant, while the agents watched gleefully. Kass left again, and after a few minutes Waxey followed him and delivered the package, in turn, to Lipsius. Later that night, Lipsius paid Waxey the final installment of $1,500. The heroin, it was discovered, was only 27 per cent pure.

Now it was time to spring the trap; the day picked was August 2. In the early afternoon, Lipsius showed up for his meeting with $3,150, half the purchase price of a half kilo of heroin. But first he had a complaint to make. He told Waxey that for the money he was paying he figured he should be getting better heroin. Waxey insisted the stuff was okay, whereupon Lipsius told him that if he couldn't offer better stuff he'd have to go elsewhere.

That did it. Waxey grew anxious and told Lipsius he'd personally guarantee the stuff. When Lipsius showed a natural hesitation at accepting a guarantee from such a source, Waxey went all the way.

"This time I won't take your money unless you're satisfied," he said. "If it's not good stuff, you can keep the heroin and not pay me a dime."

Lipsius didn't want this. After all, the money was marked. So they had a kind of Alphonse-Gaston argument, which went on until Waxey compromised and agreed to take $1,000 of the money. He told Lipsius to meet him at 6:30 that night at Second Avenue and Fourth Street. When Lipsius returned to his rendezvous with the law, final plans were made for the pounce.

Agents Morrison and Joe Ferro were assigned to cover Waxey and Lipsius in one car, with Agent Price Spivey in another, and a New York group, including Sergeant Johnny Cottone, Marco Deserio and Isaac Ezagui, in a third car. Agents Charles Ward and Joe Amato and New York Detective Paul C. Hein were dispatched to Harlem to keep an eye on Repola. An added gimmick was the assignment of Agent Ben Fitzgerald to the driver's seat of a New York cab; his job was to try to pick up Lipsius and Waxey as fares.

At the meeting place, Waxey had a surprise for his young friend. "I'll need more dough," he told Lipsius. "The mob wants another two thousand one fifty before delivery." Lipsius went back and got the $2,150 from Agent Morrison, then rejoined Waxey at First Avenue and Fourth Street and gave him the money. Here Agent Fitzgerald got into the act. He skillfully maneuvered his cab through traffic and cruised slowly toward the spot where Waxey and Lipsius were standing. They got in the cab, and Waxey told Fitz to drive to the corner of York Avenue and Sixty-ninth Street. Fitz promptly wrote the address on a piece of paper and tossed it out of the cab. Agent Ferro stopped the car he was in and picked it up.

At York and Sixty-eighth, Waxey told Lipsius to wait in front of New York Hospital; then he walked north. Lipsius waited for half an hour, then walked north, too. Waxey was standing on the corner of York and Seventy-first Street.

"I don't understand it," said Waxey. "They were never this late before." However, he told Lipsius to go back to Sixty-ninth Street and wait.

About ten minutes after nine—it was just dark—Waxey Gordon and Sam Kass hurried down York toward the corner of Sixty-ninth Street. Kass stopped near the corner, took a package out of a car parked at the curb, and handed it to Waxey. Waxey tucked the package under his arm, crossed the street and started walking toward Lipsius.

Agent Joe Ferro caught up with Waxey when he was still fifty feet away from Lipsius. He grabbed Waxey's arm and barked a terse "Hold it." Other agents closed in, including Sergeant Cottone.

"Irving," he told Waxey, "this is Johnny Cottone."

Waxey seemed bewildered. Then he broke down.

"My God, Johnny," he pleaded. "Shoot me. Don't take me in for junk. Let me run, and then shoot me!"

A couple of blocks away, other agents surrounded Kass's car and arrested Kass and one Benjamin Katz, whose legal name is Kass and who is Sam Kass's brother. Bursting in on a crap game in a Harlem garage, a third contingent of agents nabbed Artie Repola.

At York and Sixty-ninth Street, Sam Kass played big shot. He called over Johnny Cottone and held out both hands. In one were two diamond rings, in the other was $2,500 in cash.

"Take this," he said. "Take the whole business. Just let Pop go."

Pop, of course, was Waxey Gordon. Johnny Cottone smiled and turned away. When Waxey was arraigned a few hours later, his bail was set at a quarter of a million dollars.

Four months later, in December 1951, Judge Francis L. Valente threw the book at the mob. Sam Kass got ten and a half to twenty-two years; Benjamin (Kass) Katz got three and a half to seven years, and Artie Repola got ten to twenty years. Besides his two terms of from twenty-five years to life, Waxey Gordon got a tongue-lashing from Judge Valente:

"You are described in my probation report as a predatory, calloused, unmoral, materialistic person who, in your determination to live comfortably and luxuriously by unlawful means, has not been hampered by any religious scruples, moral standards or ethical concepts.

"You have demonstrated repeatedly that there is no crime or racket to which you would not resort in order to make a dollar. Your latest and most dastardly offense is typical of your hostility, and it should ring down the curtain on your parasitical and lawless life."

Judge Valente was a prophet. Irving (Waxey Gordon) Wexler died in Alcatraz June 24, 1952.

Foreign Relations

ONE-MAN NARCOTICS SQUAD

DURING CHRISTMAS WEEK, 1957, Charles (Lucky) Luciano showed up at a respectable Christmas party at a Naples orphanage and was seen in deep conversation with an American-type Santa Claus provided by a Yankee expatriate to give the shindig a home-town touch.

"Take a look at Lucky over there," an American correspondent told his companion. "He's asking for Charlie Siragusa in a block of concrete."

Possibly they were libeling Mr. Luciano, who often affects a charitable outlook, even toward cops. But there's no doubt he would reward handsomely any Santa Claus who could deliver Charles Siragusa in such a package. For Siragusa is kind of a one-man Federal Narcotics Bureau in Europe and he has been a pain in the neck to Lucky Luciano's dope syndicate.

Operating out of a wing in the United States Embassy in Rome, Siragusa's little police force of himself and two assistants since 1951 has cut the dope traffic from Europe to the United States by 40 per cent. During that time, he has staged more than 100 raids from Rome to Beirut, Lebanon, has arranged the arrest of nearly 200 narcotics racketeers and has seized 4,400 pounds of opium, heroin, hashish and cocaine ticketed for the U.S. At the retail level, the total value of the stuff seized runs into millions of dollars.

Siragusa roams about Europe and the Middle East today, spreading his reign of terror in the underworld, because his boss, Federal Narcotics Commissioner Harry Jacob Anslinger, believes in the approach direct. Shortly after the end of World War II, Anslinger was troubled by the increase of heroin addiction in the United States and by evidence that the illicit drug was pouring into the nation's East Coast cities from Europe, notably Italy. It seemed like more than a coincidence that the Justice Department had recently deported a passel of Italian-born American hoodlums—mugs who had had a fat hand in the dope traffic here. By arrangement with the Italian government, Anslinger sent a couple of his agents to Italy for a look-see in 1948 and 1949. In 1950 he sent Siragusa on a similar errand, and then the next year he assigned Siragusa to a permanent post in Rome, with orders to go anywhere in Europe and the Middle East where he thought he could do some good.

Siragusa had both the background and the personality for the assignment. A brash, glib-talking, second-generation American whose parents emigrated from Sicily, he had grown up in New York's Bronx, where he spent a typical rough-and-ready childhood on the fringes of the teen-age Sicilian gangs which roamed his neighborhood. New York University was his educational background; he had gone on to a stint with the Immigration Service and a wartime interlude with the intrigue-laden OSS before joining up with Anslinger's outfit. By 1951 he was sporting black horn-rimmed glasses, a thin mustache and an insatiable curiosity.

During his 1950 tour, Siragusa had picked up enough information to give him a start. In Greece, Turkey, Syria and Lebanon he had seen the flourishing acres of marijuana and he had peeked into huts stacked with bags of opium. Police officials and underworld informants had showed him evidence indicating that the raw opium from Turkey and Iran was smuggled into Syria and Lebanon, then into Italy for processing into heroin and finally shipped to the U.S. Everywhere he went, he saw the fine hand of those expatriates from Uncle Sam's paternalism—Frank (Three Finger) Coppola, Little Joe Peachy and Nick Gentile.

Siragusa also was properly impressed with the fact that Italy at that time imported twice as much raw opium as it needed and produced four to six times the heroin required for legitimate medicinal demands. So one of his first moves was a quiet investigation of the five legal heroin plants near Milan. Working with Italian police, he seized twenty-two pounds of bootleg cocaine and evidence that the owner of one of these plants was diverting heroin to his good friend Lucky Luciano. A few months later he joined Italian police in a raid on a little Sicilian village where they came up with a green trunk filled with heroin and some interesting papers that implicated fourteen well-known recent deportees from the United States. Siragusa was convinced that American mobsters had muscled in on the racket, and that Lucky Luciano was the chairman of the board of this new organization. It was, in fact, the old Mafia with some new bosses.

One of the first tasks was to convince the Italian government that steps should be taken to curb this illicit traffic. So Siragusa, and our then Ambassador Clare Boothe Luce, started a campaign to get Italy to ban the legal production of heroin. They were helped by the scandalous Schiaparelli Affair, in which a top official of a heroin plant admitted he had diverted $800,000 worth of heroin to hoods known as close associates of Luciano. But it wasn't until March 1956 that Italy finally banned heroin production.

It wasn't enough to crack down on the distributors in Italy; in order to curb the traffic something had to be done about the source of supply, which meant the Middle East. American agents have no police powers abroad—they must depend on the co-operation of police officials of friendly countries—and to get that co-operation they need the combined talents of a Machiavelli, a Winston Churchill and a Madison Avenue account executive.

Siragusa showed he had these talents, in spades. Prowling about the Middle East, choking over a popskull called raki, he impressed the cops in countries like Syria, Turkey, Lebanon and Greece with his sincerity. He accepted their confidences about political throat-cutting and never tattled. He lent a hand in solving an occasional local crime. He convinced them that he was a friend they could trust. A Greek police chief named Gerasimos Liaromatis—who is "Gerry" to Siragusa—says, "Charlie is the only honest man I ever met."

Thus when Siragusa was ready to launch his drive in the Middle East in the fall of 1954, he had a lot of tough and efficient cops all over the area going for him. He needed them, for in his most successful expedition he required the co-operation of four countries whose officials would much rather be at each other's throats than working in harness. Soothed by Siragusa's diplomacy, the police of Greece and Turkey forgot their differences over Cyprus, and the cops of Syria and Lebanon buried their hatchet whetted by their opposing views concerning the machinations of newly resurgent Egypt.

The operation took five months of planning and was climaxed by nearly simultaneous raids in three countries—Turkey, Lebanon and Syria. Siragusa's right-hand man in the operation was his old pal, the Greek Police Chief, Gerasimos (Gerry) Liaromatis. Siragusa, a man with a flair, calls it "Operation Old Goat."

In mid-November 1954, Siragusa was tipped by an informant in Greece that circumstances were favorable for rounding up the gang they were after, a gang whose exports had an estimated retail value in the United States of more than a million dollars a year. Siragusa picked up Gerry, and the two set off for the Turkish town of Adana, an ancient cotton center where Uncle Sam had set up an Air Force base.

The man they wanted was an opium supplier named Ahmet Ozsayar, but in order to get him to do business with them they had to have a convincing story. Siragusa solved that problem. He drove out to the Air Force base and had a chat with one of the two Air Force officers stationed there. An hour later he drove off in an Air Force jeep, wearing one of the officer's spare uniforms.

"You're a big Greek gangster," Siragusa told Gerry. "You want to buy opium. I'm a corrupt Air Force pilot who's willing to smuggle it out."

Confronted with this tale, Ahmet was charmed. He would be glad to sell them 550 pounds of opium. It was agreed the stuff would be delivered the next morning, and the trio then hied themselves to the nearest night club, where Ahmet belted himself stiff with raki and insisted on covering Siragusa's cheeks with kisses. That's when Siragusa started calling him the "Old Goat."

Siragusa chose well the rendezvous for the next morning. It was at a lonely road intersection near Adana's airport, and there was a railway shack near by in which were hidden a platoon of Turkish police. Ahmet showed up promptly at five o'clock with a British truck loaded with opium, and after submitting to a moist buss on his cheek, Siragusa started helping Ahmet and his two assistants unload the truck. Suddenly, the Turkish police burst from the shack with what sounded like Indian war-whoops and tethered Ahmet and his two helpers together with a chain.

At police headquarters, the Old Goat was persuaded to mention the name of his supplier. A few minutes later, Siragusa and Gerry, supported by a half-dozen Turkish policemen, took off for a mountain village in Anatolia. It was a 300-mile drive through wild brush and desert prowled by hundreds of wolves, and when they reached the village they were nearly mobbed by a knot of some twenty peasants. But they grabbed their man and an accomplice and 4.4 pounds of opium.

Charlie Siragusa, at that point, had an extra reason to be pleased. He had personally shot three wolves, on the run, with his revolver.

Things were happening in Beirut by that time. One of Siragusa's Rome assistants had donned the uniform of a Pan-American World Airways pilot and was making a deal with another member of the gang to buy eighty-eight pounds of opium. This gangster's name was Abou Sayia. He was an irritable little Lebanese who was the Old Goat's branch manager in Lebanon.

Abou refused to make the delivery anywhere but in his apartment, so at the agreed-on time the agent showed up and flashed his roll—a few hundred-dollar bills wrapped around a wad of paper. This was the signal for the Lebanese police to break into the place. As they did, one of Abou's teen-age sons staged a one-man battle with the cops, which gave his mother time to flush a quantity of the dope down the toilet. Still, the cops seized eighty-eight pounds of opium, nine of hashish and an ounce of morphine, and made five arrests.

The final raid was set for the next day in Aleppo, the famous walled city of Syria. The quarry was known as a dangerous man, a huge Syrian-type gangster named Tifankji who had a potbelly and a face slashed with scars. Two weeks before, according to one undercover agent, Tifankji had tackled three rivals in a raki joint and had departed, leaving one of them with a broken neck and the other two with fractured skulls. As one agent put it, "Maybe we should raid that guy with a tank."

No tanks were pressed into service, but the enforcement clan gathered for this one. On hand were Siragusa, Chief Gerry, the original Greek informant, a Turkish police chief, the agent who had nabbed Abou Sayia in Beirut, and two other agents.

They separated into two groups and started dickering with Tifankji in an assortment of coffeehouses. To give it an old-school authenticity, the two groups represented themselves as competitors, and Tifankji had the time of his life setting one group against the other while the bid price soared. During one stage of the negotiations he also demonstrated his strength by punching a hole through the coffeehouse wall. The wall was three-inch-thick mortar.

Finally Tifankji had had enough fun, and he closed a deal with Agent X for 114 pounds of opium. That night Agent X drove to Tifankji's home, a fourth-floor apartment in a respectable section of the town. In the street below were Siragusa, his policeman friends and six Syrian cops dressed in civilian clothes.

Tifankji emerged a half hour later after telling Agent X he had to go to get the opium. He boarded a streetcar, with Siragusa behind him; the police followed in a truck. Tifankji got off at the end of the line and made his way to a collection of unlighted huts, his pursuers spread out behind him. When he entered one of the huts, Siragusa and his cohorts burst in at his heels, and Tifankji was nabbed without a struggle. Also arrested were two accomplices; the 114 pounds of opium were seized.

The two-day raid had netted thirteen dope peddlers and 765 pounds of drugs, which if successfully smuggled into the United States would have sold at retail for upward to a half million dollars. In one month's time, Siragusa's combined operations in co-operation with officials of Turkey, Syria, Lebanon and Greece knocked off thirty-four drug traffickers, 1,038 pounds of opium, forty-six pounds of morphine base, fifty-three pounds of heroin, nine pounds of hashish and a well-equipped laboratory for the conversion of opium into heroin.

That Middle East campaign was a classic in international co-operation, and Narcotics Bureau men like to savor it because there are times when things can go wrong. Often, countries just don't have the diplomatic channels necessary to work together, as is illustrated by an incident in April 1955.

Siragusa had tipped off the Lebanese and Egyptian police to a hashish shipment scheduled to be smuggled from Lebanon into Egypt aboard a Lebanese vessel. During the voyage, the vessel encountered a terrific storm and had to make for Israeli waters. Israel customs agents boarded the vessel and arrested the captain when they discovered 825 pounds of hashish aboard. Obviously it was now Lebanon's move—an investigation of the charter of the ship was indicated. But since the Lebanese were not on speaking terms with the Israelis, nothing was done about it, and the ship was freed to resume its illicit trade.

The snafus, though, are becoming more and more infrequent. International co-operation, fostered by Siragusa's personable persistence and Commissioner Anslinger's devotion to daily negotiations with officials abroad, is making life miserable for traffickers whether they do business in Aleppo or Albany. And the key is the free and mutually trustful exchange of information.

Thus there came a day in January 1955 when Narcotics Bureau agents in Detroit learned that one Hussein Hider was getting regular shipments of heroin from Beirut. Authorities in Beirut were advised, and meanwhile an agent went undercover and struck up an acquaintance with Hider by posing as a dope pusher. Hider was willing to sell, but he had a better plan. He suggested that the agent go into partnership with him. Hider said he was dissatisfied with the man who was bringing in the dope from Lebanon, and he hired the agent as his courier.

Beirut is a long way from Detroit, but any trip is worth while when the result can be the cutting off of a source of supply. So the agent flew to Beirut and, after the usual negotiations through contacts, got himself an introduction to Hider's supplier, one Mounib Goureyeb. After buying a kilogram of morphine base, the agent tipped the Lebanese police and they seized Goureyeb's secret processing laboratory and put the pinch on Goureyeb. The same day, Hider was arrested in Detroit.

A tip from Lebanese police to Narcotics Bureau headquarters in Washington in January 1957 had even wider ramifications. Beirut authorities had seized a cache of heroin and had persuaded somebody to talk. The information they received led Narcotics agents to Detroit, where they hauled in Fauzi El Masri, a courier for the Beirut ring. Two days later, on the same information, French police grabbed another member of the ring in Marseille. He turned out to be Ibrahim Mabrouk Khalil, a resident of Brooklyn, N. Y. Sure enough, agents found a supply of hashish in Khalil's apartment.

Much of the credit for these cracks in the wall of secrecy built up by the syndicates of international dope gangsters belongs to Charles Siragusa. On a monthly budget of only $4,000 he has set up a vast network of informants from Hamburg to Rome to Naples to the little villages in the Middle East. The information he receives from these undercover agents is checked and then filed and cross-filed in an imposing array of filing cabinets in his Rome office. United States and European intelligence agencies feed him vital tidbits; so do members of Uncle Sam's armed forces scattered over the continent. As he puts it, "Everybody helps; I'm just the guy who sorts out the stuff."

This is partially true, of course. But both the Treasury Department and the Italian government regard Charles Siragusa's contributions with considerably more esteem. He has been awarded Treasury's highest award, the Exceptional Civilian Service Medal, "for outstanding courage in the face of danger while performing assigned duties." And in 1956 he was made a knight of the Ordine al Merito, which is the Italian equivalent of the French Legion of Honor.

Charles Siragusa, son of Sicilian immigrants, occasionally must savor a kind of poetic justice in these awards. "My uncle would get a kick out of it," he says. That, of course, would be the uncle who was murdered by Mafia mobsters on New York's Lower East Side forty years ago for refusing to kick back part of his pay envelope.

Death Is Over There

A BABY NAMED LINDBERGH

DEAR MR. IREY:

I want you to know how much we appreciate all that you have done for us. It is not possible for me to thank you sufficiently for your own assistance and that of your department. I know of nothing which could have been done which was not and I fully realize the time and effort that you have spent. It has meant a great deal to us to be able to go to you for advice and I want to thank you again for the many ways you have helped. Time and again during the past months I have realized the value of Federal organization.

Sincerely,

CHARLES A. LINDBERGH

It is true that the arrest of Bruno Richard Hauptmann for the kidnaping of the baby son of Charles A. Lindbergh was a combined operation of the FBI and the New York and New Jersey police. But the fact is that it was the Department of the Treasury which in effect told police who the kidnaper was and where to find him.

The premise is simple, and compelling. Hauptmann was nabbed because he passed a ten-dollar bill at a gasoline filling station in the Bronx on September 12, 1934. The ten-dollar bill was part of the $50,000 ransom Colonel Lindbergh had paid in a vain attempt to recover his child, and it put the finger on Hauptmann because the Treasury Department, over Colonel Lindbergh's objections, had insisted on recording the serial number of every one of the 5,150 items of currency contained in the ransom package.

To this day, few Americans are aware of the part Treasury played in the solution of one of the most grisly crimes in American annals. It was a role assumed almost casually, because a hoodlum named Al Capone couldn't resist trying to get into the act.

Capone had just started serving an eleven-year sentence in the penitentiary for income-tax evasion in March 1932, when he heard about the kidnaping. He managed to contact Arthur Brisbane, the Hearst columnist, now dead, with an offer. Al said if Uncle Sam would restore his freedom he would restore the kidnaped child to its parents. Brisbane dutifully reported Al's offer to his readers, among them Colonel Lindbergh. It was the Intelligence Division of Internal Revenue which had put Capone in jail, so Lindbergh telephoned Secretary of the Treasury Ogden L. Mills and asked if Mills could be of any help.

Mills summoned Elmer Irey, chief of Treasury's law-enforcement agencies. "Go up there and see Lindbergh," he told Irey. "Tell him we'll do anything we can to help, but I don't have to tell you that we can't make any deals with Capone."

Irey arrived the next day in Hopewell, N. J., and took a cab out to the Lindbergh home, headquarters for the manhunt. The house was overflowing with police. Irey was greeted by Mrs. Lindbergh, who asked him if she could get him a sandwich; there was a determined calm in her manner, but her eyes were frightened. Irey couldn't have swallowed a crumb at that point.

Lindbergh greeted Irey warmly and introduced him to his "adviser," Henry Breckinridge, financier. "I've asked you to come up, Mr. Irey," said Lindbergh, "because I feel I should talk to somebody in an official capacity about this Capone offer. But I want you to know that I wouldn't ask for that man's release—even if it would save a life." Irey felt he should set things straight at once. "I hate to say this," he said, "but Capone doesn't know who has the child. He claims one of his gang, Bob Conroy, did the kidnaping, but we know that Conroy was two hundred miles away at the time. We'll find Conroy and talk to him, but we know he didn't do it."

Lindbergh nodded thoughtfully. "I'll be guided by your advice, Mr. Irey."

He showed Irey the kidnap note that had been left on the window sill of the baby's room on the night of March 1, 1932. It asked for $50,000 in twenties, tens and fives, and the writing was stilted: "We warn you from making anything public or for notify the police." Two more letters assured Lindbergh the baby was well but complained about the publicity the case was getting and increased the ransom to $70,000. Lindbergh wondered whether he should accept the proffered services of a seventy-two-year-old eccentric Bronx teacher named Dr. John F. Condon, who had put an advertisement in the Bronx *Home News* offering to serve as go-between and adding $1,000 of his own money to the ransom.

Lindbergh had checked on Condon and found him to be a man of honesty, despite his eccentric ways. He was a retired New York school-teacher who occasionally substituted in the parochial schools. Friends and educators described him as a brilliant pedagogue but inclined to be cantankerous; he was a man who loved publicity and delighted in parading his rather picturesque personality. For instance, he liked to roam the tree-lined streets in the Bronx roaring the soliloquy from *Hamlet*.

"I'd appreciate it if you folks could stay," Lindbergh told Irey. "I'm at a complete loss and your advice would be helpful."

Irey said his outfit would be delighted to do whatever it could, but that at this point it seemed best to await developments. He told Lindbergh to phone him whenever there was something Treasury could do.

The phone call came a few days later, prompted by a hopeful development. Dr. Condon, known to his neighbors as "Jafsie," received a letter from a person purporting to be the kidnaper, accepting his offer to serve as go-between. Jafsie hurried down to Hopewell and put the matter up to Lindbergh. Lindbergh decided to go along with him, and told Jafsie to insert an ad—"Money is ready"—in the New York *American*. Jafsie heard from the kidnaper again on the evening of March 12, when a cab driver delivered a note to the Condon home. It told Jafsie to go to an "empty frank *further* stand" near the "last station" on the Jerome Avenue subway line; he would find a note at the stand telling him where to go next.

Jafsie drove to the frankfurter stand with Al Reich, an ex-prize fighter who was a sometime Jafsie bodyguard. There they found a note instructing them to follow a fence enclosing Woodlawn Cemetery to the corner of 233rd Street and Jerome Avenue. As Jafsie reached the corner, a voice hailed him from the cemetery: "Hey, Doctor!" The voice identified itself as a man named "John," and he and Jafsie started a conversation, with the fence between them. When a cemetery guard approached, "John" jumped over the fence and ran across the street. Jafsie followed him, and they resumed their conversation on a bench in Van Cortlandt Park.

"John" said there were five persons in the kidnaping gang. He said the baby was on a "boad," or boat, far from New York, and explained to Jafsie just how he wanted the ransom money made up.

The next day Lindbergh phoned Irey in Washington. "I'd like you to come back on the case," he said. "I'm sure your advice would come in handy." Irey went up to Hopewell with Special Agent Frank Wilson and a noted Intelligence undercover man named Pat O'Rourke, who had lived with the Capone gang for months during the investigation of the gangland czar. Another agent, Arthur P. Madden, came on from Chicago.

O'Rourke's first assignment was to investigate a gang of spiritualists who were trying to horn in on the case. Ordinarily, they would have been dismissed as nuts, but a couple of them named Peter Baritella and "Mary Magdalene" had made noises to Henry Breckinridge that made them worth a check. First, they told him that "the spirits" had told them the note was left on the window sill of the nursery. This was true, but it was supposed to be a deep secret. Then they told Breckinridge he had gotten a kidnap note at his office that morning. He checked and found the note.

Irey assigned O'Rourke to join the spiritualists' church and find out who these "spirits" were who seemed to know so much about the kidnaping. O'Rourke joined in the mumbo-jumbo for three weeks but found nothing.

Meanwhile, the kidnaper wrote Lindbergh that he should insert an advertisement in the New York *American* reading: "Money is ready." The kidnaper then would contact Jafsie to arrange for the pay-off. Refusing all offers of financial help from his relatives and friends, the Lone Eagle sold $350,000 worth of stocks for $70,000 and deposited the money in a Bronx bank. Jafsie got his note from the kidnaper. It informed Jafsie that the child was well and was eating heartily. He was told to insert an ad in the *American:* "I accept, mony is redy."

The time had come when the Treasury, represented by Elmer Irey, would have to speak bluntly to Colonel Lindbergh lest the kidnaper escape punishment.

The Lindberghs had gone on the radio and promised the kidnaper immunity if the little boy was returned. They told him none of the bills would be marked. "All we want is our son," Mrs. Lindbergh pleaded.

Elmer Irey would not go along with this. He told Lindbergh a list should be made of all the bills in the ransom package and a record kept of all the serial numbers. Lindbergh was stubborn. "I can't break my promise," he said. "I've told the man the bills would not be marked."

Irey hated to deliver an ultimatum to a man in Lindbergh's position, but it had to be done. He told the Lone Eagle that unless he complied and permitted the Treasury to record the serial numbers the department would have to withdraw from the case. To go along with Lindbergh, he said, would be to compound a felony. Lindbergh said he'd think it over.

The next day, Lindbergh capitulated. Agent Madden got a phone call from one of Lindbergh's advisers, William Galvin, telling him to go to the office of J. P. Morgan and Company and oversee the drawing up of a new set of ransom money. At the Morgan office, Madden and Agent Wilson insisted that as much of the ransom money as possible be in gold certificates, which were easily recognizable. Twenty thousand dollars of it subsequently was counted out in fifty-dollar gold certificates. The bills were bound with a special kind of string and wrapped in a special kind of paper and they were placed in a box made of twelve different kinds of wood. Samples of the string, paper and of each kind of wood were locked up at the bank. It took fourteen clerks eight hours to compile a list of the 5,150 items of currency; there were no two numbers in sequence. One hundred thousand copies of the serial numbers of the bills were secretly printed.

On April 1, a month after the kidnaping, Jafsie Condon received the important note from the kidnaper. It said the money should be ready by the next evening, a Saturday. Condon was to place an ad in the Saturday-morning *American* reading, "Yes, everything O.K." The ad was placed. At seven o'clock Saturday night a boy brought Jafsie another note:

DEAR SIR:
Take a car and follow Tremont Avenue to the east until you reach the number 3225 East Tremont Ave.
It is a nursery.
Bergen.
Greenhauses florist.
There is a table standing outside right on the door you find a letter undernead the table covert with stone, read and follow instruction. Don't speak to anyone on the way. If there is a radio alarm for police car, we warn you we have the same equipment. Have the money in one bundle.
We give you ¾ of a houer to reach the place.

Lindbergh went along with Condon to 3225 East Tremont Avenue— Bergen's Florist Shop. Under the table, held down by a stone, was a note reading:

Cross the street and walk to the next corner and follow Whittemore Ave. to the soud. Take the money with you. Come alone and walk I will meet you.

Both notes seemed to confirm the analysis of Dr. Wilmer Souder, handwriting expert with the Bureau of Standards, who had stated that the kidnaper was a German, illiterate but methodical.

Jafsie crossed the street, leaving Lindbergh in the car with the money. In St. Raymond's Cemetery, he met the same "John" and talked briefly with him. Then he returned to the car, got the package of money, and handed it to "John" over a hedge. "John" gave Jafsie a note:

The boy is on boad Nelly it is a small boad 28 feet long, two persons on board. They are innocense. You will find the boad between Horseneck Beach and Gay Head near Elizabeth Island.

Lindbergh and Condon joined police and Treasury officials at the home of Mrs. Dwight Morrow, Mrs. Lindbergh's mother, on East Seventy-second Street. And here Jafsie exploded a bombshell.

"I talked him out of twenty thousand dollars," he boasted. Irey, Madden and Wilson were horrified. "Sure," said Jafsie. "Here's the twenty thousand." And he showed the gathering four hundred fifty-dollar gold certificates—the certificates everybody had hoped would lead police to the kidnaper. Now the highest gold certificates in the possession of the kidnaper were twenty-dollar notes, which were much harder to trace because they were so much more common. Red-necked, Irey glared at Jafsie. "I could shoot your head off," he told him.

There was nothing left now but tragedy. The Coast Guard sent ships into the Long Island Sound area mentioned in the kidnaper's note. At dawn, Lindbergh took off from a Bridgeport, Connecticut, airport in a rented plane to go seeking the *Nelly*. With him were Breckinridge, Jafsie and Elmer Irey. Stowed in one corner of the cabin were clothing for the baby and a bottle of milk.

They searched the sound for hours, while Jafsie filled the air with roaring excerpts from the Song of Solomon. Lindbergh dove at every boat, flying alongside each so he could see the name. No *Nelly* was found. At dusk on Sunday, April 3, 1932, Lindbergh landed the plane at a Long Island club airport and phoned the sad news to his wife. Nobody was saying what everybody knew—that the child was dead.

Everything else was forgotten now but the apprehension of the kidnaper. Serial numbers of the ransom notes were released to banks all over the country. The banks were pledged to secrecy, but the day after the numbers were released, a clerk sold the list to a Newark newspaper for five dollars, and within twenty-four hours practically every newspaper in the country had printed it. Two days after the fruitless search of Long Island Sound, a ransom bill was passed in a Manhattan bank, but nobody could remember who did the passing.

People kept harassing Lindbergh, telling him they had information about the kidnaping. One of these was a Norfolk, Virginia, shipbuilder named John Curtis. Lindbergh was running down a tip from Curtis on May 11, 1932, when he got the message he had been fearing. The body of his dead son had been found in a woodsy glen only five miles from the Lindberghs' Hopewell home.

Agent Frank Wilson turned his attention to Violet Sharpe, a maid in the Lindbergh home. She had said that she was having a few beers with a man named "Earnie" on the night the baby was kidnaped. But "Earnie" furnished proof that on that night he and his wife and some friends were elsewhere. In the summer of 1932, Wilson was waiting downstairs in the Lindbergh home to question Violet about her story. While he waited, Violet committed suicide. Yet, there never was any evidence that Violet had had any part in the kidnaping.

Bob Conroy, the hoodlum Capone had accused of the kidnaping, made his violent exit, too. In August 1932, he and a girl friend were found dead in a New York apartment, apparently suicides. In the room was a printing press and plates for turning out counterfeit currency.

Ransom notes continued to appear, mostly in Manhattan; two were passed in a Childs' Restaurant. Wilson tried to get W. O. Woods, Treasurer of the United States, secretly to call in and retire certain issues of notes which would include the ransom money. But after conferring with other Treasury officials, Woods had to refuse on the ground that if such an action leaked out it might start a financial panic. The United States Government's financial situation in that summer of 1932 was slightly precarious.

But the following April, Wilson got what he wanted. In line with his reorganization of the nation's financial structure, President Franklin D. Roosevelt called in all gold certificates as of May 1, 1933. Frank Wilson harangued the banks anew; now was the time to be especially alert.

Nevertheless, Hauptmann slipped through this financial dragnet. In the few days before May 1, he exchanged $15,000 in gold certificates, apparently for stock purchases. Then, on May 1, a New York bank changed $2,980 in gold certificates, and the clerk dutifully made out an exchange slip with the name of the man who had brought them in. The slip listed him as J. J. Faulkner, 547 West 149th Street, Manhattan; the teller didn't remember the transaction so he could offer no description of "Faulkner."

A check showed no J. J. Faulkner living at the 149th Street address, but somebody remembered that an automobile stolen from Lakehurst, New Jersey, a few days before the kidnaping had been recovered across from 547 West 149th. It was learned, too, that a Jane Faulkner had lived at 547 West 149th Street before 1920. Marriage records showed she had married Carl O. Giessler, a naturalized German, in 1920. Giessler turned out to be a partner in a big New York florist shop, but he easily proved he had had nothing to do with the bank transaction. Hauptmann apparently had picked the name Faulkner at random.

Thirty months had passed since the kidnaping when, on September 12, 1934, a man stopped at a gasoline filling station at Lexington Avenue and 127th Street in Harlem. He paid the attendant for his gas with a ten-dollar bill. The attendant was under orders to take the license-plate number of all drivers paying in notes of ten dollars or more in case they should turn out to be counterfeit; he jotted the number on the bill. A bank teller recognized the bill as part of the ransom money.

That was the beginning of the end for Bruno Richard Hauptmann. Police first determined that the license plate had been issued to Hauptmann, then they compared the handwriting on the ransom notes to that on Hauptmann's auto registration form. They matched beautifully.

In Chicago, Treasury Agent Arthur Madden felt vindicated. In the first few months after the kidnaping, he had tried to get the authorities to check the ransom note handwriting with auto license applications in the Bronx, arguing that the kidnaper had been seen twice in the Bronx, that he had mailed many of his ransom notes from there, and that he had passed money there. Somehow nobody had thought it worth while at the time.

Hauptmann's home at 1279 East 222nd Street, the Bronx, was put under twenty-four-hour surveillance. He was followed everywhere he went on the theory he might lead police to accomplices. Investigators checked his bank account and his stock-market dealings. It was found that he had had a criminal record in Germany. Seven days after his identity was discovered he was arrested. It was September 19, 1934.

Police ransacked the Hauptmann home and garage. In the garage was found a wooden box containing $14,600 in currency—ransom currency. The box was the same one Treasury agents had built back in 1932 to hold the ransom money. Hauptmann's carefully kept records of his financial transactions were handed over to Treasury Agent William E. Frank and he came up with more damning evidence. In black and white, Frank proved that Hauptmann had spent or owned $49,950.44 more than he had ever earned since coming to the United States. The same figures showed that since the ransom was paid Hauptmann hadn't put in a day's work and yet he had handled $49,986, including the $14,600 found in the box.

Other evidence helped put the finger on Hauptmann at his trial. Arthur Kohler, a wood technician from the Bureau of Forestry, testified that part of the wood used to make the kidnap ladder had come from a piece of wood found in Hauptmann's attic. Nails in the ladder were proved to be identical with nails found in a keg in Hauptmann's home. Plane marks on the kidnap ladder were identical with marks made by a plane owned by Hauptmann. And the only eyewitness, an eighty-seven-year-old veteran of the Franco-Prussian War of 1870, testified he had seen Hauptmann drive through Hopewell on the day the baby was kidnaped.

Sometimes, during the ordered chaos which was the Hauptmann trial, it seemed as if much of this evidence was being obscured. But eventually Hauptmann was convicted and subsequently died in the electric chair for the kidnap-murder of a hero's baby. He was the first kidnaper ever to be caught as a result of the recovery of ransom money he spent.

Charles A. Lindbergh put it quite simply in a verbal thank-you note to Elmer Irey during the trial: "If it had not been for your service being in the case Hauptmann would not now be on trial, and your organization deserves *full* credit for his apprehension."

Assignment: The President

THEY COME TO KILL

OSCAR COLLAZO, the slender, olive-skinned Puerto Rican who tried to kill Harry S. Truman on November 1, 1950, summed it up for all the mental invalids who have gone gunning for occupants of the White House.

"I didn't come here to kill Mister Truman, I came to kill the President of the United States," Collazo told Secret Service Agent Joseph J. Ellis during a conversation in a Washington jail cell in early 1951.

The six men who have killed, or tried to kill, a President of the United States undoubtedly would have signed their names to the sentiment expressed by Oscar Collazo. History has shown that it is the officeholder, not the man, who incites the assassin. Former Presidents always have been able to walk the streets safely, their existence ignored by the fanatic once they walk out of the White House for the last time.

But the office has been a dangerous one for more than 120 years, because in the minds of the assassins it represents the power which wreaks fancied wrongs. Richard Lawrence tried to murder Andrew Jackson because he felt Jackson was usurping royal prerogatives Lawrence claimed as his own; John Wilkes Booth, who killed Lincoln, was determined to avenge the South's defeat in the Civil War; Charles J. Guiteau, assassin of Garfield, sought to unite the Republican party; Leon Czolgosz saw his murder of McKinley and Giuseppe Zangara his attempt to slay Franklin D. Roosevelt as blows struck against authority. And Oscar Collazo and Griselio Torresola were fired by a fanatical zeal on behalf of Puerto Rican nationalism.

To be sure, personal hatred was a motivation in the cases of Lawrence, Booth and Guiteau. But their hatred sprang from the political policies of their targets. They would have had no occasion to hate the man if the man had not been President.

There was considerable public indignation when Richard Lawrence, a house painter who called himself King Richard III, fired two shots at Jackson during a funeral procession at the Capitol on January 30, 1835. Neither bullet struck Jackson, but the country was shocked that the attempt had been made—the first such attempt in the young nation's history —and there was some agitation to assign Army guards to the President. Nothing came of it, however, and when Booth went to Ford's Theater on a Good Friday thirty years later he found no one barring his entry into the Presidential box; in fact, a policeman guarding an outer door had left his post.

Yet, within the next thirty-six years, two more Presidents would be assassinated before the government would take the step necessary to provide the Chief Executive with a formalized system of protection. James A. Garfield was shot in the back by the Republican dissenter, Guiteau, in the Baltimore and Potomac Depot in Washington on July 2, 1881. And on September 6, 1901, the anarchist Czolgosz fired two fatal bullets into William McKinley's chest and abdomen at a public reception in Buffalo.

That did it, finally. McKinley's death marked the third time in thirty-seven years that a President of the United States had been murdered; the average was one assassination every twelve years. Yet, during the 112 years between the signing of our Constitution and the killing of President McKinley, not one ruler of England, Germany or Spain was assassinated; France, Italy and Austria each had a single royal victim, and Russia had two. The reason was that these royal targets were given personal protection at all times, whereas the President moved about freely without escort or bodyguard.

Congress acknowledged these grisly statistics. Shortly after Theodore

Roosevelt succeeded McKinley, it provided legislation assigning to the Secret Service of the Treasury Department the sole responsibility for the constant protection of the President.

Since that day in 1901, no President has been assassinated. There have been attempts on the lives of two White House occupants, Franklin D. Roosevelt and Harry S. Truman, but neither was scratched. Ironically, the man who was President when the SS took over its Presidential role was wounded by a would-be assassin after he had left the White House and was campaigning to re-enter it after a four-year interval.

This, of course, was Theodore Roosevelt, who had stepped down in 1908 after serving almost two full terms and then, in 1912, had decided to run as the candidate of the Bull Moose party against his hand-picked successor, William Howard Taft. On October 14, 1912, while sitting in an open car in Milwaukee, Teddy was wounded in the chest by a bullet fired by a New York saloonkeeper named John F. Schrank. At this time, Teddy was not under SS protection, since the Treasury has never guarded Presidential candidates but only Presidents and Presidents-elect.

Yet the first Roosevelt had a narrow escape while still in the White House, and after the Secret Service had taken over. It was his habit to receive visitors, by appointment, between nine and ten o'clock every evening in his study, and one night a man drove up to the front door of the White House and informed the usher that the President was expecting him. He was wearing white tie and tails and looked like the kind of man the President would be expecting.

He gave the usher his name and a visiting card, and the usher took his cloak and hat and asked him to wait in the Red Room. Then the usher went to Roosevelt's study and notified the President that he had a visitor waiting.

"I don't know the man," Roosevelt snapped. Then, as the usher started to leave, "Wait a minute. I'll go downstairs and see him. I seem to remember asking someone with a name like that to call tonight."

Downstairs, the President strode into the Red Room and closed the door after him. About three minutes later the Chief Usher's buzzer sounded. The usher practically ran to the Red Room to find Roosevelt in the doorway, his face grim but his manner calm.

"Take this crank out of here," Teddy told the usher quietly.

At the gate, SS men belatedly frisked the caller. He had a revolver in one back pocket.

Nearly thirty years elapsed before violence brushed against another President, and then it came close to ending the Presidential career, before it had officially started, of one of the most controversial figures in

American history. The name here was Roosevelt, too, but a man from a different branch of the family and a President whose policies even the progressive Teddy might have found startling.

It was February 15, 1933, and a warm breeze gentled the Miami evening. More than 10,000 persons had gathered in Bayfront Park to hear a speech by Franklin Delano Roosevelt, who in the previous November had won an overwhelming victory over President Herbert Hoover. FDR had been on a fishing trip aboard the yacht *Nourmahal* as a guest of the elegant Vincent Astor, and when the yacht had docked at the Miami pier, local Democrats had asked the President-elect to say a few words to the citizenry in near-by Bayfront Park.

Living in Miami at the time was a thirty-three-year-old immigrant from Italy named Giuseppe Zangara who was obsessed with a hatred of authority, particularly as personified by heads of state. Zangara had been forced to go to work at the age of six, and all his adult life he blamed his lack of education on constituted authority—beginning with the King of Italy. For eight years after his arrival in this country in 1923, Zangara had worked in New Jersey as a bricklayer, but in 1931 he had quit his job and migrated to Miami, where he hoped the sunshine would have a beneficial effect on his chronic indigestion.

Brooding on his troubles, real and imagined, Zangara made up his mind to go to Washington and assassinate President Hoover. It was not so much that he blamed Hoover for the depression; he merely felt the world would be better if there were fewer kings and presidents. But while he was waiting for spring to arrive in Washington, he read in a Miami paper that President-elect Roosevelt was coming to the city to make a speech.

To a man like Zangara, there was little difference between a President and a President-elect; he was certain that once Roosevelt got in he would be just as bad as any other head of state. For this reason and for the obvious reason of convenience, he decided to kill FDR. For eight dollars he bought a thirty-two-caliber revolver at a pawnshop, and on the night of February 15 he went out to Bayfront Park to use it on his fancied enemy.

When Zangara got there, the park already was jammed with people, although FDR would not be showing up for another hour and a half. The closest he could get to the spot where Roosevelt would speak from his automobile was a standing-room spot in an aisle about fifteen feet to the rear of the front row.

Roosevelt's car drove into the amphitheater at about nine-thirty o'clock. FDR was sitting in the rear seat and with him were Mayor R. B.

Gautier of Miami and George E. Hussey, chairman of the Reception Committee. Behind Roosevelt's car was a touring car carrying Secret Service agents. Zangara couldn't shoot his prey as the procession moved into the park because everybody was standing up and he was too short even to see over the heads of those in front of him.

At a spot in front of the stage, about twenty-five feet from where Zangara was standing, FDR's car stopped and the President-elect hoisted himself up to the top of the rear seat to deliver his off-the-cuff speech. First, however, he waved to a man sitting with the big wheels on the stage and shouted an invitation. "Come on down," FDR yelled to Mayor Anton J. Cermak of Chicago. Cermak smiled and held up a finger signifying he would be down to greet Roosevelt when the latter had finished his speech.

Roosevelt's speech consisted of only 162 words and contained nothing more significant than the news that he had caught a lot of fish. When he finished, several newsreel men climbed on the running board of his car and pleaded with him to repeat his talk for their benefit. FDR refused to do so; instead he slid down onto the seat again. Then he turned to greet Mayor Cermak, who had come down from the stage. The two shook hands and chatted for a few moments, and Mayor Cermak moved away toward the rear of the car.

Just then somebody handed Roosevelt one of those long telegrams signed with hundreds of names, and as FDR reached for it Zangara swung into action. Somebody had vacated a seat near by. Zangara jumped aboard and, standing on the wobbly perch, started pressing the trigger of his revolver.

Five bullets spewed from the gun. One smashed into the right lung of Mayor Cermak and he slumped to the ground. Another struck a Miami woman in the stomach and she fell, too, seriously wounded. Three other persons, including a New York detective on vacation, were struck in the head but were not seriously hurt.

Roosevelt wrote a story about the shooting that was carried in various newspapers around the country. He reported that immediately after Zangara fired his last shot, the Secret Service agents ordered his chauffeur to drive out of the park.

"I called to the chauffeur to stop," wrote Roosevelt. "He did, about fifteen feet from where we started. The Secret Service men shouted to him to get out of the crowd, and he started the car forward again. I stopped him a second time, this time at the corner of the bandstand, about thirty feet farther on.

"I saw Mayor Cermak being carried. I motioned to have him put in the back of the car. He was alive, but I didn't think he was going to last. I put my left arm around him and my hand on his pulse, but I couldn't find any pulse. He slumped forward. . . .

"After we had gone another block, Mayor Cermak straightened up and I got his pulse. It was surprising. For three blocks I believed his heart had stopped. I held him all the way to the hospital, and his pulse constantly improved. . . ."

Meanwhile, police and SS men had seized Zangara and taken away his revolver. Then they threw him on the trunk rack of one of the cars in the Presidential procession and three policemen sat on him while the car bore him to jail. Cermak died on March 6, three weeks after the shooting. Zangara died in the electric chair at the State Prison in Raiford, Florida, on March 20, only thirty-three days after his shooting spree.

Secret Service agents still suffer a little shiver of fright when they recall the Zangara attempt. Spontaneously conceived and haphazardly executed as it was, it nevertheless nearly succeeded. A better shot than the nervous Zangara undoubtedly would have managed at least to wound Roosevelt. In contrast, Oscar Collazo and Griselio Torresola had virtually no chance of assassinating Harry S. Truman.

It is true that when they went after Truman, on that beautiful Indian-summer day in November 1950, the Man from Independence was living in Blair House, diagonally across Pennsylvania Avenue from the White House, which was undergoing extensive repairs. Unlike the White House, which is surrounded by a high iron picket fence, Blair House abuts a public sidewalk, with only a flight of ten steps between its front door and the walk. Theoretically, a man can stand in the middle of Pennsylvania Avenue and send bullets whistling into Blair House's windows.

But there was a guard booth at each end of the house, on the sidewalk level. In each booth the assassins could expect to find at least one White House Police guard who had been required at semiannual examinations to maintain his rating as a marksman. Additionally, at least two and probably three or four Secret Service agents ordinarily would be lurking inside the house. Making a reconnaissance of the neighborhood the morning of the shooting, Collazo and Torresola noticed the manned guard booths; it must have occurred to them also that a President would have inside protection as well.

Collazo and Torresola had arrived in Washington from New York the night before the shooting and had taken two separate $3.50 rooms at a hotel near Union Station. Like Collazo, Torresola was a zealot of the Puerto Rican Nationalist party, but unlike Collazo, who was a model husband and father, Torresola was known as a ladies' man. He was also an expert marksman, whereas Collazo had never fired anything but a .22 rifle, when he was a youth in Puerto Rico.

After casing Blair House from a cab on the morning of November 1, Collazo and Torresola had lunch and then returned to their hotel. There Torresola spent nearly an hour showing Collazo how to fire the German P-38 revolver he had bought for him in New York. Torresola had a German Luger. They left the hotel about two o'clock, their guns loaded and their pockets stuffed with cartridge clips, and took a cab to the Treasury Building on Pennsylvania Avenue, a block from Blair House.

The pair was determined to be professional about it. First they walked by Blair House for another look; by that time President Truman had had lunch and was napping in a second-floor front bedroom, but the conspirators had no way of knowing that. Back in front of the Treasury Building, Collazo and Torresola separated. Collazo walked along the north side of Pennsylvania toward Blair House, while Torresola took the south side and strode past the White House and the old State Department Building, now known as the Executive Offices Building. As Collazo approached the guard booth on the east end of Blair House, Torresola crossed the avenue and started toward the booth on the west end of the building.

Collazo stopped in front of the Blair House steps. Standing on the first step, with his back to Collazo, was a White House policeman, Donald T. Birdzell. Collazo pulled out his gun, aimed it at Birdzell and squeezed the trigger. But the gun misfired—the only sound was a metallic click. Birdzell wheeled and saw Collazo holding the gun in one hand and pounding it with another. As he did so, the gun fired and a bullet buried itself in Birdzell's right leg.

Birdzell scampered into the street as bullets sang about him. He drew his own gun and started firing back. Meanwhile, from the east booth, Collazo came under fire from two marksmen, White House Policeman Joseph O. Davidson and Secret Service Agent Floyd M. Boring. But the steps are flanked by iron picket railings, and Boring's and Davidson's shots kept spattering against the pickets. As Collazo crouched on the second step, reloading, one bullet nicked his nose and another scratched his ear.

Torresola was busy, too. Walking up to the west guard booth, he stood in the doorway and pumped three shots into Private Leslie Coffelt of the White House Police. When Coffelt fell, Torresola turned and fired three times at another White House policeman, Joseph H. Downs, standing near a basement door, and again every bullet hit its target. Leaping a hedge, Torresola came to Collazo's aid. It was too late. With several guns barking at him, Collazo collapsed with a bullet in his chest and lay still on the sidewalk.

Torresola turned his gun on Birdzell, out in the street, and sent a bullet into the policeman's left knee. Then he crouched down and began reloading his gun. He never finished the job. Coffelt, although bleeding from mortal wounds, managed to take one last aim and pulled the trigger. Torresola seemed to shudder, then he dropped to the sidewalk, a fatal bullet in his brain.

Inside Blair House, Secret Service Agent Stewart Stout had grabbed a Thompson submachine gun from a cabinet and squatted down beside it in the hall to cover the elevator and stairs leading to the Truman bedroom. Truman, awakened by the shots, had reacted normally. He had rushed to the window just after Collazo fell but quickly retreated when a guard yelled to him, "Get back! Get back!"

Meanwhile, the affray was getting spot coverage by a carload of White House photographers, including Charley Corte of United Press Pictures, Harvey Georges of the Associated Press, Al Muto of International Photos, Bruce Hoertel, then with *The New York Times* but now a CBS newsreel cameraman, and Matt Zimmerman of Time-Life. The photographers had left the West Wing entrance on West Executive Avenue seconds before the shooting and had started to drive to Arlington Cemetery where Truman was to speak at two-thirty at the unveiling of a statue to Field Marshall Sir John Dill, British member of the World War II Combined Chiefs of Staff.

The cameramen's car had just stopped for a red light at the intersection of West Executive Avenue and Pennsylvania Avenue when Collazo opened fire on Birdzell. Never before were so many pictures taken in so short a time.

But they were pictures that told the story of a tragedy. Policeman Coffelt died in the hospital that afternoon, during an operation. Downs and Birdzell survived and so, amazingly, did Collazo. The bullet which struck him in the chest had been turned aside by the breastbone and after passing through his right armpit had buried itself in his right arm.

Collazo went on trial on February 27, 1951, in the United States District Court in Washington. He pleaded not guilty and insisted that he had come to Washington merely to "make a demonstration" and not to kill anybody. He refused to consider a suggestion by his counsel that he plead insanity. "This is not a farce," Collazo said quietly.

He was convicted on four counts involving the murder of Coffelt and assaults on the President, Birdzell and Downs. Judge T. Alan Goldsborough sentenced him to die in the electric chair for the Coffelt murder and for the assault on President Truman and, rather anticlimactically, sentenced him to serve from five to fifteen years on each of the other two counts. Six months later Truman commuted the sentence to life imprisonment.

The Insolent Chariots

BY JOHN KEATS

ILLUSTRATED BY ROBERT OSBORN

EDITOR'S NOTE

Do you ever wonder why today's cars look the way they do, and why they cost so much? Is the public at the mercy of Detroit? Or vice versa? Are the new highways drawing the nation together—or are they merely homogenizing it? What goes on behind the façade at your friendly dealer's, and when you buy a car do you know how to penetrate the Byzantine snarl of auto "financing"?

Wielding a rapier tipped with wit, edged with anger and forged with facts, John Keats slashes aside myth and chrome to reveal some amazing stories of the automobile industry.

Author Keats turned from his reporter's job on the Washington *Daily News* to full-time, free-lance writing a few years ago. He has written many magazine articles and two books, *The Crack in the Picture Window* and *Schools Without Scholars*. He lives with his wife and three children in Philadelphia. He drives, but is not attached to, a large station wagon.

Through his drawings in numerous books and magazines, Robert Osborn, whose pictures appear in this volume, has become one of our outstanding social critics. He and John Keats make natural fellow conspirators.

AUTHOR'S NOTE

The title of this book was suggested by a speech by Mr. Lewis Mumford to the Thirteenth International Congress of Local Authorities, at The Hague, on 12 June, 1957.

"SOUNDS LIKE 'DEAD CELL'"

—The Game

WHEN IN THE COURSE of human events it seemed necessary to the Ford Motor Company to bring forth on this continent a brand-new motor car to be called the Edsel, care was taken that the American populace was not uninformed of the company's intentions. Ford's advertising campaign hewed to the same dispassionate standards that have distinguished it since the day it proclaimed the first Fordmobile to be "Boss of the Road. The latest and best. It is positively the most perfect machine on the market, having overcome all drawbacks such as smell, noise, jolt, etc., common to all other makes of Auto Carriages."

The time—the fall of 1957—could not have been more propitious for the introduction of a basically new automobile, because 1957 was the end of an era. Detroit seems not to have noticed it, but the nation in that year was beginning to look for new values of every kind, having begun to emerge from a decade of noisy, glittering drift that was itself a reaction to the prior years of depression and war. During the years 1947–57, the nation engaged in a shapeless orgy. Wages were high, employment was at record levels, nobody wished to think of yesterday, and everyone seemed ready to believe that every tomorrow would be bigger and better and twice as yummy. The pursuit of happiness seemed to be the nation's single-minded intent, and although there were plenty of people who understood that every action contains its own reaction, it was hopefully suggested by practically all hands that the reaction, if any, would take place at some vague, future time, if at all. Ironically enough, it was a Russian rocket that brought most of the nation back to earth.

A dissection of the decade is not the proper concern of this volume, however. It is enough for our purposes to note that, in the fall of 1957, prior to the Reds' rocket glare, more and more people were leaving the carnival to return to the mainstream of civilization. They were beginning to listen to serious men who were questioning the shape of our cities, the value of conformity, the prevailing know-nothing philosophy of the public schools, the nation's true role in world affairs and—among a thousand other things—the meaning of our automobiles. There was already a cloud no bigger than a Volkswagen on Detroit's horizon.

It was into this climate, so ripe for change, that the Ford company introduced its Edsel. Not only was the time exactly right for something really new, but there was also no company in a better position to bring new wares to the market place. Sales of foreign cars were proceeding briskly; people were waiting as long as nine months for Volkswagen deliveries. Sales of American makes were slipping; already Detroit was cutting production. Nevertheless, General Motors, Ford and Chrysler still owned 95% of the American market, but of these companies, only Ford could gamble the $250,000,000 necessary to bring out a new car. General Motors saw no reason to change a formula that had won it nearly 50% of the market. Chrysler was committed to its then-current line of dreamboats. American Motors was trying to worm its way to the top of the remaining 5% of the market with an automobile that was a compromise between the small foreign car and the smallest of the Detroit dreamboats.* Studebaker-Packard was in dire straits. Only Ford, under eager young administration, had the money, the facilities and the desire to bring out a really new American automobile, the latest and the best, having none of the disadvantages that so distinguished all other makes.

If Ford had actually done so, its preliminary ten-million-dollars' worth of Edsel advertising would not have been necessary. Such was that public mood in the fall of 1957 that, if Ford had unveiled the first Edsel in dead silence on a lonely county crossroads at midnight, every literate child in the land would have been aware of the event ten minutes later. If, that is, the Edsel had in fact been a really new automobile. As this is written, nearly a year after the Edsel's arrival, the Edsel's qualified failure seems to be reasonably well established from a sales viewpoint. We might wonder why. Wondering, we might find some additional light to shed on that murkiest of all questions, to which there seems to be no one good answer, Does the public, or does Detroit, make taste?

There seem to be two reasons why Ford missed the boat. First, it is apparently impossible today to bring out a new car overnight, and second, nobody at the Ford plant cared about Tom Wretch. Now, the only reason why Detroit can't bring out a new automobile tomorrow is because none

---

* Later, in the early months of 1958, it succeeded.

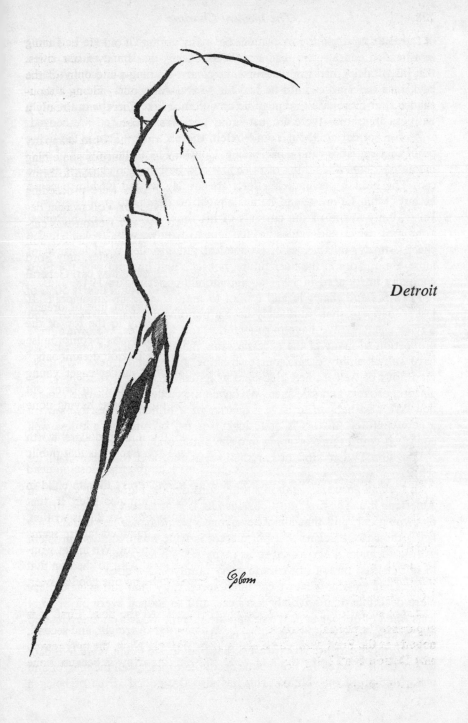

Detroit

of Detroit's three giant corporations have any vestige of old Henry Ford's iron-headed courage, or obstinacy. When Henry was finally made to see that his Model T had run its course, he closed his plants and didn't come back into the market until he had his Model A to offer. Henry took a chance, but there don't seem to be any chance-takers in the automobile business any more—there are just wrong guessers whose bets are hedged.

As for not caring about Tom Wretch, there's a pity. Tom is the living proof that statistics can be misleading. Contrary to all the studies of buying habits, Tom does think of price first and he buys the cheapest car he can. The hidden persuaders' efforts are largely wasted on him because he buys what he must, and he has almost no depths to probe, anyway. He is dimly aware of the currents of his time, however, and his questioning of prices and values has led him to wonder why he can't find a cheap, sturdy, reliable, safe, economical automobile. We'll learn a lot more about Tom in the near future, but let's first find out why the Ford company introduced in 1957 an automobile conceived in 1948.

Let's pretend that you and I want to manufacture an automobile. It just so happens that we already have a nationwide chain of dealers and service agencies. We have huge factories and foundries. We own a large proportion of many of the necessary raw materials, such as ore, and we have sub-assembly plants, our own ships, trains and trucks. We have thousands of well-trained blue- and white-collar workers, designers, engineers, brokers and salesmen. We have an excellent, world-wide reputation. We also happen to have a quarter of a billion dollars to blow on a new venture. All this is quite lucky for us, because no one less well equipped could think of going into the automobile business.

Question: What kind of car shall we make, and to whom shall we sell it?

In seeking answers, we thoughtfully consider the automobile's place in American life. The first, most obvious fact is that almost everyone drives, or owns a car, and that almost everyone else imagines he should. That being the case, it seems that our market is wide open, and our problem will be to make a car to sell to as many people as possible, preferably, to sell at least one of our cars to every family in America.

Next, we wonder what we can offer, specifically, that will make our car more desirable than anybody else's car, and so induce every buyer to at least *think* of our car first. We size up the current models on the road, and conclusions immediately spring to mind.

First, most cars are so expensive that people are going years into debt to buy them. Therefore, it might be desirable to undersell the market and make our profit on volume. This has also the added virtue of being a

The Public

patriotic act, because going into debt is unhealthy for the individual, and a nation of debtors is a sick nation.

Second, automobiles are obviously dangerous, because each year they kill more than 40,000 Americans—the population of a middle-sized city —badly wound a million more, cause $1,100,000,000 worth of property damage and cause another $1,700,000,000 to be paid out annually in wage losses, medical expenses and insurance. Therefore, we want to build as safe a contraption as we can possibly devise, both because of our humanitarian impulses and because of a desire to offer something different that will help us make money.

Third, we notice that our cities are becoming more and more congested, and that parking is becoming more difficult, and so we will want to offer the public a car that is shorter and easier to park, both as a personal and as a public favor.

Fourth, we notice that other manufacturers are making cars that are increasingly expensive to repair and operate. Thus, our car will be simple to repair and will easily work on the cheapest fuels.

If we go on thinking in this way, we'll come up with a car the like of which Detroit has yet to see.* Since we have the plant, the time and the money, all we need to make our ideas reality is a courageous faith in the essential common decency and good sense of the American public.

The trouble with this kind of reasoning is that it is unfair, because it is the kind of thinking more and more people began to turn to in the post-Sputnik winter of 1958, and we can't say now that this was the kind of thinking that should have occurred to the Ford Motor Company in 1948, when the public mood was quite different, and when the Ford Forward Products Planning Committee began work—that was to culminate in the Edsel. All we can fairly say is that our kind of thinking did not enter the minds of the Ford company in 1948, and because it did not, Ford lost a magnificent opportunity in 1957.

The mood of 1948 was generally orgiastic, as noted, and that of the Ford company was optimistic. Well before the end of World War II, Ford had been losing a fantastic amount of money each year, but when Henry Ford II took over the seasick corporation, profound changes were wrought not only in factory conditions and pricing methods, but also in the quality of the wares. Young Henry, as the second Henry Ford was known, raided General Motors Corporation for ideas and talent, and General Motors' methods of production, cost accounting and design were

* Mr. Romney's American Motors, however, seems to be working in the right direction here.

installed at the Ford plants. The result, of course, was just another General Motors Corporation on a smaller scale.

One of Young Henry's concerns was to establish a "family" of cars akin to the family of Chevrolets, Buicks, Pontiacs, Oldsmobiles and Cadillacs. Ford had three cars—the Ford, the Mercury and the Lincoln. While the 1949 Ford began to compete with Chevrolet in the low price field, the Mercury was less than quicksilver in the middle bracket and the Lincoln was not at all competitive with the Cadillac. Thus, one of the Ford company's decisions was to create a line that would not only compete with the General Motors family in all respects, but also a family that would have as recognizable a family relationship as General Motors cars enjoy. This meant making sure that just as the Chevrolet bore some resemblance to the Cadillac, so the Ford products must be generally alike. It also meant either that the price ranges of all three Ford cars must be widened by use of more, slightly different models of each of the three makes, or that a new, middle car be introduced to help Mercury cover the competitive ground between the highest priced Chevrolet and the lowest priced Cadillac; specifically to compete with the highly successful Buick. Ford's Forward Products Planning Committee was handed the problem, and it came up with a six-volume answer in 1955, the gist of which was, "build another medium-priced car."

Note that there was no indication that the Ford company considered the idea of building something new to sell to as many people as possible. The view was of a narrower market—the medium price market. Remember that the mood of 1948 was expansive; manufacturers were selling anything they could make as fast as they could make it and a car-hungry public was willingly being fleeced by unscrupulous dealers. In 1948, there was every indication that automobiles could grow longer, lower, wider, more powerful and much more expensive—and the public gave every indication of being willing and able to choke down whatever was spooned out.

When Ford's Planning Committee reported in 1955, the mood was still expanding. It was the gaudiest sales year in automotive history. On the basis of market research, the extrapolation was made that, by 1965, one-half of all American families would be earning $5,000 a year; that the middle car market would increase to 60% of the total market; that there would be 20,000,000 more automobiles on the road. It thus seemed reasonable to Ford's planners that, of those who bought middle-priced cars, at least 3½% could be persuaded to buy a new Ford brand, and since 3½% of the middle market was a profitable figure, the decision was made to wedge a new car into this middle market. No claim was made that the middle-car-buyer was crying his baby blue eyeballs out for something really *new;* the idea was simply that there was 3½% worth of room in the market for *another* car.

Whereupon a clutch of Columbia University depth-probers and motivation researchers was called in, and in their arbitrary way, the social scientists interviewed 1,600 unsuspecting citizens in Peoria, Illinois, and San Bernardino, California. (Why places like Peoria and San Bernardino seem to invite this sort of thing is beyond the scope of our argument. Apparently, they are believed to represent a kind of All-America rock bottom.) In the cant of their trade, the depth-probers were after "image intensity." They wanted to know if the people's images of their cars compared with the images they had of themselves, and the findings were next used to build an "image" of the car that was to become the Edsel. The images were measured on three scales—sex, age and social class.

The results alleged to show that Peorians and San Bernardinians thought that a lower class of people bought Mercuries than bought Fords; that while a middle-class Ford owner might want to step up to a bigger, more expensive car, he would consider a Mercury a step down, and he didn't—or couldn't—step two steps up to a Lincoln. The good burghers were believed to have thought Mercuries were for young lightweights, such as jazz-band leaders, while Buicks, Pontiacs, and Dodges were for the elderly. Mercuries were believed to be purchased by men, while it was thought women bought Dodges and Pontiacs. The probed citizenry figured Pontiacs, Dodges and Mercuries were bought by working-class people, while Buicks and Oldsmobiles were watchfobs of the well-to-do.

Therefore, Ford's market researchers decided, the new car would be for the young, but not too young; for the kind of people who indefinitely think of themselves as the young married set. It would be for the man who was almost well-to-do; who imagined he might one day actually become the kind of man who could buy a Buick. The new car should not have sex—that is, it shouldn't be thought of as a car women would buy, nor as a car that only men would buy. It should be, said Ford's chief of research, "the smart car for the younger executive or professional *family* on its way up." This is the reason the Edsel's advertising said "They'll know you've arrived" when you drive up in an Edsel, and why the pictures showed a middle-class family in its late thirties arriving at a middle-class house in a middle-class suburban Never-Never Land.

Instead of thinking about what a new automobile design should or could be, Ford merely thought in terms of a specific product to fit Ford's view of a specific consumer market.

At this point, there was still a chance for Ford to have done something more or less reasonable. Despite the narrow view of a product for a market, Ford could also have tried to make that product safe, simple, and cheap to operate and maintain. You would normally not think *that* too much to ask for the quarter of a billion dollars Ford was ready to sink into the new product. Unfortunately, those terms did not comprise the frame of reference of 1955. Decisions relating to the Edsel were made on other grounds.

It will be remembered that one basic concept of Ford's postwar recovery was to create a family of cars analagous to General Motors'. It will also be remembered that Detroit is congenitally opposed to sudden change. Thus, the new car could not be *too* different, and, as far as possible, its parts should be interchangeable with those of other cars in the family. Thus it was that the two smaller Edsels would use the basic body of the Ford Fairlane series; the two larger Edsels would use basic Mercury bodies and components. The "new" Edsel engines would merely be Ford and Mercury engines, rebored to different dimensions. Because of the many interchangeable parts, Ford, Mercury and Edsel dealers would be able to give service to all three makes. Thus it was that while Ford was claiming to have sunk $250,000,000 into introducing the Edsel, Ford was actually hedging its bets. The "new" Edsel factory was the old Ford Continental factory with a new name on the door—the familiar scene of a prior mistake. (Two years earlier, some readers may recall, Ford decided to produce a super-luxury car, to be called the Continental, designed to out-sparkle the most sparkling Cadillac. But even in lush 1955, the market wouldn't bear the weight. The Continental was a fiscal flop of no mean proportion.) If the Edsel proved a similar fiasco, Ford could still recover $150,000,000 by using Edsel facilities and parts to make Fords and Mercuries, just as Continental equipment was absorbed by Lincoln. The remaining $100,000,000 could presumably be charged off to future Ford and Mercury customers. Meantime, all the Fords, Thunderbirds, Edsels, Mercuries and Lincolns would look somewhat alike, and when it came to choosing a generic style, the company chose the low rectangle of its sports car, the Thunderbird, the most blatant and least practical of its products.

The Edsel's basic design and production decisions having been made, the Ford company next faced up to the problem of a name. Ask any advertising man, "What's in a name?" "Money," he'll say. Since the Ford company wanted to make money, several dozen of the highest paid brains in the world smoked and burst as they considered the gigantic problem of finding the magic, money-making name for what was essentially to be a car specifically designed to be sold to mediocre people. In desperation,

Ford turned to the fine arts for help, enlisting the services of the poet Marianne Moore. Miss Moore, charmed and delighted, supplied a lengthy list of first-chop suggestions, including "Utopian Turtletop," but somehow even her efforts were found wanting. A middle-class man, however much he might aspire to rise, still would not aspire to Utopias.

Great ideas are often enough found right around the house, so to speak, and the longer the Ford company considered the nature of the product they had designed for a special market, the more natural it seemed to name the new creation the Edsel, after Edsel Ford, the Company's unknown middle president. If ever there was a younger executive perpetually on his way up, and never getting there, it was Edsel Ford. If ever there was a middleman, sandwiched between giants, it was Edsel. He was a man overpowered and outlived by Old Henry, his father, who allowed him no real authority, and outdistanced in memory by Young Henry, his son. Moreover, the name Edsel was neither lowly, like Ed, nor royal, like Edward. It was a Texas Leaguer of a name, just as the Edsel was meant to be a Texas Leaguer of a car.

We know you will understand, the company wrote to Miss Moore, when we tell you we have decided to name the new car the Edsel.

Miss Moore doubtless understood, being a poet, and poets possess compassion. Detroit, too, understood, because everyone in that provincial city was familiar with Edsel Ford's career, and, considering the product, the name seemed no more than just. It did not occur to Detroit that perhaps no one outside the city had ever heard, or cared about Edsel Ford, because, as *Harper's* magazine pointed out, the conversations in Detroit are 75% about automobiles, 15% about sport, and 10% about last night's TV programs. Were it not for Detroit's limited *Weltanschauung,* "the selection of a name like Edsel, for a multi-million dollar investment, would have been impossible," *Harper's* said. "Their own wizards of market research, left to their own devices, would never have come up with such an answer.

" 'Look at the associations,' " *Harper's* quoted an advertising man. " 'Edsel, diesel, pretzel— Good Lord! It's a wonderful name for a plow or a tractor, but a car? They can make it elegant, but it will take them two or three years and fifty million dollars to do it.' "

The most the admen salvaged was the naming of the four Edsel models, which they promptly christened the Ranger, the Pacer, the Corsair and the Citation. Here were associations aplenty—and none of them were prosaic. The customer had his choice of pretending to be somehow related to the keeper of a royal forest; or to a horse of peculiar gait, or to a Barbary pirate, or of receiving an official summons to appear before a court. No doubt the Citation's name was a logical free association with its more than 300 advertised horsepower.

Conceived, designed, manufactured and named, the Edsel was now displayed and offered for trial to the press. The results were uniformly disappointing, for even such favorably inclined professional automobile writers as Tom McCahill of *Mechanix Illustrated* praised the car with faint damns. In a September, 1957 article, Mr. McCahill compared aspects of the Edsel to beasts of prey, bombardment aircraft, a music hall, boomerangs, a bag of bolts, a sausage, runaway horses and snakebites. From all reports, it was evident that the Edsel was not new, was not cheap, was not economical and was far from the safest thing on four wheels.

Let's pause for two words on this matter of safety. Each year more than 4,320,000 cubic feet of American earth is excavated to make graves for what the newspapers call our traffic victims. You'd normally think this fact would inspire some sort of action in Detroit; that it would at least lead the manufacturers into a working agreement with the nation's undertakers, if not leading perhaps one manufacturer to want to produce a somewhat safer product. Detroit's view, however, is different, because Detroit sees itself as selling nothing but dreams of speed, sex, luxury and horsepower. It would no more occur to Detroit to try to sell safety at the same time than it would occur to a fashionable restaurant to provide sodium bicarbonate and a stomach pump with every place setting.

Besides, if Detroit were to sell a safe automobile, it would have to offer a radically different car, and we have seen that Detroit loathes radical differences. A relatively safe automobile would have a well-supported, noncollapsible roof, circumferential bumpers, and no exposed metal inside the cab. The interior would be padded with collision matting; seat harnesses, not belts, would be standard equipment and the passengers would ride with their backs to the motion, so that in event of sudden stops they'd sink into padded chairs and not go flying through space to crack their pates on the windshield. A safe car would have no deep-slanted, vision-distorting wrap-around windshields; there would be dull, anti-glare paint on the unornamented hood, and the instrument panel would not glitter with chromium and leer with lights but would softly glow with ultra-violet light, as airplane instrument panels do. A safe car's wheels would be larger, to provide more braking area, instead of being made constantly smaller, with less braking area, as is now the trend with most new cars. A safe car would have its wheels at its outer corners, both for maneuverability and stability. The long, long cars that overhang their wheelbases fore, aft and amidships cannot be safely turned at speed, and they bounce like ping-pong balls when wrenched to panic halts.

None of these suggestions is either novel or impossible, but none has been adopted, despite the fact that it is faulty design that fills our graves. The National Safety Council studied 685,000 accidents in one year and discovered that 87% of them took place at 40 miles an hour or less. A Cornell University research team working with Indiana State Police estimated that of 600 fatal accidents studied, only 16% were non-survivable in any case, and that the remaining 84% of lives lost could have been saved by proper interior design. There is some evidence that you can operate an Indianapolis racer at 100 miles an hour with greater safety than a professional racing driver can operate your Detroit dreamboat at 70.

It is Detroit's contention that speed has less to do with accidents than is generally supposed; that the chief killer is bad judgment, and that the judgment of the driver is something Detroit obviously can't control. So, Detroit defends its ever-higher horsepower by saying if you have sufficient speed in reserve, you can flee from an accident before it happens. Hence the passing gear that accelerates you from 35 to 70 miles an hour in a

matter of instants; hence the cars that leap to 60 miles an hour in less than ten seconds from a standing start.

All this is so much hoopla, because our automobiles are so poorly designed as to be unsafe at *any* speed, and more speed simply increases the danger. For instance, it is possible for a man to be impaled on his steering column like a bug on a pin in the course of a panic stop at 25 miles an hour. You can, at 10 miles an hour, be jerked off the front seat and lose every tooth in your skull when you fetch up on the dashboard. Furthermore, if most accidents can be attributed to bad judgment, then it would seem poor taste to supply poor judges with an opportunity to exercise their poor judgments at high speeds when there will be even less time for making any kind of decisions. Moreover, momentum equals mass times velocity, and a 3,300-pound automobile whistling along at 70 miles an hour is going to have far greater impact than the same automobile moving at 30—and so will its passengers, who go flying off the seats toward the windshield at the moment of collision. To say that most accidents occur at speeds lower than 40 miles an hour is to say nothing; it is more important to wonder how many more of the same people would have been killed in the same cars had they all been doing 80, and how many less would have died in either case had the cars been better designed against collision damage.

We should wonder about such things, because Detroit keeps building more and more powerful automobiles with higher and higher advertised speeds, while making only derisive efforts to provide safe design. In all fairness, it must be said that the Ford Motor Company has said and done

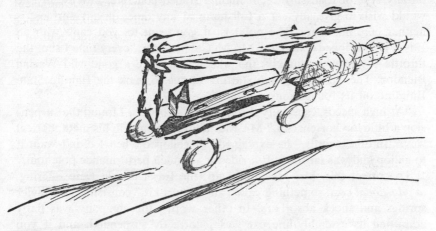

more than most companies about safety. Ford came out with the collapsible steering wheel, which is designed to bend under the pressure of your frantic, stiffened arms at the moment of impact, instead of snapping off to permit the steering column to skewer you. Ford pioneered the slow-rebound plastic padding on the dashboard and suggested that seat belts be anchored to firmly-anchored seats. At the same time, however, Ford kept on raising its speed and horsepower and provided the padding and the belts *as optional equipment available at extra cost.* Ford thus said, "Here's a hot car. Now, if you want to try to be safe in it, you'll have to pay more."

All of which brings us back to the Edsel and to our recital of missed opportunity. Given Ford's interest in safety, and given Ford's chance to produce a really new car, you'd think that Ford would have come out with the newest, safest thing on the road. So you might think. The facts are different.

Tom McCahill of *Mechanix Illustrated* wrote of the Edsel's "gigantic V-8s; the Pacer and Ranger with 361 cubic inches and the tiger-eating Corsair and Citation with an engine bigger than Carnegie Hall, displacing 410 cubic inches—at this writing the biggest automobile engines in many years. Most of my testing was done with the big bombers."

Mr. McCahill said the first fault he discovered was that he couldn't tell how fast he was going. "The revolving speedometer," he said, "develops inertia but will unquestionably be fixed before these cars are turned over to the public."

Next, it seemed "the bolt bag," as Mr. McCahill called the Edsel, had so much torque that it was impossible to give the car a "full jump start on any type of road surface, including ribbed concrete." (Why anyone would wish to give any car a full jump at any time, on any surface, is neither here nor there. The point is, if you want to, you can't with an Edsel.) "On ribbed concrete," Mr. McCahill wrote, "every time I shot the throttle to the floor quickly, the wheels spun like a gone-wild Waring Blendor. The car has enough starting torque to yank the Empire State Building off its foundations.

"At high speeds, especially through rough corners, I found the suspension a little too horsebacky," Mr. McCahill continued in his metaphorical way. "In other words," he explained, "it galloped when I didn't want it to gallop and was far too soft a ride for so much performance potential."

To correct this, Mr. McCahill said, the Edsel people were offering, *at additional cost,* something called an "export kit," consisting of heavier springs and shock absorbers. In other words, the company was flatly admitting its assembly-line car was incorrectly suspended, and if you wanted one that was correctly suspended, you'd have to pay extra for it. "For my dough," Mr. McCahill told *Mechanix Illustrated's* fascinated readers, "I wouldn't own one except with the export kit; without stiffer suspension, a car with so much performance could prove similar to opening a Christmas basket of King Cobras in a small room with the lights out."

Mr. McCahill discovered the Edsel, despite its wildly spinning wheels, could achieve 60 miles an hour in 8.7 seconds from a standing start, and 30 miles an hour in three seconds from ground zero. Still, there was some small difficulty. "To do this," Mr. McCahill explained, "I was

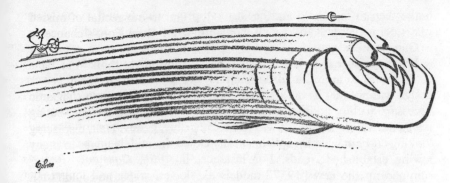

forced to feather the throttle to avoid wheel break and I couldn't help but wonder what this salami would really do if it had enough road adhesion to keep the wheels from spinning and you could shove the throttle through to the front axle."

Perhaps all this is not the fault it seems, however, because it might just be that cars should not instantly respond to the desires of people who want to jam throttles through the floorboards in an attempt to jump from nothing to 30 in *less* than three seconds. It would seem that the Edsel is already lethal enough, because let us suppose that a man is stopped at a traffic light. He is the kind of person who jams throttles to axles the split second a light changes.

There he is—let's call him Sneed—not looking at the red light facing him, but at the yellow caution light diagonally across the intersection. The instant that yellow light blinks, Sneed will leap ahead.

At the same moment, a school child starts to run across the street on what is left of the yellow light. The light blinks off. The child hesitates, starts to continue across the street, thinks better of it, and starts back to the curb. Meantime, Sneed, watching the yellow light to the exclusion of all else, has jammed his accelerator. Then, horrified, he sees the running child who is now pelting back toward safety. Sneed jams on the brake.

Unfortunately, Sneed's salami, as Mr. McCahill would call it, is already traveling across a yards-wide intersection at nearly 20 miles an hour, gaining speed and momentum every inch of the way. Under perfect traffic conditions, given normally-functioning brakes and a normal human reaction time, the average driver in the average car traveling at 25 miles an hour cannot possibly come to a halt in less than 44 feet from the spot where danger was first perceived.

Hence, in the instant it takes Sneed to see the child, realize his error, take his foot from accelerator and slam it on the brake, and for the brake then to take hold and begin to stop the wheels, and so cause the vast steel juggernaut to lose all momentum, the child is dead.

One wonders why.

What dream has Detroit fulfilled? What illusion made real?

To return to more humdrum matters, the basic tragedy of the Edsel's design was not that it was a hot car improperly suspended, nor that it was necessary to buy additional equipment to cure its little faults, but that it was not a *different* car. It was just another big, gaudy, not-too-unusual-looking entry in what is euphemistically called the middle price range, following established trends. For instance, in 1956, *Consumer Reports* summed up the new "1957" models as "lower, wider and longer, but having no more room inside; more power and, despite higher compression ratios, lapping up more and more super-fuel; more speed and hotter performance; a little better handling; more inadequately supported hardtop roofs, more glass area, increasingly wrapped-around windshields embodying more entrance difficulty and glass distortion; added weight not always reflected in stiffer structure; fatter and squealier tires that make parking harder without power steering and lastly, higher prices." In 1957, when the "1958" models appeared, *The New York Times* summed them up as follows: "They will cost more. They will have more horsepower. They will have improved engines, which may give more miles to a gallon of [more expensive] gas. They will cost more to repair. There will be more models . . . about the only thing there will not be more of is comfort, especially when the new six-passenger car has a full load." The Edsel was in this tradition. The only reason to believe the Edsel was the particular car for the younger executive family on its way up was that the advertisements said so.

"Edsel specifications," *Consumer Reports* said in 1957, "reveal no major engineering advances and offer few mechanical—or functional—details that won't appear on Ford or Mercury for 1958."

The Ranger and Pacer models, *Consumer Reports* said, had the same components as Ford Fairlanes "including the Ford Fairlane's far-from-roomy body structure." Likewise, Corsairs and Citations were filled with Mercury components and the only thing *Consumer Reports* had to say about the new Edsel engines was that they "were going to have big appetites . . . but . . . they almost certainly will require super-premium fuel."

The Edsel, *Consumer Reports* said, "appears to be an unexciting automobile mechanically; durable, no doubt, probably longer lasting, probably better riding than the Ford, but in the main offering the Ford and Mercury virtues over again at slightly different prices. But Edsels are, indeed, very highly gadgeted . . . there are enough flashing lights on the instrument panel to satisfy pinball machine addicts.

"Merchandising advantage," the report concluded, "rather than the desire to create a really new, different or better automobile, seems to be the Edsel's reason for being."

Truer words were never cast in movable type.

The big question remaining is whether the Edsel achieved any merchandising advantage for Ford that the company could not better have achieved by bringing out a new kind of car. At this writing, the answer seems to be fairly clear.

The Edsel arrived in showrooms on September 4, 1957. By September 30, the nation's 1,160 new Edsel dealers had their first forebodings —people weren't buying. In fact, some were snickering. October sales were even lower than September's; November sales were lower than October's. By midwinter, some Edsel dealers were bankrupt—cleaned out in three months—and others were trying to get out from under as fast as they could. Desperately, Ford sank another ten million dollars into Edsel advertising, but so far this seems to have had no effect other than

to prove you shouldn't throw good money after bad. There is every indication that the decision to manufacture the Edsel was one of the most costly blunders in all merchandising history, and many an advertising man is beginning to take his own long, second look at the practitioners of motivation research and market analysis.

With the gift of hindsight, we can say yes, if Ford had introduced a really new car in the fall of 1957, its chances would have been better than the chances of the look-alike, act-alike models of "1958" Chrysler, Ford and General Motors products. It is equally easy to see that a genuinely new car will capture the market tomorrow because someone will someday have to reverse the current trends if for no other reason than the simple fact that cars cannot indefinitely grow longer, lower, wider, more powerful, more wasteful and more expensive. Also, if Detroit is going to market automobiles like dresses, Detroit will have to steel itself against flighty Dame Fashion's abrupt changes, and the first company really to do something radically sensible is going to corner the market.

At this point, I'll suggest that the possibility for a company to make a fortune existed at least since 1947, and that the only reason—apart from a lack of courage and a surfeit of blind greed—that nobody took advantage of it was that nobody in Detroit remembered, or cared about or understood Tom Wretch.

Tom is a member of that great middle majority that reaches from the upper-lower through the lower-middle class. In a word, he doesn't have much money and he's not too bright. Tom drives his car to work. He buys a car and drives it until it's worn out, and then he has it fixed and drives it a little longer, because he just can't afford a new one every year. Most often, he buys a used car. At the same time, Tom reads all about the new models, and in his own good-natured way, he actually believes what he reads. He thinks cars *are* getting better and better, just as the advertisements say.

Tom is a little slow, but he's not entirely a dunce. He might be easy to mislead, but he is honest with himself, and he's not given to venting his aggressive impulses by endangering the life of every kid on the block at fifty miles an hour through a residential zone. He doesn't buy a car because it reminds him of his high school sweetheart's underwear, or because the car permits him to think he's General Patton. For example, he has a spotlight on his old General Chrysford coupé. He didn't buy it because of some hidden urge to pretend he was a fire chief. He bought it because he really uses it to find door numbers in strange neighborhoods. Likewise, that extra-long antenna doesn't reflect Tom's urge to attract attention. Tom bought it hoping it would (as advertised) improve his radio reception. (It didn't.) There is no doubt that Tom will buy any gadget he thinks he can use, if he has the money. Tom buys the cheapest model in the low price field because that's all he can afford if, indeed, he can really afford *that*. We're going to look in on him in 1953, when a marketing revolution was underway, and when the car that seemed

76

poor Wretch!

to offer Tom the most for the least was a General Chrysford Stylepack Super. Tom liked everything about that car, including the price, which, like all automobile prices, was far beyond his means.

As we follow Tom Wretch through his little problems, remember this about him: Tom really wanted that Stylepack Super. If, however, there had been a less gadget-bedizened contraption on the market, selling for $495—or nearly $2,200 less than Tom paid for his Stylepack—would Tom have taken it?

Our $495 figure doesn't come out of thin air, by the way. In his *Get a Horse,* Mr. H. M. Musselman reports that Detroit could have manufactured a light, practical machine for that price in 1950. And, in *My Forty Years With Ford* (Norton, N.Y., 1956) Charles E. Sorensen, the man who had as much to do with the Model T as Henry Ford, says a light, cheap car in the Model T tradition "is possible today, but only under certain conditions.

"One is a reversal of the present trend in auto design and in public preference," Mr. Sorensen writes. "Today's cars are more wasteful of power and fuel than any that have gone before. . . . For speed and power the American people are paying dearly, not only in safety but in unnecessarily inefficient operation and gas consumption. . . . The most economically operating cars today are the light, small, low horsepower ones of foreign make. They come from countries which tax horsepower instead of size or weight. . . . Even with import duties, some of them can be sold in the United States for less [than our cheapest cars]."

When Tom went into the market in 1953, there were no bargains, foreign or domestic, and Tom bought what he could. Now, just for the sake of argument, let's say that Tom had some depths to be probed, after all. Let's say he really would be pleased with a Cadillac; that he dreams futile dreams of wealth and satyriasis. It is obvious he cannot buy a Cadillac, but there are two cars he *can* buy—on time. They're both new. Both are two-door sedans. One looks very much like a small version of the Cadillac that haunts Tom's subconscious mind. It costs $2,500. The other has only the Roman virtue of practicality and the Scottish virtue of thrift. It travels forty miles on a gallon of gasoline and it costs $500. Are Tom's dreams worth $2,000 to him?

Well, sir and lady, it's difficult to say. History can be confusing. There is no question the Model T lost its sales leadership to Chevrolet when the Chevrolet trended diffidently into dreamboat realms. In 1927, however, everybody might have wanted a car, but not every man could afford one—not even a Model T. Is it not more correct to read into the Model T's demise the presumption that any man who could buy a Model T could also find a way to buy something flashier, given the chance? And that now, when people like Tom Wretch are dependent on automobiles, those Wretches would buy a latter-day version of a Model T, given the chance?

Is not the real reason why Detroit builds dreamboats simply so that it can sell six million $2,500 cars on the installment plan, and thus make *five billion more dollars* than if it sold twenty million $500 cars? Is this not the real reason why there is no latter-day Model T on the road, no matter *what* the public wants? If Detroit thinks of Tom Wretch at all, does it not merely regard him as the kind of clod who will have to buy a *used* car—a purchase which has the virtue of keeping the whole zany scheme of automobile financing in something resembling balance?

As this is written, only two kinds of new automobiles are selling well in the American market. One is the foreign car Mr. Sorensen describes, and the other is the American Motors' compromise, the Rambler. The Rambler is not as small as the foreign car, yet it is shorter than the smallest Detroit dreamboat. It is slightly more expensive than the foreign car; slightly less expensive than the cheapest Detroit make. It is cheaper to operate than the Detroit thing; a little more expensive than the foreign car. Do the sales of Ramblers and foreign cars portend a bright future for any manufacturer willing to gamble all on the success of a really new, really cheap, serviceable car? Will somebody discover Tom Wretch and make another Woolworth fortune?

I mention this *en passant* for what it might be worth: The Volkswagen people are so busy trying to fill their orders that they do not need the services of market analysts, researchers, psyche-plumbers, hidden persuaders and twenty million dollars' worth of advertising.

Meanwhile, let's now join Tom Wretch as he goes to market to fall victim to a pattern of merchandising first devised in a Levantine *souk*.

HEIGH HO, COME TO THE FAIR!

THERE WAS NO DOUBT Tom Wretch needed an automobile. His position as elevator captain at the Mausoleum Self-Service Products Corporation depended on his arriving punctually at 7:30 A.M. five days a week, and Tom lived in a housing development twenty miles from the heart of Metropolis. There was neither train nor bus, and nobody's car pool left the development at six in the morning. There was, however, Tom's 1950 General Chrysford two-door coupé, and its doors were sprung, one window was broken, the valves leaked, the fenders were nearly rusted off, the muffler was shot, the wheel bearings were noisy, the gears didn't mesh until the third try, and the tires were threadbare. From time to time, Wretch thought about another car, by which he meant another used car, because his $75 salary seemed to set certain limits on his ambitions.

Tom's ambitions, however, were as unimportant as his capabilities, because while he was considering his automotive needs, forces quite beyond his control were conspiring to give him not a new used car, but a brand-new car. It is an irony of our time that the same forces entirely depended on Tom's existence for their own, as we shall see. Meanwhile, Wretch finally said to himself, "I'll buy a car" one Saturday morning in 1953, not knowing that he would actually do so before the day was out. It was Simon Greed who made up Tom's mind for him. Mr. Greed had been laboring mightily all the week before to do just that, not quite without out Tom's being aware of it.

Mr. Greed, president, general manager and sales director of Honor Bright Motors, Inc., was essentially a simple man. He simply wanted to sell more automobiles, and all of his considerable energies were concentrated on his problem. At last, one night, while he was nibbling his wife's ear, a great light flooded his mind. He would stage what the auto industry

was first to call the "blitz," and then to come to know as a way of life.
At this point, permit me a slight digression. I have chosen to send
Tom Wretch to Mr. Greed's market in 1953, because—according to testimony before the United States Senate—1953 was the year the blitz first
appeared in finest flower, and because the Senate has been kind enough
to document the case. All of Mr. Greed's curious business practices (as
well as a complete account of his troubles) will be found in "Automobile
Marketing Practices," a 1,225-page typescript of hearings before the Senate's subcommittee of the Interstate and Foreign Commerce Committee,
eighty-fourth Congress, second session, published as Document 73438
by the U. S. Government Printing Office at Washington, D.C., in 1956.
As we follow Tom Wretch through his purchase of an automobile, please
bear in mind the fact that nothing has been made up. Senate testimony,
according to the Senate's published document, indicates that my mythical
Mr. Greed merely followed in detail the sales advice furnished him by
at least one major manufacturer. Not all dealers are Simon Greed, of
course—but Simon Greed is the sum of all dealers as described by themselves and other witnesses before the Senate. On this thought, let's now
look in on Mr. Greed as, his sales force assembled about him, he waited
for an abject silence, and then said huskily into this silence:

"Fellows, we're going to make history. Fellows, Honor Bright's going
to sell one hundred brannew Stylepack Supers in one single, solitary day."

The salesmen stirred suspiciously. Honor Bright normally sold fewer
than 400 cars in an entire year. Mr. Greed, however, was well aware
that most historical events require a certain amount of mundane preparation, and he therefore let his troops in on the practical details.

First, he said, there would be extensive local radio, television and newspaper advertising, climaxed by a parade of one hundred new Stylepack
Supers led down Main Street by a marching band. Pretty girls from Metropolis High would ride in the cars, and airplanes would soar overhead,
towing signs reading HONOR BRIGHT.

Two cashiers would be hired for the day, Mr. Greed said, and hot
lunch would be served to the salesmen at their desks in order to create
in the customers' minds the idea that Honor Bright was so busy selling
cars that its salesmen didn't have time to go out for lunch. A cameraman
would be on hand with a Polaroid camera to take a picture of salesman
and customer every time a sale was consummated, and the lucky customer
would be given the picture as a souvenir. Meanwhile, a band would play
"music suitable to this occasion," as Mr. Greed put it, and all the while
girls would serve free coffee to salesmen and customers alike.

"Fellows," Mr. Greed said, "it's going to be a *great* day. I'm going

Osborn

to give every man in this organization five silver dollars every time I see him being extra polite to a customer, and I'm going to give it to him right on the spot so the customer can see the value we put on courtesy.

"We're going to start selling at nine A.M. on Saturday morning and we're going to sell right through the night—oh, sure, there'll be search-lights and the band will be playing and you'll have food right along, and we're going to keep selling until nine A.M. Sunday morning when the customers can knock off and go to church. And we're going to sell a hundred cars in that day.

"Gentlemen," Mr. Greed said, drawing himself to attention, "I salute you."

Whereupon, he saluted them.

Next, Mr. Greed told his army that he wanted every man on the telephone all week before the sale, but not to make calls on the quarter hours, when Honor Bright's commercials would be running on radio and television. He drew diagrams, he outlined sales talks, but above all, Simon Greed gave his infantry a cause for which to fight. The cause was Service, because Mr. Greed was a public-spirited citizen. In his office there was a sign that ever reminded him, "Boost, don't knock." Wholly apart from his perfectly normal desire to make money, Simon Greed honestly wanted more people to own new cars, because he thought it was good for them, good for Metropolis, and good for him. He often said as much at Rotary revels. "What's good for Greed is good for Metropolis," he'd say.

Thus, it is only fair to say the whole idea of Mr. Greed's blitzkrieg was to help other people. Mr. Greed had asked himself this question:

"Who needs help the most?" His answer was automatic. It was, "The people who can't afford a new car." Mr. Greed's problem was therefore clear. It was to find a way to sell new cars to people who couldn't afford them. Mr. Greed had found the way, and his solution was staggering in its awesome simplicity, and when he realized that the less able a man was to buy a car, the more money that he, Greed, would make, the better this made Mr. Greed feel. He experienced that soaring of the soul that had led Mr. Henry Ford to his tremendous dictum: "We know now that anything which is economically right is also morally right."

Here, briefly, was Mr. Greed's idea:

Only one kind of customer was to be kept out of the shop. That was the man who wanted to pay cash. A man like that, Mr. Greed figured, didn't need help.

"On a sale like this, cash customers can kill you," Mr. Greed said. "We're practically giving the car away as it is. So if a guy hauls out a checkbook and says 'how much?' you write the order and send for me. I'll explain to the guy that Gee, we've been selling so fast the salesmen don't know we don't have a car left in stock, and all we can do now is take orders. I'll tell him we'll be glad to take his order, but it might take him a couple of months to get the car, and meanwhile, can we show him the convertible."

Cash customers were a remote danger, however, and it was for the overwhelming bulk of his clientele that Mr. Greed had two prices in mind. The first, to be charged relatively solvent customers, would guarantee Honor Bright a barest minimum profit of more than $12,000 if all 100 cars were sold. The second price was more of an elastic plan than it was a price, and there was no possible way of reckoning the day's profits in advance, except to say that $12,000 would be chicken feed if all 100 cars were sold according to the plan.

Since Mr. Greed's sale did make history indeed, and became not only the rage of 1953, but was recommended as a model by one giant manufacturer, and reached gaudy heights in 1955, and has remained the vogue to date, it is instructive to follow Mr. Greed's arithmetic in some detail.

First, Mr. Greed knew the factory would charge him $1,726.97 for a Stylepack Super loaded with radio, heater, overdrive, white sidewall tires, and other odds and ends. He figured he could give a $30 commission to his salesman (above salary), spend—or at least, charge—$15 to have the car put into running order (this is called the handling charge, of which more later), tack on a $39.38 gross profit, and offer the car to a "solvent" customer for $1,811.35. (Of course, Mr. Greed could have put a stripped-down car on sale for $354.97 less, but he wanted his customers to have the very best. He thought they not only deserved it, but would want nothing less.)

If Mr. Greed's "solvent" customer provided either $454 in cash, or turned in a used car worth that much, this would leave the customer owing an unpaid balance of $1,357.35. Mr. Greed would then add in $144.50 for thirty months of insurance, leaving the purchaser to finance a balance of $1,501.85, on which there would be 6% interest for thirty months. This was not interest on a declining balance, however—it was more in the nature of a carrying charge—and thus the customer would be faced with a total of $1,772.18 to be divided into monthly payments. In other words, the customer would first have to pay $454 down in one shape or another, and then $1,772.18 in monthly payments, or—to be blunt about it—it would cost the customer a grand total of $2,226.18 to buy a car that cost Simon Greed exactly $1,771.97 to sell.

It must not be imagined that Mr. Greed would make anything like a $454.21 profit on each deal, however. His gross profit was $39.38 on the car, plus an $82.97 profit on the finance and insurance charges. Thus, Mr. Greed himself would make only $122.35 on each deal, but then, he was simply out for volume, as he said. If he sold 100 cars in one day on these terms, his profits would be $12,235 for the day, and he could expect his profits on the finance charges of his used-car sales to more than wash out the cost of advertising his new-car blitz.

It will be seen that Mr. Greed's profit on finance charges was more than twice the gross profit on the sale of the car itself. If, like many other dealers, Mr. Greed's profits on parts and service had paid for the entire overhead of his sales agency, and if Mr. Greed had further owned his finance company, Mr. Greed's profits would tell a much longer and more interesting story. Alas, this was not the case. Mr. Greed, like many more dealers then and now, earned only .8% net profit on sales of new and used cars, parts and service, and his real profit was made on financing and acting as an agent for an insurance company. It is precisely this point that gave rise to the truly monumental phase of Mr. Greed's blitz—the plan for the customers who couldn't afford to buy. The plan for people like Tom Wretch.

For one solid week, Wretch could not look up on his way home from work without seeing Mr. Greed's airplanes. He could not turn on his radio or television set or read any page of the Metropolis *Morning & Sunday Patriot* without being somehow aware of Honor Bright's story. On Saturday morning, the story appeared on the *Patriot's* centerfold in 64-, 36- and 24-point type:

IT'S WHEEL AND DEAL AT HONOR BRIGHT!

Never before, and never again, will we be trading as high,
wild, handsome and zany!

WE'LL POSITIVELY TOP ANY DEAL IN TOWN!

Yes, folks, even if your car has to be *towed* to our lot,
we may give you at least $800 for it! Up to
$1,500 on your 1950 car! But that's not all!

WHEN YOU BUY TODAY, WE'LL GIVE YOU $300 IN CASH, TO BE USED FOR ANY PURPOSE!

No, folks, this isn't part of your trade-in! It's a
bonus from us to you!

WE CAN DO THIS BECAUSE WE'RE GOING TO SELL 100 BRAND NEW STYLEPACK SUPERS IN *ONE DAY!*

Yes, folks, 100 cars must go even if we have to give 'em away!
Trade-ins? WE DON'T CARE! Down payments! WE DON'T
CARE! Terms? WE DON'T CARE! Profits! WE DON'T
CARE! WE WANT VOLUME!

Yes, folks, Honor Bright is going volume crazy! And here's
why! We want people to have the best car made! We know,
and you know, the bigger the volume, the more you can cut
profits, and the more you cut profits the more friends you
make! So come on out to Honor Bright today, have a free
lunch on us, tell us your terms, and don't feel obliged to buy!
Of course, you'll want to buy when you see the new Stylepack Super and find out that we'll meet any terms you set!

WE'LL MAKE DEALS WITH NOTHING DOWN!

to properly qualified customers

The advertisement was tastefully embellished with photographs of girls
kissing young men who were buying them Stylepack Supers. The automobiles were strangely long and low, because Mr. Greed used the manufacturer's press-release photographs in which, by clever distortion, the
center section of each car is increased by one-third, and the girls and
young men stand on boxes well in the foreground to make the cars seem
even lower. It was another magnificent illustration of the fact that the
camera does more than writers can to justify Detroit to man.

Wretch, whose unconscious ear had been bombarded all week by Mr.
Greed's drumfire; Wretch, weakened by his obvious need for another car,
was nevertheless still somewhat suspicious of what seemed too good a

thing to be true, but Henry Clapperclaw finally disarmed him. Mr. Clapperclaw, city editor of the *Patriot,* privately was given to understand there just might be a special deal at Honor Bright for him, particularly if Mr. Clapperclaw's sense of news judgment led Mr. Clapperclaw to want to run a little something of his own, in the news sections of the paper, concerning Honor Bright's one-day philanthropy. Like many city editors, Mr. Clapperclaw was something of a junior-grade back-scratcher, and in order that Honor Bright should not be uninformed as to who were Honor Bright's friends, Mr. Clapperclaw modestly signed his name and title to the page one story that Tom Wretch read. And reading, Wretch concluded that if the paper said so, it must be true. Wherefore, Wretch roused himself, put on hat and coat, and rummaged for his car keys.

"Where you goin', hon?" Mae Wretch asked.

"Out," Tom explained. "Be back soon."

Wretch smiled to himself. That'd make Mae mad, not knowing where he was going, he thought, but she'd be tickled silly when she saw the surprise he'd bring home. He was still smiling to himself when Honor Bright's doors were flung open to give him entrance.

"Hello, sir, we're *real* glad *you* came to see us today," Bob Joy boomed, pumping Wretch's hand and grasping him by the sleeve. "It's sure good of *you* to drop by, but then, heh, we know why you're here."

Wretch, barely past the doorjamb, looked a bit at sea. Five men had converged on him, but this one had caught him and was leading him to a desk. Bob Joy was Simon Greed's star salesman.

"Siddown," Joy said generously. "Have a cup coffee? Here, let me light that *for* you."

He snapped a silver lighter before Wretch's cigarette.

"*You* don't really want to *see* the new Stylepack Super, do you?" Joy rattled on, before Wretch could say a word. "I can see *you* know just as well as we know that it's the best thing anybody ever put on the road. You look to me like the kind of man that *really knows cars*—the kind that reads the specifications before he ever comes to the shop. Right?"

"Well, sure I read about—" Wretch began.

"Right!" Joy said. "So the only thing *you* want to know is style, color, how soon you can have it, and the terms. Right?"

"Ah," Wretch said.

"Right!" Joy said. "How soon can you have it? Ten minutes from now. Style? It's the Stylepack Super, fully equipped, the hottest thing in the whole General Chrysford family, the car that wowed 'em at the auto show. Color? Most of 'em here on the lot today are the new tri-colors—

bile green, jararaca red, and prune-pit puce. I mean, they're the same crisp tri-colors that took the auto show big. So I guess that's what you'd want anyway. But if it isn't, well, we have others to choose from. So let's not worry about color."

"Could I—" Wretch said. "I just came to look around . . . I . . . well, I have a car. Outside. I mean, I don't know what kind of . . ."

"What kind of deal you want to make?" Joy grinned. "Tell you what —let's see your car."

He jumped around the desk, swept Wretch from his chair, pushed Honor Bright's door open, and hustled Wretch outside. There, across the street from the glittering Stylepacks, was Tom's 1950 coupé with its eroded fenders.

"Glad to see you have one of our General Chrysford family," Joy said. "Plenty of life in this baby. You took good care of it, didn't you?"

"Well, yes, kind of," Wretch agreed.

"I believe you," Joy said. Then, doing some quick arithmetic in the tumblers of his mind, Joy thought to himself that Wretch's wreck would bring $400 at most at auction after the tiny rust holes in the fenders were filled with wax and lampblack. Joy felt he could sell it to a customer for more, of course, but $400 would have to be a basing price. That was $54 less than Wretch would need as a down payment on Simon Greed's $1,811 price schedule. Obviously, Wretch wouldn't have $54 in his pockets, much less in a bank. But Wretch might be good for sixty a month. So, Joy thought, I'll slip him the pack. . . .

"Tell you what, friend," Joy said, "I'll give you seven hundred for that car of yours, and that's what I'd call a deal, hey?"

"But this is a 1950 job," Wretch said. "Your ad said you'd give fifteen hundred on a 1950 car, and eight hundred even if it had to be towed to the lot."

"I don't think it said *that*," Joy smiled. "It said we *may* give you eight hundred on a car you have to tow to the lot. Like, if you had a new Rolls-Royce and the battery was dead, so you had to tow it in, we might go up to eight hundred on it, and like, if your '50 was a fully equipped convertible with only ten miles on it, we'd maybe go up to near one thousand five hundred.

"But I tell you true," Joy said seriously, "seven hundred is a top price for your car, because we couldn't sell it for that. Not with these new Stylepacks out now, that everybody wants. But, if you think you can get a better deal, why that's all right with us.

"Besides," he confided, "if you make the deal, we'll take your car as the down payment, so there'll be nothing down to you, nothing at all, and—on top of that, if you buy today we'll give you $300 in cash to use for any purpose.

"Now, nobody's got a deal like that," he said. "This way, we're really giving you $1,000 for your old car, aren't we? But don't tell."

There was something infectious about Joy's grin, and so, Wretch smiled at Joy.

"Come on in," Joy said, "have a cup coffee while we figure it out. . . ."

The whole key to Simon Greed's blitz lay in the fact that nowhere in his advertising, nowhere in his shop, did Greed once mention the "list price" of his wares. The actual price to be quoted by salesmen was left to that salesman's discretion, as long as it did not go below the $1,811 figure that was the basic "list price" to solvent customers. Following Mr. Greed's formula for selling to people like Wretch, Bob Joy raced through a series of transpositions. First, as noticed, he had inflated the worth of Wretch's old wreck by $300. Next, he added $300 to the original $1,811.35 that was the basic "list price" of the day's sale, to quote Wretch the figure of $2,111.35 as the "list price" of the Stylepack Super. The mythical $300 was what Joy called the "pack."

Joy thereupon deducted $700 allowed on Wretch's car as the down payment, on the theory that $700 was one-third of $2,100, and that any 36-month term contract should carry at least a third down.*

This left an unpaid balance of $1411.35, to which Joy quickly added $144.50 for insurance, and then added the "$300 cash gift" to bring the unpaid balance to finance up to $1,855.85. Next, figuring three years at 6% on all this, he added in $334.05 to bring the total for Wretch to finance up to an imposing $2,189.90, which he expressed in these terms:

"So it's only $60.83 a month to you."

Thus, Wretch would be paying out $2,589.90 in notes and investment to buy the car that cost Mr. Greed precisely $1,771.97 to sell, or, to put it another way, it would cost Wretch exactly $363.72 more to buy the same car than it would cost anyone able to meet Mr. Greed's "solvent customer" price on a thirty-month deal.

Wretch would now be paying a 6% "interest" on a balance that never declined; he would be paying it on $300 that turned out not to be a gift, but a loan; he would be paying 6% on a $300 "pack" that was pure

* Four hundred dollars, you see, was not one-third of $1,800, but $700 was one-third of $2,100. The reader will object that neither is $454 one-third of $1811.35, but mysterious are the ways of auto finance. Greed arrived at his $454 figure on the basis of $1,362, which is what a stripped Stylepack cost him. He did not count the $354.97 worth of optional equipment in making his down-payment estimate.

whimsy; he would be paying 6% on Mr. Greed's insurance commission; he would be paying state sales and personal property taxes on a base of $2,189.90 when his purchase was really worth $1,771.97, so that he would also be paying taxes on the very interest he paid. We might redundantly reflect that Wretch would be paying more taxes on his purchase than a rich man who paid cash would pay on the same purchase.

In sum, Wretch would be paying a total of $478.10 in charges on a $2,100 deal, and since Simon Greed made a 20% profit on gross charges, this meant that Greed would make a $95.62 profit on this amount, plus his $39.38 gross profit on the sale of the car itself, or a total of $135 profit on a sale to Wretch. Thus, Mr. Greed would earn $13.65 more per car by selling to people like Wretch than he would by selling to anyone who met his other price. In this way did Mr. Greed work his wonders to perform; in this way did he help those who seemed least able to help themselves; in this way did Mr. Greed do his bit to help make Metropolis great. No knocker, but a booster, he.

But how was Wretch going to be able to pay $60.83 a month for a new car when his salary was only $75 a week? When he also had a mortgage to pay and a wife and three children to feed? In view of Wretch's financial structure, why didn't he buy a secondhand bicycle instead?

Curiously enough, these questions are easy to answer. Like most Americans, Tom Wretch thought of the automobile as a means of transportation, indeed, as the only means of transportation, and then at once dismissed the thought. Like most Americans, Tom Wretch thought of the automobile as more than that. To him, the automobile was really not so much a means of transportation as it was a state of mind. It must be understood that Tom Wretch *really wanted* that Stylepack Super. Not only did he want a Stylepack, but he also really wanted all those optional doodads with which Mr. Greed had thoughtfully festooned it. Mr. Greed's estimate of Mr. Wretch's desires was exact. More—much more—will be said on this point; please note it now and have MacArthur's faith that we shall return.

The next thing to understand is that Wretch signed on hope—on the hope that tomorrow will be just as good as today, and probably better. Further, he thought he was getting a whale of a deal, getting $1,000 for his old car. He did not believe the thief in himself was, in fact, the victim. To Tom Wretch, the fact was this: he'd drive home with a new Stylepack, kiss his wife at the door, and hand her $300 in cash. If a pinch should come in the days ahead, we may be sure Wretch could gladly pinch himself, because as sociologists Robert and Helen Lynd pointed out in their *Middletown,* people earning as little as $35 a week reported "We'd rather do without clothes than give up the car . . . I'd go without food before I see us give up the car." In the midst of the Depression, the Lynds found the family car the one depression-proof commodity—everything else was more vulnerable. Marriages, new babies, clothing and food disappeared from the American scheme of values while the automobile remained. There was no depression in 1953, of course, but in the intervening twenty years since the Lynds' report the automobile had become even more important in the American scheme of things. Who has not seen the Cadillac parked before the hovel? The government estimates that two million Americans who earn less than $750 a year somehow own cars. So naturally, Wretch signed up; gladly he drove home with his debt.

Wretch's attitude is significant; it made Simon Greed's blitz possible. Yet, Mr. Greed's blitz is significant too, because it started a nationwide trend that, in retrospect, leads us to envision Robert Joy as Galahad and Simon Greed as sweetly pure as Candide.

Joy's "pack" quickly became known to an expanding trade as the "top pack," which can take the form either of a purely fictitious list price, or an inflated turn-in price on a used car with the same price added to the new car purchase price. In addition, there emerged, and there is the "plain pack"—a purely mythical amount of money charged for various mysterious services which either do not exist, or are not performed, or, if performed, actually cost much less.

Then there is the "finance pack," whereby dealers more than make up in finance charges for any gross profits that might be squeezed out of a sale by low "list prices." Using rate charts furnished by finance companies, dealers can set their rates so high that they can sell the contract to a finance agency at a discount and still receive an extra profit for themselves. Overcharges on insurance provide a rich vein of ore, and when finance and insurance charges are added together and then presented to the customer in the form of "here's your monthly payment" —which, despite the Federal Trade Commission's orders governing itemized bills of sale, is often done—then the customer has no way of knowing what in the world he is paying to whom, or why.

There is the "switch." This simply consists of advertising a genuine bargain, and then telling customers it's been sold, switching their attention to quite another deal.

What automobile dealers call "the bush," or "bushing," means offering a bargain, then hiking the price during the course of the sale. A salesman may actually quote one price, get a customer to sign a blank sales agreement, and then, when all is signed, write in a much higher price than he quoted. Or, he may write his quoted price on the sales agreement, have the customer sign the document, and then say, "I'll have to get the manager's approval."

Instants later, he's back with an irate manager at his heels.

"My God, the kind of salesmen we get these days," the manager apologizes to the customer. "One more mistake like that and I'll have to fire him. Look, friend, he gave you the wrong price. The real price is $2,597, not $2,465, and even then I'm giving it away with no profit at all, just because of my man's mistake."

Then, while the chastised salesman cringes in the background, the manager concludes the sale to which the customer is already emotionally committed, but at the higher price. "Bushing" is so profitable it has deprived Broadway of some major talent.

Then, there is the "highball." There is also the "lowball." To highball, a salesman verbally offers a customer a high price on a trade-in while they're outside the shop, and then offers much less when the customer has picked out and is about to sign for a new car. When a salesman throws a lowball, he either "bushes" or gives the customer less for his used car than it is worth, or both.

"Would You Take" is a simple highball. A card is tucked under a windshield wiper on your parked car. The card says "would you take $10,000,000 for this dog as a trade-in on a new Jetzoom?" Sure, you'd take it. But when you get to the store, you're bushed, highballed, lowballed, packed plain, top-packed, finance packed, or, possibly, "unhorsed."

Of all the sales practices in vogue, unhorsing is perhaps the ultimate refinement. "This is a rising market in used cars," the salesman says. "Tell you what. You give us your car. We'll lend you a new car. By next month, we'll get you $500 more for your used car than you can get now, and then we'll sell it and close the deal on the new car. Your new-car guarantee starts when you actually buy it next month. What could be fairer than that?"

Nothing would be more fair if that happy chain of circumstances should, by chance, be forged. But at the end of the month, the salesman says, "Gee, Mac, we sold your old lemon. But all we could get for it was $600 less than we thought we'd get, because the market went down instead of up. So now you don't have a car, but here's the dough. Now, are you gonna buy that new car, or not? If you don't, we'll have to charge you rent on all the time you've been driving it."

Finally, for the man who really can't afford to buy a bag of popcorn on time, there is the "balloon." A deal is worked out—no down payment, other than the used car or perhaps a judgment note or chattel mortgage against everything you own. There are as many as forty-eight months to pay, and the payments are fantastically low. All except the last one. Heretofore, the payments have been almost pure "interest," which is to say, the carrying charge, but the last payment is so large that the whole note must be refinanced, at, naturally, "interest" again.

We remarked that Mr. Greed's blitz occurred in 1953, but all of his sales practices have been in use since the first days of the automobile, or, perhaps, since the invention of the wheel. Greed's contribution was to use every gimmick all at once in a blitz—he was original only in the sense that Carlyle's most original man was he who adapts from the greatest number of sources. The important thing to understand about Mr. Greed's operation is that his combined attack—his military phrases, his girls, his Polaroid camera, his music, his parade, his searchlights, hot lunch, free coffee, 100-car day and so on—was recommended as an ideal by the Ford Motor Company in the pages of the September 10, 1953, issue of Ford's *Car Merchandising Bulletin,* published by Ford's Car Sales Department. Indeed, the Ford company seemed so happy with blitz operations that witnesses were to complain to the United States Senate that Ford deliberately set up company-owned dealerships to use blitz methods in competition with more reliable, established Ford dealers, in an effort to jazz up sales.

Similarly, Mr. Greed's misleading advertising, quoted above, is simply a combination of newspaper advertising bought by dealers. Such advertising has been repudiated by the manufacturers, but still, we note that it appears in nearly every big city newspaper nearly every day.

As for the sundry packs and the questionable, if not usurious trade practices, it should be clearly understood that no automobile manufacturer approves of them. Senate testimony indicated that manufacturers' sales division managers were firmly telling the dealers something like this: "We don't like the pack. All we want you to do is sell cars or lose your franchise. If the other guy down the street is using the pack, you may have to think about this. Remember, we don't like packs. All we want you to do is sell cars, make your quotas, or lose your franchise. So suit yourselves."

Nevertheless, it must be said that one witness told the Senate that, in 1955, General Motors Acceptance Corporation, General Motors' favorite finance company, practiced a singular duplicity. The witness, a former GM dealer, said, "GMAC has two charts. If the dealer wants more kickbacks, they give him a high-priced chart."

Other former GM dealers were to testify that honorable sales practices which had prevailed during the pre-World War II regime of Alfred P.

Sloan, Jr., as company president seemed to have been tossed overboard after Harlow Curtice took command of the giant corporation.

Indeed, the testimony moved Sen. Monroney to suggest that "the renaissance of responsibility [and] ethical leadership enunciated by Mr. Sloan" had "gone into the limbo of forgotten words in Detroit."

Rather than connect Mr. Curtice with this state of things, we should recall Mr. Greed, and we should remember Mr. Wretch. It was Mr. Greed's knowledge of Mr. Wretch's business naïveté that made Mr. Greed's blitz possible, and Mr. Wretch's willingness to be blitzed that kept the thing going, and all this captured the imaginations of the division sales managers of the corporations. The division sales managers fed the blitz, and it spread like crab grass in 1953. By the end of 1955, the blitz had thrown the automobile retail market into such turmoil that Senator A. S. Mike Monroney (D., Oklahoma) remarked that the business of selling automobiles had taken on all "the morality of an Oriental bazaar."

Between January and March, 1956, Senator Monroney presided over a Senate hearing requested by—of all people—the automobile dealers. It seemed they wanted Congress to protect them from the manufacturers, from the public, and from themselves. As Senator Monroney remarked, it was astonishing to find the dealers asking Congress for legislation, because automobile dealers as a class generally tend to have as little use for what they call "government interference" as anyone to the distant right of the late Colonel Robert McCormick.

Meanwhile, blitzing had reached such proportions that a noise level seldom equaled by P. T. Barnum's pitchmen pervaded the bazaar. From New York to Portland new cars were being offered for "10¢ down, 10¢ a day," or for "sale at a 1¢ profit." A Cleveland dealer offered two new cars for $2,999. Another Cleveland dealer offered 500 gallons of free gas with a new car purchase; the offer was doubled in Providence, Rhode Island. Detroit Chevrolet dealer Saul Rose said he'd give a customer a sleeping bag, a hammer, an ax, boots, a compass, a Geiger counter, maps of likely terrain, and, in event of his customer's failing to count any Geigers, he'd give the disappointed prospector 100 shares of somebody's uranium stock. Another Detroit dealer said he'd take a dollar off the price of a new Plymouth for every pound the customer and his wife weighed, or $1.50 off per pound on a Chrysler deal. In Denver and Portland, Oregon, customers were wooed with visions of trips to Hawaii; Bostonian purchasers were given a choice of Florida or Hollywood. Cleveland Pontiac purchasers were lured by a trip for two to Bermuda; uranium stock was offered in Birmingham; Alcoa stock in Maryville, Tennessee; General Motors stock came with a new car purchase in Miami and one dealer said he'd toss in three free shares of Ford stock to every man who bought a '56 Mercury. In Los Angeles—well, in Los Angeles all this sort of thing had never been particularly unusual, since as Frank Lloyd Wright points out, all our unstable elements seem to collect in lower California. In Los Angeles, smoky home of seven million automobiles, Senator Monroney's "Oriental bazaar" was a Hollywood production of an Oriental bazaar.

From one end of the nation to the other, dealers were buttonholing drivers at stoplights; fast-talking men in "boiler rooms" whirled telephone dials all day, running through the phone books. The "wheel and deal" was in full swing, and, let us note, the dealers were not alone. The manufacturers were adding their not-inconsequential weight to the fun. American Motors and Studebaker-Packard were offering free life insurance policies covering the buyer of a new car and his wife for the first year of their ownership. Dodge and Plymouth dealers were branch offices of a national lottery free to all—get an entry blank at your local dealer, fill it out, no obligation at all, and you just might win a new Dodge for every year of your life, or maybe, you would win $500 a month forever.

Advertising became more and more expert. Some advertisements turned out to be combinations of one car's price, another's picture, and the name of a third. At the same time, the "bootlegger" put in his appearance.

An automobile bootlegger, also called a "supermarket operator," does not sell a hot car. He buys cars from overstocked, but franchised dealers, paying slightly more than the dealer's wholesale price, but selling below the franchised dealer's "list price." Sometimes he sells his cars as "used— 200 miles." Sometimes he sells them as "new used cars"; sometimes as "new." Most often, he will not say they are brand-new, all hot and crunchy off the assembly line, but he will say they are "1958 cars." He provides no parts, no service, and usually, no warranty. If he provides a new-car guarantee, he says you must go to a franchised dealer for your checks, services and repairs. Typically, he's just a lonely man with a neon sign and a vacant lot on the edge of town, and all he sells is cars, and he sells them with what Senator Monroney calls "a soldier's farewell." Cars come to him from a variety of sources, and one of the more popular is the Detroit dealer. Often, the cars are driven hundreds, if not thousands of miles from Detroit to the bootlegger, chained together in pairs, their speedometers disconnected. If the trip is a long one, the original "breaking in" oil is drained before the trip starts, and is replaced with regular oil. Or, oftener still, the cars are driven to the bootlegger by some wayward adolescent, their breaking-in oil still in the crankcase. In either event, the result is the same; the motor is more broken than in.

And, speaking of results, one result of all the hoopla in the bazaar was that somebody, surely somebody, would eventually have to pay for all the advertising, for all the free trips, for all the free stock, for all the free gasoline, for all the national lotteries. Somebody owed a large bill for all the razzmatazz, not to mention also owing a large bill for all those automobiles. It was perhaps inevitable that the customer—Richard Rich or Tom Wretch—should have to pick up the tab. Therefore, the net worth of General Motors dealerships, for example, climbed from 249 million dollars in 1940 to 2,200 million dollars in 1956, and the profit on 17,000 GM dealerships for the first nine months of 1955 alone was $414,000,000. It was completely incomprehensible to Harlow Curtice that his, and other dealers, seemed to be quite raddled with fear at this moment of their greatest prosperity.

Despite the blizzard of inflated dollars that drifted against their doors, the dealers were a hag-ridden lot. They didn't know how much of their net worth was real worth, and how much was pure pack. They told Senator Monroney's committee they were forced by the manufacturers to do things that were in the dealers' opinions unwise if not plain dishonest.

"When this thing became a shell game instead of a business," one former dealer said, he quit, "so I could live with myself."

Dealers said the manufacturers were locked in battle to see who could sell the most cars. General Motors, they said, was kneeing in the groin to maintain Chevrolet's sales lead over Ford; Ford was gouging and biting in the clinches to capture the lead from Chevrolet. This, in turn, compelled other manufacturers to bite, knee and scratch, too, if they were to compete at all with the giants. The dealers' position was peculiar. The manufacturer sells only to dealers; thus the manufacturers were really trying to see who could sell the most automobiles to dealers. Of course, the dealers would have to sell to somebody else, and if the manufacturers increased their volume to dealers, the dealers must do a greater volume of business with the public. If the dealers didn't reach the volume the manufacturer expected them to reach, the dealers would lose their franchises to sell the manufacturers' product.

So if we don't blitz, the dealers said, we lose our franchises. It was the manufacturers who told them to pack, some dealers said. The manufacturers had overproduced, and were cramming unwanted cars on the dealers, and then telling the dealers what subterfuges to employ to unload the junk on the public. At the same time, the dealers told the Senate, some manufacturers forced them to pay cash for cars when ordered, not when delivered, and this tied up so much of their working capital that they were strapped. One former dealer said he was shipped—and charged for—cars he had never ordered and had said he did not want.

Listening to an automobile dealer whine about his cruel fate would ordinarily send a reasonable man into gales of laughter, but when the whines are extended over hundreds of pages of testimony, they take on a certain shy poignance, not without charm. One dealer said his manufacturer told him to set aside a certain quota of his cars for sale to a bootlegger; in other words, to set apart a certain amount of poison and then swallow it, for how can a franchised dealer sell cars at one price when the bootlegger sells them at a lower price? One dealer said he could get no new cars from his manufacturer while a bootlegger down the street had no trouble getting seventeen of them.

A Buick dealer said his manufacturer criticized him for not finding enough things wrong with cars brought to him for service. His sale of parts, it seemed, was too small. Another witness said sales division chiefs of Ford and General Motors requested dealers falsely to register cars in the names of their relatives and employees, to help win the sales race. A Chicago dealer said his sales boss told him he could bootleg his cars to Texas, for all the company cared, just as long as all the cars were registered as sold in Cook County, Illinois. The whines went on and on, and the clear burden of the song was that the manufacturers had put the dealers in great pain, and that it was the sales managers that were the villains of the piece. Dealers, Senator Monroney said, "show you letters from sales managers that you wouldn't write to a dog. . . . They [sales managers] have gone so far in some states as to require the dealer to violate the law. . . ."

The testimony was, that under pressure to sell and sell, the dealers adopted the pack as a way of life. Since the pack must surely come out of the car's price at some point on its road to the junk heap, this meant a simply incredible amount of dollars did not exist anywhere but on paper. In other words, many a customer owed more money on his car than that car was worth; thus the loan was unsecured. Some dealers said they had their names on the back of as much as $500,000 worth of paper, and that they frankly didn't know, and couldn't know whether this meant they were rich or bankrupt. On a 36-month sales contract, they said, eighteen months was the break-even point. For the first eighteen months, nothing was supporting the loan.

Dealers said they feared the 36- and 48-month terms on 1955 contracts would mean that 1955 buyers would be out of the market for the next three years, and they saw bleak days ahead. In this, of course, they were dead right. Dealers today tell you they haven't seen a profit for the last three years, but their wail leaves the public eye singularly dry. The public only too well remembers the bastinado it absorbed from the dealers in 1946–49, when the dealers had too few cars to sell, and sold them mercilessly. The public remembers (how can it forget, when a large part of it is still paying) the pack of 1955, when the dealers had too many cars to sell, and sold them mercilessly.

Senator Monroney, a patient man, listened to all the testimony, and it left him muttering darkly about "the juvenile delinquency that we are finding all over the country in the automobile business."

The shaky financial structure of the thing worried the Senator, and he summed up the dealer's position thus:

"You sell all the good credit risks, then the intermediate credit risks, then the ordinarily bad credit risks, and finally you get down to a guy who you don't know whether is going to wind up in Mexico in two weeks or not. But you sell him, with three years to pay."

Yes, the dealers nodded, that is so. But, they said, it's all the fault of the manufacturer, when it's not the fault of the public. Their complaint against the public was much like the complaint of the bandit against the rich man—the fellow had money, and this tempted the bandit, and if the rich man hadn't had money, there would have been no banditry.

All this led George Romney, president of American Motors, to make a curious remark:

"I have found dealers," he said, "as a group, are just as honest and just as farsighted as manufacturers."

General Motors' Harlow Curtice didn't see matters in this same, reasonable light. He came scorching to Washington, called the dealers a pack of liars, blamed them for bootlegging and assorted evils, denied everything, and said that General Motors never pushed an unwanted product on anybody.

Then, a bit later, Mr. Curtice returned to Washington a calmer man. The gist of his new testimony was that he wanted to take back some of the hard things he'd said. He explained, in the homely turn of phrase that so often characterizes the speech of General Motors officials, that it had since occurred to him "that where there was smoke, there must be some fire." It turned out there *was* something in what the dealers had been saying, but now, Mr. Curtice said, he'd investigated, made "suggestions," and that new "policies and practices that all agreed were reasonable and practical" had been adopted, and no legislation was therefore necessary, thank you.

There was now in effect, Mr. Curtice said, a new formula that would convert the manufacturer-dealer relationship into a lilting song. Meanwhile, he conceded General Motors *had* condoned price packing, but said pressure from competition had forced GM into this disreputable, reprehensible practice. The competition, apparently, consisted of the fact that General Motors sold only slightly more than 50% of all the cars sold in America. One can imagine Mr. Curtice's hurt astonishment to find that almost five of every ten buyers were purchasing either a Ford, or a Chrysler, or a Studebaker-Packard, or an American Motors, or a foreign product, instead of wisely buying Mr. Curtice's own. A thing like that can shake any honest workman's faith in himself.

Henry Ford II, president of Old Henry's empire, followed Mr. Curtice to the stand to explain that a lot of curious things must have happened— if they happened—while he was out of the office. But all that, Mr. Ford said, was bygones. He, too, was going to help dealers to a new plane of finer understanding. Like Mr. Curtice, Mr. Ford did not, and would not condone misleading advertising and spurious sales practices by dealers, if discovered. Like Mr. Curtice, Mr. Ford saw little need for legislation.

In short, the manufacturers' reply to the indictment was exemplary, fully worthy of them, and if anything remains now to be desired, it might be that the manufacturers' eyesight for dealers' frauds could be improved, because six years after Tom Wretch struck his bargain with Bob Joy; three years after the Senate hearings; the plain pack, the top pack, the finance pack, the bush, the switch, the highball, the lowball, the bootlegging, the usury, the unhorsing, the unsecured loan and the grand competition are still as much with us as the blitz and the quaintly scented advertising.

The only real changes in the bazaar since Tom Wretch was last there are that the prices are higher and the noise level is several decibels lower, because the crowd is smaller. The entertainment and the wares remain the same.

"Detroit's answer to overproduction or slow sales is kind of interesting," one dealer explained. "It used to be the law of supply and demand said if you get too much supply for the demand, what you do is lower the price. What Detroit does is cut production and *raise* the price. They just kind of amended the law of supply and demand so they'll always get theirs."

The crowd at the bazaar is slimmer because Tom Wretch hasn't come back in great numbers this year. He's still trying to pay for that Stylepack Super he bought in 1953. He refinanced his note in 1955, 1956, and in 1957. A good many other souls have left the bazaar's chrome-plated Midway to go across the street to look at the small cultural exhibits from Europe.

Wretch will be back soon, however, because we remember he bought more than a pack when he bought that Stylepack. He bought dynamic obsolescence with a vengeance, for not only is he sick of looking at his 1953 car, but now, in 1958, it's coming apart. In a way, it is wonderful to contemplate how a piece of machinery that cost Wretch $2,589.90 could, in five years, come to be worth nothing to Wretch and only about $100 to a used car dealer.

Let's not consider the finance charges Wretch paid. Let's merely estimate the allowances for depreciation, and the cost of insurance, license fees and taxes, gasoline, oil, tires, grease, repairs, cleaning, and the money Wretch tied up in a non-paying investment. We discover that it costs Wretch $.1042 to drive his car one mile.* Since Wretch drove 12,000 miles a year for five years, we discover it cost him at least $6,252 to acquire and drive a car for five years, or $1,250 a year.

This is absurd, of course. How can a man spend $1,250 a year on an automobile when he earns only $3,900 a year?

He can't.

But he does.

His family goes without new clothing and they buy three pounds of hamburg for a dollar and that's their supply of meat for the week, and Mae Wretch gets a part-time job and so the little Wretches go without parents, but, by George, the Wretch family has a car. It is the focal point of their lives.

Very well, we will admit their lives are somewhat out of focus, and I'd go so far as to say who are we to try to save the Wretches from themselves? Still, these admissions do nothing to banish the gamey flavor of the entire business we have been considering thus far. Let's shove Wretch aside and ask these general questions:

Where is the morality in two, or two hundred prices for the same automobile? What effect do you think this kind of pricing has on all other merchandising? The automobile, central to our economy, is the most expensive so-called necessity anyone can buy except a house. If it has no price, what else can have a price?

Where is the morality in selling a car to a man who is obviously incapable of paying for it unless he is willing to deprive his family of many necessities? Where, for that matter, is the morality in burdening an oaf with a debt, simply because he is an oaf? What effect do you think this sort of sale has had on the sale of all other things to the public, except to make our national economy more unstable and our business morality in general even more whimsical than it is?

* The current average operating cost for a car priced at $2,300.

But wait—we are not through. Tom Wretch is not the end of a line, but the beginning of one. When Wretch walked from Honor Bright's door, twirling the keys to his new car, he was startled to find Bob Joy standing beside his old car, talking to a young man with sideburns and a black leather jacket.

"I know you won't believe it," Joy was saying, "but God help me, it's the truth. This car had only one owner, a retired schoolteacher. She never drove it except back and forth, up and down her driveway, on alternate Sunday afternoons in the summer. Only reason she turned it in was that a kid had busted that window with a rock. It's a late '50 and we gave the full $1,500 for it. Tell you what—we'll split the difference, because we have to move the used cars we're taking in today. It's yours for $750, and we can work out a nothing-down deal and give you $300 in cash besides. . . ."

At this point, it should be understood that dealers do a larger business in used cars than in new cars, and Honor Bright is no exception. About two-thirds of all Americans buy old or new cars on time; on trade-in and installment. Wretch buys a new car; Doe buys his old car; Roe buys the old wreck Doe traded in, and meanwhile turns in a fourth car himself. One new car is sold, and somewhere along the line, one old car is led to the junkpile and meanwhile, nobody really owns any of them except, perhaps, the junk dealer. All along the line cars are sold to people who can't afford them; to people who must pay with promises instead of cash, and so the entire economy of the automobile industry is secured by promissory notes. But what secures the notes? Only a long line of automobiles, all unpaid for, moving toward a junkyard. As Lloyd Morris points out in *Not So Long Ago* (Random House, N.Y., 1949) each car in the procession is so far removed from the note it secures that nobody cares where it happens to be, or who has it at the moment. The procession, he said, supports the promissory notes exactly as the gold at Fort Knox supports the national credit—nobody's really seen it, but everybody believes it's there, and thus a national faith in a junkyard-bound stream of cars that no one owns ultimately keeps the assembly lines humming in Detroit.

"Somewhere along that dismal road," Mr. Morris says, "even very poor Americans [are] able to intercept cars that they could afford to buy—on the installment plan. They paid more for these cars than they were worth; so had the dealers who originally accepted them as trade-ins. For it was not to the industry's advantage to permit a cash—and competitive— market in used cars; such a market would inevitably depress prices to a point where Joe Doakes might find it more advantageous to buy a good used car than a new one."

Here, we might pause to reflect that Mr. Charles Wilson, late of General Motors, late of the Defense Department, remarked that what is good for General Motors is good for the country, and vice versa. This might strike some people as a rather parochial viewpoint, because what is good for General Motors is obviously installment buying, but the net effect of buying automobiles on time might be to contract, not to expand, the national economy. Briefly, if Wretch and his wife go without food, clothing, shelter, cleanliness and medical services in order to swing the note on the new Stylepack, the effect is that all the people providing the Wretches with food, clothing, shelter and sundry goods and services, will fare worse. In theory and in practice, the manufacture and sale of automobiles is an index of prosperity. Because the automobile industry is the heart of our economy; because so many jobs are dependent on the industry in all its ramifications; it is true that employment and wages are at high levels when many automobiles are sold. But if buying an automobile means the customer not only pays for an overpriced car, but also assumes a staggering debt, the money he pays out on his debt cannot be spent for anything else. Thus, there is less money available for butcher and baker. Thus, presumably, butcher and baker are less able to buy or to operate cars. Thus, presumably again, fewer cars are made and sold and driven; thus the economy contracts. The facts would seem to indicate that when one perches on a spiral, one can either spiral up or spiral down.

CRIME

OF

PASSION

DERICK GOODMAN

EDITOR'S NOTE

The crime of passion—or *crime passionel,* as the French call it—is an established institution in the French legal code. Since the war it has not even incurred the death penalty. The reason for this, in the French mind, is that *crime passionel* is a private crime, committed from motives untainted by any thought of gain and not disturbing the public peace.

This point of view, considerably at variance with British and U.S. ideas of justice, is dramatized quite intensely in the case of Pauline Dubuisson, who was only seventeen when she became the mistress of a fifty-five-year-old German Colonel, and then shot her French lover ten days before he was to marry someone else.

"Strong stuff, yes," comments the *Buffalo Evening News.* "It is often sordid, frequently incredible—but consistently fascinating and inoffensively presented by an international crime expert who is a good reporter."

Foreword

"THE IDEA THAT A WIFE can shoot down with impunity the husband who is deceiving her has taken solid root in France. I fully agree that the degree of responsibility varies with the degree of the 'crime passionel' in question. Extenuating circumstances can be admitted in certain cases but I do not agree with invariable acquittal even for the crime committed in a moment of anger. The loose title of 'crime passionel' must not be allowed to become a synonym for such automatic acquittal . . ."

This can be taken as a more or less semi-official view of that Latin crime *par excellence,* the "crime passionel"; it was framed by the Commissaire Principal Ducret of the Paris Police Judiciaire.

With the exception of five women, child-murderers and abortionists, who were executed between January 1941 and July 1943 because Marshal Pétain, with his great cult of family-love, refused to grant what should have been an automatic pardon, no woman has been guillotined in France in this century . . . But even Marshal Pétain would not have allowed a woman to lose her head for a crime passionel. In France, motives of love and hate are understood and discussed intelligently in the courts instead of being thrust beyond the pale as they are in England.

But what is crime passionel? The expression is widely used not only in newspapers and novels, but in the courts themselves. You will see later how Pauline Dubuisson was condemned to imprisonment for life because her defence failed to establish that the murder of her ex-lover was in fact a crime passionel . . . But you can search the statute books in vain for a mention of crime passionel. It does not exist. It is a psychological term responding to a definite need in Latin countries where temperament drives women—and men as we shall see—to gun law. It is especially characteristic of France. Can you imagine a placid English housewife going to the local sports-goods shop to choose an automatic pistol to murder her lover or her husband?

It is almost impossible to purchase a revolver legally in England. In France, providing you have no police record and have a good reputation, you have only to go to the police station and say your life has been threatened, or that you have to walk home late alone at night—as Pauline Dubuisson did when she bought the gun with which she was to murder her ex-lover—and you will get your licence.

Quite obviously, cold-blooded murder such as poisoning is ruled out from the definition of crime passionel. An English court, however, would say that the very purchase of a revolver establishes clear premeditation and the only price for murder with premeditation is the death penalty. Likewise in the United States, where premeditation means first-degree murder which carries an automatic death sentence when proved. But premeditation exists in France, too. Clause 296 of the French Penal Code states:

"Every murder committed with premeditation or by lying-in-wait is termed assassination."

And the only admissible sentence for assassination even in France is the death penalty. Nevertheless, although crime passionel does not legally exist, it can become such an important factor in a case that it *overrides* the considerations of premeditation. In England, the law is remarkably clear . . . It could not be more simple; you are not guilty and you go free, or you are guilty and in capital cases you were previously executed. There were no niceties or shades of understanding in between. It may be a convenient yardstick but there is nevertheless something rather barbarous and medieval about this system in the twentieth century. The English law is as dogmatic as . . . a Communist directive. But in France, if the law is slow, it is supple and filled with understanding. The crowd is no longer screaming for blood and the average case of murder does not come before the courts until two years have passed. This long period, so frequently criticised abroad, has one great benefit. It cools passions. It ensures that the crime, already committed in passion, will at least not be judged in passion. Swift retribution is seldom the most just, as every schoolboy knows to his disadvantage.

Is crime passionel a crime committed in a moment of passion? Almost, but not quite. Here is a very short explanation, made by Maître Raymond Hubert of the French Bar, a great defence lawyer who specialises in this type of crime.

"I have often appeared for murderers or murderesses," he said. "Some of them had killed because they loved to excess, the others because they loved no longer."

There you have the definition of crime passionel in a nutshell. Let us reduce and combine the two expressions, and add the word murder. *Crime passionel is murder committed in a moment of passion either for excess or for lack of love.* It is both a human and humane expression coined by a great people who have produced some of the world's outstanding jurists and philosophers. At the same time, it is not a confession of weakness, a loose acceptance of immorality, as English critics sometimes point out.

"The English claim that we are helpless in France when faced with crimes of passion," Président Marcel Leser, a French High Court Judge, said recently. "That is not my view. On the contrary, we have a magnificent scale of punishment to fit the crime. It can range from life imprisonment . . . to total acquittal . . ."

Then Président Leser stressed a point which is never admitted by English jurists but which is wholly logical: "Public law and order is not upset by crimes of passion. For the man in the street, they are a private matter, an affair purely between those involved, between lover and mistress. And although he has every desire to see the common malefactor punished, he willingly pardons the passionate murderer."

May I add to that: do you know why? Because it could so easily happen to *him* . . . Because, if you were a Latin, living in France, it could so easily happen to *you*.

For my part, I find it difficult to understand any form of modern society not based on totalitarianism which does not admit the theme of crime passionel. Is modern man so perfect that he must never lose his temper, must never deceive his wife or his lover? They are perhaps the burning, the brutal reasons for crime passionel, but at the other end of the scale there are the pathetic reasons, the poor and ugly lame duckling . . . who shot her lover when he brutally proposed to leave her, or the woman, growing old, abandoned by a young lover who left her pregnant.

Men, too, commit crimes passionel with the same facility as women. Take the last three years in Paris alone; in 1954, in 25 cases of murder for love, 15 men and 10 women stood in the dock. In 1955, 15 women and 14 men. And in 1956, 14 women and 11 men.

I am not writing this book as a defence of crime passionel. I do not advocate the use of a .32 automatic every time there is a domestic drama at home in Acacia Road or Beeches Avenue. But I do plead for greater understanding of the motives for crime passionel in those rare cases where it crops up in England. For, as the greatest French woman novelist of this century, Colette, wrote, just before she died:

"There are only two sorts of human beings in the world; those who kill and those who do not kill . . ."

But Colette would never have judged, she was too full of human understanding for that. Moreover, she belonged to the sort of human being that did not kill. Perhaps she knew what an easy physical act it is to pull a trigger. Have you ever considered it? It is difficult to stick a knife into a human body, but oh, it is so, so easy to pull that little trigger. Just a few pounds pressure and you belong to that *other* sort of human being: those who kill.

THE PROUD MURDERESS

IT WAS THE MORNING of March the 17th, 1951. It was still cold for the time of year but the morning sunlight was a mute promise to Parisians that Spring was on its way. Spring, when a young man's fancy turns lightly to thoughts of love. In ten days' time, Bernard Mougeot was thinking, Félix Bailly, his best friend, was going to marry the girl of his choice, Monique Lombard, young, blonde, beautiful, a perfect match for the gifted young medical student, now in his final year. Such were the thoughts that flitted through Bernard's mind as the taxi took him from his home near the Trocadéro on the northern bank of the Seine to the rue de la Croix-Nivert where Félix lived. And as he yelled at the chauffeur to make better time in the thick mid-morning traffic, Bernard thought of the 'other' woman, that dark-haired bitch from the North, a girl whom even Félix, the kind-hearted Félix, had termed *ma ravageuse*. The word was eloquent, and now Bernard was rushing to Félix's flat to protect him against the cold fury of his 'spoiler', for she had arrived from the North filled with the unpredictable sentiments of a woman scorned. But even as he yelled again at the taxi-driver, the vehicle got bogged down once again in the hopeless traffic-jam. Bernard gritted his teeth and prayed he would arrive in time.

Félix Bailly was to die in a few moments' time because Fate had decided that there should be a traffic-jam on the Quai de Grenelle just as Bernard Mougeot's taxi arrived there on its frantic rush to the rue de la Croix-Nivert. On such small incidents are based the threads of a human life, a young human life, vigorous and filled with promise for the future.

When Bernard Mougeot leapt out of the lift and ran towards the door of Félix Bailly's flat, he suddenly realised as he reached the entrance that he was too late. He was less than five minutes too late. Only half-an-hour had passed since Félix had telephoned him, begging him to rush urgently to his flat because the 'spoiler' had returned. And now there was the acrid smell of smokeless powder in the air mingled with a second more compelling smell of domestic gas. The front-door of the flat was still open. It must all have happened very quickly.

Félix lay dead in a slowly widening pool of blood on the floor of the lounge. In the kitchen, the 'spoiler' was lying unconscious on the floor, the gas-pipe to the cooking stove in her mouth. Bernard Mougeot's features were grim as he pulled the gas-pipe away and turned off the tap. That would have been all too easy for *her*. He returned to the lounge, and avoiding his friend's body with his eyes, dialled 17 for 'Police-Secours'. A few minutes later the first policemen arrived, followed by the firemen with their artificial respiration apparatus and oxygen cylinders.

Pauline Dubuisson was brought back swiftly to consciousness—and arrest. . . .

Two days later, in the family home at Malo-les-Bains, near Dunkirk, her brother was imploring their father to engage a leading lawyer to defend Pauline. But-the only reply the old cavalry officer could make was: "She has already killed me."

Georges Dubuisson sat down at his desk and slowly penned a long letter in impeccable copper-plate writing to the parents of Félix Bailly. He expressed his compassion, his humility, his shame. Then he went into his own kitchen and made certain adjustments to the gas piping. Being an expert engineer he did not fail in *his* suicide bid.

Sister Saint-Gerard, a wardress at the Paris women's prison of La Petite Rocquette, was making her early morning rounds. It was November 1953 and dawn was late in coming. Quietly, she opened the judas-hole of each cell to peer inside. She stopped outside Pauline Dubuisson's cell. The young woman was due to appear before the Assizes of the Seine that day to reply to the murder of Félix Bailly, but as the sister peered through the judas, her hand dropped automatically to her whistle. Pauline's features were blanched and blood dripped slowly from the veins in her wrist on to the stone floor of the cell. Sister Saint-Gerard called for help and went inside. Using her own medical training, Pauline had applied a tourniquet to her arm and then opened the vein with a needle and a fragment of glass. Two blood-stained letters lay on the bed beside her.

Rushed to the prison hospital, Pauline received an immediate blood transfusion. Dr. Paul, the French 'Médecin-Légiste', was summoned. At ten o'clock he ordered further blood and plasma transfusions, for Pauline had lost over a litre of blood in her suicide bid. By midday, her life was out of danger, but there could be no question of her taking her place in the box at the Palais de Justice that day. The court nevertheless was convened in the afternoon and Dr. Paul was called to the witness-box.

"I examined Pauline Dubuisson at the Petite Rocquette prison this morning," he said. "According to the governor of the prison and the doctor there, the young woman was found unconscious in her cell at six o'clock this morning. She had used her medical knowledge to apply a tourniquet around her left arm to bring out the veins. Then, she had attacked the radial vein with a piece of glass and a needle. . . . She will be in too serious a state of anaemia for several days to be able to take part in her own defence properly," Dr. Paul concluded.

The Advocate General, Maître Lindon, appearing for the prosecution, then stood to his feet, with a crumpled letter in his hand. As he opened it, spectators craned their necks to peer at the blood-stains on the paper. Then he read slowly:

"Monsieur le Président,

I am obliged to write to you in the dark as I do not want to turn on my night-light. I do not know whether you will be able to read this. Perhaps you will not even want to. But there was nothing to be done to avoid this and everything possible was tried. I do not want to die without thanking all those who have been so good to me despite my faults, that is, most of my friends and those others who in their own way have shown me friendship and affection. I regret having been so unkind and I would have liked to have thanked each of them personally. I think that my family is accursed and myself also. I only hurt those whom I love the most in the world. I have already lost over a litre of blood but I am still all right. Let Monsieur and Madame Bailly pardon me if they can; let them be sorry for Mummy. Pardon for all the evil I have done. You can say that I am infinitely sorry for having killed Félix but at the same time I do not want to submit myself to a justice which is so lacking in dignity. It is not that I refuse to be judged, but I refuse to deliver myself as a spectacle to a crowd which reminds me so exactly of those crowds of the Revolution. I would not have minded a case held *in camera*. But I am happy to have turned the tables finally on those who wanted to make a Roman Holiday of my trial."

The Advocate General finished reading the letter, then in a sarcastic tone said it contained the whole character of Pauline Dubuisson, the proud actress. He added his scepticism as to the sincerity of the suicide attempt, saying it was a trick to gain the sympathy of the jury.

"It was a simulation," he said, before sitting down.

Pauline's lawyer, Maître Paul Baudet, got slowly to his feet, very pale, his hands trembling with emotion. He had some difficulty in controlling his voice which quivered with disdain as he stared with undisguised hostility at the Advocate General.

"I will not tolerate the use of the word 'simulation'," he said. "It is utterly absurd and wicked to allege that a woman who has already lost over a litre of blood was only trying to simulate suicide. In point of fact, she was disgusted with the procedure in this case. She knew that the prosecution was setting great store on dragging out the more revolting details of her unhappy life. In seeking that way of dying, Pauline Dubuisson only wanted to show this court her contempt for its conduct, a way of giving us a slap on the face. . . ."

A murmur ran through the court as Maître Baudet pronounced these last words but he continued: "As she will return here, she will return to show us her true face, that of her love, not to seek your pity, but to ask for justice. She will, I think, be healed, and above all, healed by her own self."

His voice almost breaking under the strain once more, Maître Baudet concluded:

"From certain details Pauline wrote in a personal letter to me last night before attempting suicide, I feel I must tell you that henceforth there is an invisible barrier between me and Maître Lindon."

The Advocate General flushed but made no reply. The Presiding Judge, M. Raymond Jadin, adjourned the case until such time as the accused could be present.

A fortnight later, on November the 18th, the court was reconvened. This time, Pauline Dubuisson, pale but with her head held high, took her place in the box, overshadowed by two huge gendarmes. The spectators who had been queueing since dawn tensed in their seats as the Roman Holiday opened before them.

They were not to wait long for the carnage to begin.

"Pauline Dubuisson, you stand accused of assassination and are therefore liable to the death penalty. . . ."

A shiver ran through the courtroom as Advocate General Lindon pronounced the word "assassination". It meant that the State was going to demand the death penalty against a woman in an affair of crime passionel for the first time in over forty years. For in France, under Clause 296 of the Penal Code, any murder committed with premeditation becomes assassination and if proved carries an automatic death penalty.

But the petite 26-year-old brunette standing in the box did not flinch at the words. She continued to stare arrogantly at the jury. Pauline Dubuisson bowed ironically when the court gave her permission to sit, then leant forward to hear Lindon open the case against her with the same impassive features—"The Mask of Pride"—as the press was to dub it.

The mask did not change as Lindon outlined the damning facts. Pauline, the mistress of a Nazi colonel at the age of 17, had been expelled from college, and from her earliest experiences had kept a notebook in which she wrote down the names of all her lovers and her comments on their capacities. Pauline, who had poured three bullets into the man who had spurned her less than a fortnight before he was due to marry another girl. Now at the age of 26 she had taken two lives—for her father had committed suicide because of her action—placed her own in jeopardy, and wrecked the happiness of three others.

Lindon was in his stride now, flaying her with merciless words. She did not flinch when he called her a 'hyena', but despite herself, Pauline's proud features paled when the Advocate General said bitterly:

"I have often prosecuted women. I have felt pity or disgust for them. Today, I stand revolted. In the name of my own love of justice and in the name of the love she has destroyed, I demand the supreme penalty. . . ."

A hush fell on the courtroom and Maître Paul Baudet, at that time an almost unknown middle-aged Paris lawyer, patted his client encouragingly on the hand as the first of the witnesses took the oath. Alone among the men in the jury-box sat one woman juror, Mademoiselle Raymonde Gourdeau. She was later to turn the scales which would save Pauline from the death sentence.

Pauline was born at Malo-les-Bains on the extreme northern coast of France on March the 11th, 1927. The whole of her education was in the hands of her father, a brilliant engineer in charge of the regional public works department, a former cavalry officer from the First World War. But he was a strange man, a practical believer in Nietzsche. The psychologists might well affirm that the Dubuisson case began with her childhood. Pauline did not have a happy upbringing at home although there was nothing lacking materially. Her father, a perfectionist himself, set almost impossible standards for his daughter. Georges Dubuisson resorted to cold scientific 'cramming' for her education. Pauline became a brilliant and precocious scholar, but friends in the neighbourhood often whispered the word 'Pygmalion' when referring to her. In the home, her father's word was law. Her mother, browbeaten and resigned, no longer dared to express an opinion. Later in her trial, Pauline spoke of these years of childhood when she said:

"At home we were in the habit of keeping our moments of joy and our moments of sorrow to ourselves. So you see, I have kept them to myself ever since. . . ."

Thus was her character forged in these early years, the character which would eventually send her to life imprisonment. Apart from her reserved nature, her father taught her never to accept defeat. The precept was to prove her undoing.

In 1939 she entered the Jean-Bart College at Dunkirk. Her father refused to leave his home when the Germans arrived the next summer and it is impossible to estimate today the full extent of the effects which the scenes of battle and carnage must have had on the sensitive 13-year-old girl. But Georges Dubuisson, despite his conduct in the first war which had gained him the Légion d'Honneur, was no longer anti-German. His years of study of German philosophy had changed his outlook. Pauline was not slow to share his new views. She was only 14 when two French policemen indignantly led her away from a park bench where she had been sitting hand-in-hand with a 20-year-old German soldier. The incident took place during the college holidays. Several days later, the school authorities notified her father that they did not want Pauline to return for the next term, or indeed at all, on grounds of her "outrageous immoral conduct". Her father was already carrying out contracting work for the German Army in the region and Pauline became his interpreter. She was frequently seen out riding with German officers at the age of 15.

When she was 17, at the beginning of 1944, Pauline decided on a medical career. She entered the German Hospital at Dunkirk and lost no time in becoming the mistress of the Director, 55-year-old Colonel Von Domnick.

"You must admit there was something shocking in this difference in age," the Judge told her severely. "Did he take you by force? Did he seduce you?"

"No," Pauline replied in a level voice.

"How then?"

"It happened little by little," Pauline replied. She stressed that Von Domnick had been her first lover.

At all events the affaire was not to last long. The same year, Dunkirk was liberated by the allies and Pauline decided to move out of a neighbourhood which had become distinctly antipathetic towards young women who had cohabited with Nazi officers. But she was too late.

Local Resistance courts had already put her name on the list of feminine collaborators and Pauline was dragged on the main square and held on a stool while grim-faced men cut all her hair off with shears. For the time being, she was a marked woman. Pauline fled to an aunt in Lyons where she nevertheless succeeded in passing her preliminary medical exams. The following year, in 1946, she returned to the North and was admitted to the Medical Faculty of Lille University. The report on her at the end of her first year said:

"Intelligent, her work is brilliant at times but she is not a steady worker. She is well-balanced but haughty, provoking and a flirt. Her conduct is mediocre."

In the meantime, Pauline had already started to keep her infamous "carnet" in which she set down the names of her lovers and added her own dry appreciations of their physical qualities and needs. The list was later to do her nearly as much harm in court as the evidence concerning the shooting itself.

In the spring of 1947, Pauline met Félix Bailly for the first time. They were both just 20 years old. Félix was tall and broad, exceptionally good-looking and one of the university's leading athletes and hockey players.

Within a few days of their first meeting, Pauline had inscribed Félix's name in her "carnet". A week later and she was already being unfaithful to her new lover with one of his best friends, a dental student. Nearly everyone at the faculty knew about it, except, of course, Félix.

Their hectic and generally stormy affaire lasted just over two years, until October, 1949. It was of vital importance in Pauline's defence for she had to prove that she *loved* Félix during this time to support her plea of crime passionel. Yet there was little evidence to show that Félix was anything more than an agreeable bedfellow for her. When the Judge asked her whether she had loved him, Pauline unfortunately replied she had "had a lot of affection for him".

Another witness testified that Pauline had described Félix during this period as: "decorative but always hanging-on". It was an unfortunate beginning. The basic fact of the matter was that Pauline was out to have a good time in the physical sense. Félix, coming from a very Catholic family, was unable to resist her temptations and his moral sense found its outlet in asking Pauline to marry him. It is uncertain and we shall never know whether he really wanted to marry her, but at all events, he thought he ought to because they slept together. Poor Félix, he thought he was the only man to share Pauline's amatory favours. She was having a simultaneous affair with one of the doctors supervising the studies, 30-year-old Dr. Senéville. Félix knew something of this and one night rushed to Senéville's house to demand whether Pauline was there or not. The doctor received him kindly, assured him Pauline was not there, and told the young student that he was making rather a fool of himself over the girl. Upstairs Pauline lay in the doctor's bedroom, listening to every word. When Félix had finally departed, calmed down by the older man's words, Senéville had to reproach her for laughing over the incident. "I've tried to break with him but he will keep running after me", Pauline told Senéville that night. Later in the case, Dr. Senéville was called to the witness-box. This was his opinion of his former mistress: "She was an unlucky girl. Men said she could be had 'easily' but nevertheless they ran after her. Some even put pressure on her for their own ends. In all truthfulness, I believe she was seeking a love which she never found. She was looking for a disinterested affection from someone who needed her. Had she been able to find this, she would have been saved."

But the Senéville incident began to change Félix's feelings. Little by little he began to experience a diminishing physical desire for Pauline. And with the weakening of his physical desire, his purer conception of marriage began to fade into the background.

Other and perhaps more important differences appeared between them. Pauline and Félix had basically different conceptions of the value of medicine as a career. When Félix said with the ardour of youth that he wanted to become a doctor for the poor, like his father, Pauline tossed her head and replied disdainfully:

"The only thing that counts for me is the science of medicine. I intend to work in a laboratory with guinea-pigs, well away from the sick."

Then she added:

"Medicine would be such an agreeable career without them. . . ."

Repeated remarks of this kind ran directly counter to Félix's high ideals. The gulf between them broadened gradually. There was another important reason for this gulf. Pauline's family were strict practising Protestants, while the Bailly family were strict Catholics. On these grounds alone, marriage between them would have been almost impossible. And finally, Félix took a definite step to break up their affaire. At the end of the term in July 1949, he told Pauline that everything was finished between them, and that he had decided to go to Paris to complete his studies. Almost at the same time, Pauline learned she had failed her exams. She returned bitterly to the family home at Malo-les-Bains for the summer holidays.

At the beginning of the autumn term, Félix returned to Lille to the college for the weekend to collect some personal effects he had left there. Pauline made a half-hearted attempt to regain his affections, but the few months' separation had strengthened Félix's resolve. He said brutally he was returning to Paris at once. Pauline threatened to commit suicide and rushed upstairs to her room. A friend confirmed that she was in the habit of carrying a tube of cyanide she had taken from the laboratories in her handbag. Félix rushed after her and descended alone a few moments later, the tube in his hand.

Here came a period which remained an enigma throughout the whole case. Félix left for Paris after this weekend in Lille in November, 1949. Pauline did not see him again and *did not attempt to see him* again until the fatal month of March, 1951. It was this separation of eighteen months which did much to destroy the theory of crime passionel.

France's greatest criminal lawyer, Maître René Floriot, was appearing in the case to defend the interests of the Bailly family and to obtain damages for them. This method of appearing for the *Partie Civile* is considerably more complicated than in England, and frequently the lawyer appearing to defend a family's interest takes on the cloak of a veritable prosecutor, especially if he be a man of the calibre of Maître Floriot. This was the case in the Dubuisson trial, where Maître Floriot actually attacked Pauline with more venom than the Advocate General himself. In effect, the girl was subjected to two prosecutions, and there were many in court who termed Maître Floriot's handling of the accused as *persecution*. He pounced on Pauline over the question of this long period during which she did nothing to see Félix, although she claimed to still be in love with him.

"Paris and Lille are only two hours' train journey apart," Maître Floriot said. "I suppose it never occurred to you how little separated you?"

"Never," she replied.

"One can hardly say you were devoured with passion," Advocate General Lindon broke in, supporting Maître Floriot.

"I did not know Félix's address," Pauline said.

"When you decided to kill him, you found it easily enough," Maître Floriot's voice rasped.

There was something grotesquely unfair in the situation, providing you could manage to forget that Félix Bailly was dead and Pauline's father had committed suicide. The slight girl sitting in the box, defended by a kindly yet unknown lawyer, attacked by aces of the bar like Lindon and Floriot.

There was something rather indecent in the attitude of Maître Floriot during the case. He was briefed to defend the memory and honour of Félix Bailly, and also to obtain 2,000,000 francs damages for the boy's family. In private life, Floriot is an ardent game shot and big-game hunter. His collection of heads is one of the best in France. In private, in the corridors of the Palais de Justice, his colleagues will say that he is also a collector of human heads. He has frequently proved it to be the case. In defending a family name, there was no need for him to have treated Pauline Dubuisson in the way he did. Lindon alone was sufficient adversary for this girl with her own sincere lawyer who had none of the panache or biting sarcasm of the others. From the beginning of the case, it was obvious that Maître Floriot wanted Pauline Dubuisson's head for his trophy room. It was sufficient to be in court to realise it.

During this long period, Pauline did not lack for amatory distraction. She went to Germany for her next summer's holidays and renewed her friendship with the now ex-Colonel Von Domnick. Then she met a young engineer, Jean Legens, in the mountains in Austria. She swiftly seduced him and, in a short while, he was begging her to marry him. November came again and with it the start of a second college year without Félix. Legens wrote to her and Pauline replied: "I have enough wonderful souvenirs of you stored in my memory to be able to wait for you. Your kindness and tenderness mean so much to me. I love you with all my heart. . . . I fell in love with you very quickly without realising it at the time. . . . I embrace you fifty thousand times, I remain your repentant Pauline, and I want to prove to you that I am still the same Pauline you knew in Austria. . . ."

When the letter was read aloud, Judge Jadin looked perplexed: "I would like to understand," he said to Pauline.

"Talk to us about fidelity. What does it mean to you?" Advocate General Lindon fired at her.

French judges play a far greater active part in cases than their English counterparts and frequently carry out long cross-examinations themselves. Once again, you got the impression that Pauline was at bay in the box with implacable gowned hunters firing shot after shot at her.

In a cold dispassionate voice, Pauline tried to explain that at that moment she had not given up hope of marrying Félix. But she sounded confused as she said: "I wanted to force myself to love other people, in order to persuade myself I was capable of having lasting sentiments for him."

Maître Floriot, Advocate General Lindon, and Judge Jadin fired poisoned barbs at her in quick succession. What kind of a love was this? If love it were, it was self-centred and purely egotistical. Pauline continued to hold her head high, her features frozen in her "mask of pride".

Then a mutual friend, Janine Lahousse, told Pauline she had been in Paris and had met Félix. Félix had asked after his former mistress, saying: "And Pauline, is she still the same as ever?"

That was what Janine told Pauline when she mentioned the incident. But she told the court later that Félix's real words had been: "And Pauline, is she still as loose as ever?"

There was obviously little doubt in Félix Bailly's mind about his former mistress. And in the meantime, he had met a charming young blonde studying literature, Monique Lombard. Here was no experienced lover as Pauline had been, but a chaste young girl, whole-heartedly in love with Félix. Moreover, there was complete agreement between their respective families about the forthcoming marriage. It was the following February when another friend who had been to Paris confided to Pauline:

"I ran into Félix with an absolutely smashing blonde the other day. They're going to get married in a few weeks' time and look wonderfully happy."

For a full fortnight, Pauline thought about Félix. He was young, desirable, of a wealthy family, and his medical career was full of promise. Furthermore, Félix Bailly had been her *property*. Later, Advocate General Lindon was to explain to the court:

"To Pauline Dubuisson, love was possession. . . ."

And now this former property, this former possession, was going to be sacrificed to a chit of a blonde who probably didn't know the first thing about the facts of life.

That, at least, was the psychological side. The prosecution brought in another motive to explain why Pauline suddenly decided to make one last attempt to reconquer Félix. Her father was in deep water financially, and there was a question that she might have to renounce her studies and work for her living. Moreover, Pauline had found out that Legens was neither as wealthy nor in as good a situation as he had told her.

In early March, 1951, Pauline went to Paris and stayed with an uncle. The next morning—by chance, she claimed—she met Félix at the Odéon metro station. He asked her to dinner in his flat that evening—she claimed. From this point onwards, the testimony was based largely on Pauline's evidence, for the only person who could have confirmed or refuted her words was dead.

Pauline claimed she spent the night with Félix in his flat. . . .

Thunder and lightning in the courtroom! A triple attack from Floriot, Lindon and Judge Jadin. Impossible, they cried at her! This essentially honest and moral young man, engaged to a charming fiancée with the date of marriage approaching, how dare a slut with your morals insinuate that he so debased himself as to spend the night with you!

"I am astounded for many reasons, especially because of the moral character of your victim, acknowledged by all," Judge Jadin told her severely.

Advocate General Lindon took up the hunt:

"There was a photo of his fiancée beside the bed?"

"Yes."

"In short, he behaved first of all like a rotter to her and then as a rotter to you!"

"One lets oneself go sometimes, Monsieur, and one commits certain weaknesses to be regretted later."

"I don't believe Félix Bailly would have behaved in such a way," Lindon retorted.

During her first interrogation by the Examining Magistrate, Pauline had first stated she had not spent the night with Félix. Maître Floriot seized on this point:

"How delicate on your part, to begin with!"

"It was natural," Pauline replied.

"But you retracted," Floriot said. "He was dead and you alone know the truth. You had all the time to *construct* your crime passionel."

Paler than ever, Pauline made no reply.

"Look, I am quite convinced he threw you out that very evening. You don't judge others as you would judge yourself. Félix Bailly was incapable of the rotten act of which you accuse him."

Pauline pulled herself up even straighter:

"But he did. He kissed me and everything was just as it used to be. I felt I was coming out of a nightmare. Then, in the morning, he threw me out. Life didn't mean anything more to me . . ." her voice broke for a moment and then she whispered: "It was at that moment that I decided to kill us both."

And with these words, Pauline broke down for the first time, sobbing hopelessly in the dock. Maître Baudet looked pleadingly at Judge Jadin. The Judge suspended the sitting and as the two huge gendarmes took Pauline out, a wild hubbub broke out in the courtroom. This was a Roman Holiday with a vengeance. The spectators had heard the extracts from Pauline's private carnet, of the most damning sexual nature. Now they were presented with a girl who had loved other men while claiming to still love Félix. When he rejected her, she admitted to having decided on his death—and her own suicide. Was it all a vast charade invented by Pauline to invoke the crime passionel motive? Could people in love behave in such a way?

Whether or not Pauline had spent the night with him, one thing was certain. Félix had rejected Pauline for the second time and for good. Her pride could not countenance this second rebuttal. But before continuing, I would like to voice a personal opinion. I fail to see any reason why she did not spend the night with him. I have been a student myself. . . . You have a healthy and vigorous young man, who has been used to having a bedfellow. Suddenly he is engaged to a young girl whom he cannot touch until they are married. An attractive girl comes out of his past. You have a dinner tête-à-tête, with some wine, some brandy. Is it so unnatural? And what would be more natural than to feel disgusted with yourself the next morning and banish the girl from your flat for ever?

But at all events, thrown out and rejected, Pauline then committed the act which established her clear premeditation. She went back to Malo-les-Bains on March the 10th. It was her birthday and her father gave her 5,000 francs. She went to the local gun-shop and asked how to get a licence. The armourer explained and Pauline asked for a certificate at the police station, saying that she often had to return home late at night, alone. The certificate was granted at once and Pauline bought a small .25 calibre automatic. The stage was set.

Pauline returned to the medical school at Lille, the automatic in her handbag. She remained in her lodgings two days without coming out, but in the evenings, discussed her affairs with her landlady, Madame Gérard, with whom she was on friendly and intimate terms. On March the 15th, Pauline suddenly left her lodgings with a small suitcase and not even a word of farewell. Madame Gérard went up to her room and found a strange form of will lying there on the table. It stated Pauline's intention of killing Félix and then herself, and left several odd bits of jewellery of no great value to various friends. The landlady had also seen the gun in Pauline's handbag. The deadly significance of the document was not lost on her. Realising the deadly peril for Félix, Madame Gérard rushed a telegram off to him:

"Pauline left for Paris. Avoid any meeting. Telephone me urgently. E. Gérard."

She also telephoned to Félix's father and told him what had happened. He also sent his son a telegram warning him to be careful.

The next morning, Pauline went to Félix's flat. He was just leaving, intrigued by the telegrams he had received. He refused to arrange a meeting with her, and telephoned Madame Gérard at Lille who told him about the will and the automatic. Félix arranged for his student friends to provide him with a twenty-four hour guard. He reasoned that Pauline would never dare to try anything when he was accompanied. That night he stayed in a friend's flat, saying: "My 'spoiler' is in Paris with something dangerous in her handbag. . . ." He only returned to his own flat, accompanied by a friend, Georges Gaudel, the following evening. He was visibly nervous. Gaudel told the court how Félix had stopped the lift at the sixth floor, to tiptoe up to the seventh floor where his flat was, to see if Pauline were waiting there.

The next morning, March the 17th, Pauline knocked on the door of Félix's flat at breakfast time. Félix opened the door on the chain:

"What do you want now?" he asked.

"To see you."

"Impossible. I'm not alone here."

"But I want to be alone with you, just for a moment. . . ."

"Why alone?"

"Because I'm afraid of crying."

Kind-hearted as always, his suspicions almost lulled, he agreed finally to meet her in public outside the flat. Surely that would be safe. They would meet in three-quarters of an hour on the Place Cambronne:

"But I shall have a friend with me," he warned.

Then came the second and perhaps the more diabolical part of Pauline's premeditation. She did not go to the Place Cambronne and indeed *had no intention of going there*.

Pauline concealed herself in a café opposite the flat and waited for Félix and Gaudel to come out. As she had planned, they set off for the Place Cambronne together. Félix and his friend waited a whole hour in the square but there was no sign of Pauline.

"It's all a false alarm," Félix told Gaudel at last. "You'd better get on down to your lectures. I'll go home and catch up on my work."

Gaudel was more sceptical. He insisted that Félix should ring up another student to replace him. Félix rang up Bernard Mougeot who lived near the Trocadéro. Bernard promised to come right away to the rue de la Croix-Nivert in a taxi.

It is a journey that should only take twenty minutes. . . .

Félix returned from the Place Cambronne and from her vantage point Pauline saw him go up the stairs to his flat. She paid for her coffee, and verified the mechanism of the object in her handbag. Then she crossed the street and took the lift to the seventh floor. She rang the bell.

Félix must have thought it was Bernard Mougeot arriving. He opened the door—without the chain. . . .

Less than half-a-mile away, Bernard's taxi-driver was struggling with the traffic.

We are left with Pauline's evidence. . . .

"I begged him to come back to me. He persisted in his refusal. It was then I told him there would be nothing left for me but to do away with myself. I told him I couldn't live without him."

"Then you shot him?" Judge Jadin's tone was accusing.

"He moved towards me. I don't know what happened."

"I can tell you what happened. Three bullets struck Félix Bailly. Each was fatal."

From Doctor Paul's medical evidence, Félix had been hit by three bullets, each in a fatal area; one in the forehead, one through the back which penetrated his lung, and one behind the right ear.

"The last was the *coup de grâce*," said the Judge.

"I don't know, I don't know," Pauline whispered, on the verge of tears.

"You aimed well, Pauline Dubuisson!" Advocate General Lindon said, taking over. "You fire a first time and Félix, the man you love, falls to the ground. Do you take him by the shoulders and say: 'Félix, speak to me, what have I done?' No. You fire a second bullet into his back. Do you have a nervous breakdown or cry for help? No. You fire a third bullet behind his ear at point-blank range!"

The act was terrible but so was the retribution. Pauline alone, facing these three implacable men. Maître Floriot took over.

"All said and done, you didn't give him time to speak?"

"He seemed distant."

"I understand you went there to speak to him?"

"He said nothing."

"He didn't have time. You thought he seemed distant and that was enough for you, you shot him. You didn't waste time!"

"I don't know how it happened, I tell you." Pauline always stood up better to Floriot than the other two. There was cold hatred between them, a bond shared by rival hunters. It sustained her.

"A good shot, too. You open up and he falls. How do you manage it?"

"I don't know."

"He fell at the first or the second bullet?"

"How can I know?"

"When you shoot someone at point-blank range, you can see where you're hitting."

"If I knew I would tell you."

"I doubt it."

"After everything I've admitted to today."

"Well, be frank about the rest of it. What about the third bullet?"

"I don't know."

"Splendid indifference!" Floriot waxed sarcastic. "You put a pistol on the ear of a man you love, you act like a real killer, and you don't remember a thing about it."

This was cruelty now on Floriot's part. Everyone sensed it.

"For once and for all, you're a liar, Pauline Dubuisson!"

"No."

"Let's go on to your suicide. You're sure that you didn't wait a little before attempting it?"

"No."

"You didn't wait to hear someone arriving before turning on the gas?"

"No."

"You were used to that sort of thing. It was the third or fourth time you bungled your suicide. Decidedly, you only succeed with your murders!"

It was too much. Maître Baudet leapt to his feet:

"Don't defile everything with your hunter's allusions!" he shouted at Floriot, his voice filled with bitter contempt. The defence counsel continued:

"I defy anyone to pretend that there was any moment of reflection between the three shots. They came out in a burst. Murder was committed, aren't you satisfied with that? Why go on torturing this girl, inventing and imagining things? What do you want next?"

Maître Floriot did not reply directly, but those close to him heard him say sarcastically:

"That she says all the truth and not the bits which are useful for her. . . ."

For the time being, Pauline's part was over. It was the turn of the witnesses. Maître Baudet had a superhuman task before him. He was one against three, including René Floriot, the great hunter. And nobody in the Palais de Justice had ever seen Maître Floriot so implacable, so cruel, for no lesser word could describe his questioning.

Facing them was 46-year-old Maître Paul Baudet, pleading his first big case, with the tremendous handicap that he knew from the beginning that he was defending a lost cause. He did not possess the stinging sarcasm of Lindon, nor the dexterity of Floriot's rapier thrusts. He relied on one weapon—sincerity. Baudet was frequently overcome by his own emotion.

"In this case," he had said, when opening for the defence, "everything has been a question of excess."

From the moment that the Advocate General had claimed premeditation, Baudet knew he was fighting for his client's life. Quietly, he had been forced to admit the terrifying immorality of Pauline's past. But therein, he sought to excuse her. Speaking of her upbringing, he had stressed:

"Right from the beginning, her father had taught her that her features must never reveal her feelings. He taught her to adopt a universal mistrust of fellow creatures. That was the infernal, the monstrous education which thrust this girl along the paths of pride and domination."

And he had recalled Pauline's own words: "At home we kept our moments of joy and sorrow to ourselves."

But how could this kind of defence stand up against the cold, impersonal report of the famous forensic doctor, Dr. Paul, who said:

"There was no doubt as to which was the last shot; it was that which entered the head behind the ear, a veritable *coup de grâce*. It reminded me exactly of the action of the non-commissioned officer who finishes off the man shot by the firing-squad."

Note this extraordinary statement by a *witness*. There is frequently too much liberty in a French court; a doctor who started to explain what a fatal shot reminded him of in an English court would be swiftly called to order. But Dr. Paul has become a legend in the French courts and his word is also law there.

The evidence of the firemen who brought Pauline back to consciousness with their oxygen equipment proved to be in her favour. They had noted what they termed a "second degree asphyxiation with foam on the lips". Their solid testimony undid some of the harm wrought by Maître Floriot when he had attempted to browbeat Pauline into admitting that she had 'simulated' this other suicide. It also added strength to the plausibility of her second suicide bid in prison. But there was little else in the way of favourable testimony. The gun-dealer of Malo-les-Bains said he had loaded the automatic and had *put a cartridge into the breech* ready to fire—but on Pauline's request. Strange country where gun-dealers sell loaded guns to young girls. . . .

A Dr. Boutet gave a rather jumbled picture of Pauline's responsibility for her acts:

"She is easily stirred to anger, and an impulsive person who has an entire lack of affectionate sense. Perhaps this is the result of her education which was directed to one single end; to develop her intelligence even to the detriment of her morality or normal good nature."

Advocate General Lindon jumped on him:

"You speak of anger. But she said herself that she acted in cold blood."

"Let us say a state of anger," the doctor replied. "That makes no difference. She is an angry person by nature, and this does not exclude her maintaining, nevertheless, a certain cold-bloodedness."

Lindon returned to the questions of suicide. He was trying hard to wipe out the favourable evidence of the firemen. What did Dr. Boutet have to say about that?

"She was brought up in the belief that suicide is sometimes the logical and necessary ending to life; and that in any case, one has a natural right to commit suicide," Boutet replied.

"But you have yourself spoken of a *theatrical* suicide," Lindon said.

"I weighed my words carefully," Dr. Boutet replied. "I considered the question for a long time. Theatrical does not mean simulated."

Somewhat disgusted with a witness who did not say exactly what the prosecution wanted him to say, Lindon dismissed the doctor and turned to a witness who was one hundred per cent on his side, Félix's best friend, Bernard Mougeot. As if by previous arrangement, and indeed, probably by previous arrangement, Maître Floriot took over.

"Did Félix tell you he had spent the night with Pauline in his flat?" he asked.

"On the contrary he told me that she left at one o'clock in the morning," Mougeot said firmly.

"Had they had any sexual relations on that occasion?"

"Certainly not!" Mougeot sounded shocked. "They talked together and that was all. Félix would never have let himself go to such an extent of committing what would have been an act of treachery for him. He worshipped his fiancée and was a straightforward, loyal and pure fellow. He had a far more exalted conception of love than most of us. He would certainly not have lied to me about that night. There were no secrets between us."

Mougeot's voice trembled as he recalled the arrival of the telegrams. "I feel guilty even today about the affair. I didn't take it seriously enough. If we had all been a little more scared, we could have prevented the crime."

Recalling the moment when Félix had asked him to become a bodyguard and had shown him the telegrams from his father and from Pauline's landlady, Mougeot said:

"Félix said to me: 'Here, take care of these for me. If anything happens to me, you will be able to establish premeditation.' . . ."

Terrible words for Pauline but her features did not change.

Then came another of Félix's close friends, Yves Fruquet. He spoke of the relationship between Félix and Pauline when they had been lovers at Lille University.

"Félix was a wonderful type and Pauline Dubuisson just wasn't worthy of him. I think he knew it moreover, and I certainly did. She cuckolded him with everyone but she knew how to pull the wool over his eyes. Terribly proud, very intelligent, very egotistical, she knew what she was doing alright. When Félix left for Paris, he warned me never to give her his address. . . ."

What could Maître Baudet do for the defence when faced with such witnesses?

Then Monique Lombard stepped into the witness-box. She had hair the colour of golden corn which contrasted sharply with the lustreless brunette hair of Pauline which had grown dull and neglected during her eighteen months' prison detention pending trial. But the greatest contrast showed on their features, the difference between the pure classical beauty of Monique, and the proud, cold mask of disdain worn by Pauline.

Monique told her story simply, her hands clasped together on the edge of the box. It was strange that both women should be wearing plain black suits, each with a simple white blouse.

"He told me right at the beginning that he had been intimate with this," Monique had some difficulty in speaking, "with this . . . woman—but said that everything was finished between them. He also said that she had been a devil in his flesh. . . ."

Then came the dreaded moment for the defence. Maître René Floriot, perhaps the greatest lawyer in Europe, prepared to add his weight to the already damning factual testimony. He began by openly admitting his cruelty:

"I will begin by asking the court's pardon," his voice rasped. "I cannot promise to plead without passion. On various occasions during this case I have been forced to be cruel. I have been reproached for it. It is because I have a mother in tears next to me and you will excuse me if I think more of her sorrow than of the embarrassment of the accused. . . ."

Maître Floriot turned to Pauline's private "carnet" and the terrible record of depravity it contained. Slowly he read its contents, beginning with the name of Colonel Von Domnick. The spectators, the 'crowd' so despised by Pauline, was having its fill of Roman Holiday.

"She tries to hide everything," Floriot said, "and she only recognises her successive lovers in the last extremity when faced with witnesses and documents. It would have been different had Félix Bailly been the only, the unique, the irreplaceable lover. Then we could admit crime passionel. But look at this list. Look at Legens, Senéville, Colonel Domnick. . . .

"She meets Félix Bailly and once she had definitely conquered him, when she knows she has him in a position from which he is incapable of extricating himself, she takes a sadistic pleasure in seeing him come to cry on her shoulder, to groan, to plead with her, to give in to her every whim. For a proud being such as Pauline Dubuisson, the satisfaction is without parallel. . . .

"One day he understands and flees. His comrades had begged him to break with her. He didn't want to but finally found the necessary courage.

He left for Paris and his wounds healed quickly because he found a person worthy of his love, a person whom we have heard in this court."

Here, Maître Floriot stretched his hand out towards Monique Lombard, in what might seem a theatrical gesture in an English court. But Floriot never overacts. He knows only too well what he is doing with every word, with every gesture.

No detail of Pauline's life was too intimate, no reminiscence was too revolting for him to spare it from the court's ears. Maître Baudet turned anxiously towards his client during the crucifixion, and for a brief moment, Pauline's features flickered into what might be described as a half-smile. Then she turned back to face the jury, her head unbowed.

"Eighteen months pass," Floriot continued, "and she does not make one attempt to renew her relations with Félix. She finds new lovers and even returns to her very first. She cuckolds each of them. And then, at the end of eighteen months, at the very moment—and I stress this carefully —that she sees that Legens is only a little engineer without a future and that her father Monsieur Dubuisson is in serious difficulties, she thinks afresh of Félix—the only man I ever loved, she said—but the only man capable of straightening out the difficulties which she feels are approaching. . . ."

Maître Floriot paused, then stooped down to pick up a pathetic bundle of letters tied with pink ribbon. Now he was going to play his master card, he was going to paint the picture of Félix Bailly, the healthy young medical student on the threshold of a magnificent career, who had set aside his wild oats, and who was desperately in love with Monique Lombard. Floriot began with the letter Félix had written to his parents asking for their consent to marry Monique:

"My dear Mummy and Daddy,

I hope that this letter will not come as too great a surprise to you for I think that you have both been waiting for me to make this request for some time now. Dear Mummy and Daddy, I am asking you to take Monique into the family as if she were your second daughter. I think that you both know her well enough fully to appreciate her qualities. I do not know what I can add about her that you do not already know. In fact, I think that you both know quite as much about her as I do myself. It is hardly necessary to tell you both just how much I am in love with her for you must have realised by now. All I have to do is to wait impatiently. Oh, please tell me quickly how pleased you both are. I know that I can be sure of your reply but at the moment, it is giving me as much anxiety as the result of my exams. I embrace you both, as well as Maguitte, who I hope will love her new sister as much as you. Your little son who is very impatient and very much in love.

Félix."

Maître Floriot finished reading the letter. There was almost dead silence in court but Monique was sobbing very quietly to herself. Pauline was paler but as impassive as ever.

Floriot suddenly broke the silence. He swung towards the jury, one accusing arm pointing to Pauline:

"And that letter was written by the same boy who had written to his parents less than four years before, asking to leave Lille for Paris, *so that he would not be plagued by this . . . bitch!"*

Maître Baudet was already on his feet to protest, but the moment for protestation was passed. The shot had been mortal, Floriot, the great hunter, the wizard of the bar, had the court, the judges, the jury, the spectators, in the palm of his hand. He knew it.

The next letter was from Félix to his parents after they had told him how happy they were to give their consent to his marriage with Monique:

"I am very happy and I embrace you both dearly. I think that it is all I am able to say to you at the moment for I am so overcome with happiness. I have said nothing to Monique because I want it to be you two who will tell her the wonderful news and that it will be you who share her joy.

"May I just promise her that a surprise is coming. Mummy, please be gentle with her because her joy will certainly overcome her emotions. . . ."

There was the same silence as Floriot finished reading the letter and turned to the letters Félix had written to Monique:

"Only a week ago we were together here in Paris. It was so wonderful to be together. In only a few weeks time we will be together for always at Saint-Omer in our new house.

"Darling, it is sad to be without you for even these few days but we will be together again so soon."

"My darling darling little baby.

"There are thousands of things I want to tell you but for the moment, my heart is too filled with happiness and love.

"Darling, I love you with all my heart and all my strength.

"I am dreaming that we are already in our home and that after coming back from my day's work, I am giving you a tiny kiss on the doorstep. I will kiss you like that when I get up in the morning, too, so as not to awaken you.
Your little Teddy Bear,

Félix."

But this was not the rasping voice of René Floriot. It was uncanny and even macabre. The lawyer in his gown was no longer there. By force of his prodigious talent, Floriot *was* Félix Bailly. The words belonged to Félix, the voice and the intonation, too. It was not the voice of a lawyer reading the letter. It was the voice of the young man who had written it, the young man who had been in love with the girl to whom he was writing. Nothing had ever happened quite like this before in a French court of law. Floriot came to the last letter written to Monique by Félix, within days of their intended marriage. Even the gendarmes in the box were straining to catch every word. Alone in the courtroom, Pauline Dubuisson remained magnificently indifferent. It required courage.

"I often dream of the moment when we will have baby Moniques all as blonde and as good as their mummy, and baby Félixes all as horrid as their papa.

"When they are naughty we will look at them and say how adorable they are. And when we go to Paris to spend a few wonderful days together, we will leave them to be terribly spoiled by their grandmother.

"Darling, everything about life is wonderful. The moment that we met, now, the future. I feel I am living in a real-life fairy tale.

"Oh, my darling little fairy, my little golden-haired princess. Darling, I am so happy, we are so happy. Everything around us is happiness.

"Darling, I embrace you like one possessed, with all my strength.

Your little Teddy Bear,

Félix."

Maître Floriot finished reading the letter, took off his heavy horn-rimmed glasses, wiped them, and then turned again towards the jury. He had become the lawyer again:

"Darling, everything about life is wonderful. . . . Everything around us is happiness. . . ."

His tone changed and he shouted across the courtroom:

"That dream of happiness was shattered beyond mortal repair by three pistol bullets, the last one fired at point-blank range behind the ear!"

Maître Floriot put the pathetic bundle of letters down and began the last part of his speech.

"Just what exactly did happen? We cannot be certain for Félix Bailly is no longer there and Pauline Dubuisson can say what she pleases. All that I can say is that this crime has no resemblance whatsoever to a crime passionel. There is nothing vague about the way Pauline Dubuisson spent her time. She returns calmly to the North, buys a pistol, and returns to Paris to ambush her victim.

"She tracks him like a killer, watching his moves from the café opposite his flat with her weapon in her handbag. She knows that later he will be sacrificed to its shots. That is the way of a killer. I am forced to present the facts in this way. They are terrible, I know. But it is my duty.

"As far as the order of the shots are concerned, nobody, not even Doctor Paul has been able to fix them with certainty. However, I have asked myself if Pauline Dubuisson did not shoot Félix Bailly first in the back. You will see that this theory stands up. Félix Bailly was frightened, as you know. He hid himself, from his friends first of all, and then even more from Pauline Dubuisson. She enters his flat and her peaceful attitude deceives Félix. She sits down and Félix, standing, is no longer afraid. At the moment when, for one reason or another, he turns his back, Pauline fires. Félix, in falling, turns, and the second shot catches him in the centre of his forehead. Then it is the third bullet, the *coup de grâce,* the frightful gesture of this girl who puts her pistol on the head of the man she loves. Does a girl in anger, does a girl terribly in love, kill like that? This is only a theory, I repeat. But find me another way of explaining that bullet in the back. And remember well, she has an outstanding memory and has forgotten nothing, everything right down to the slightest details remains in her head. Everything except one scene, that of the murder, everything except the pistol shots. Everything except the way in which Félix Bailly met his death.

"You will say, therefore, that Pauline Dubuisson has not committed a crime of love, a crime passionel, but murder dictated by her wickedness, her pride, and her spite."

Maître Floriot had finished. Advocate General Lindon had still to wind up for the prosecution, and Maître Baudet for the defence. But Lindon knew his task was superfluous. The great counsel for the defence, René Floriot, had just made the greatest speech of the century for the prosecution.

His performance, based on the age-old call for a family's vengeance, weighed stronger than the demand for justice from the State.

If Floriot had set the scene, it was nevertheless for Lindon to demand the penalty. His speech was not long. One by one, he dismissed the possibility of crime passionel and the authenticity of her suicide bid which, even if it were sincere, was carried out purely to avoid paying her bill to society. There was no defence in her education. Her sisters had married normally and her brother was a decorated war hero. There was no question of her being unbalanced. She lived in a world of medical students and doctors and none of them had ever suggested it. Then the Advocate General came to the point:

"What punishment should I demand? I cannot speak without emotion for it concerns a woman. But I consider her like an evil being who has committed an unpardonable crime. This death which she meted out without pity, I ask that it should be hers. You will not accord her any form of extenuating circumstances, neither that of crime passionel, nor that of a bad upbringing. Félix Bailly called her his 'spoiler' and he had good reason. She despoiled everything around her. The marriage of Félix and Monique Lombard was something clean and beautiful. But she did not want clean and beautiful things. She killed for pleasure and today I am even more intransigent than when I am prosecuting some common killer. Pauline Dubuisson wreaked a veritable carnage of happiness. She decided on it and she carried it out to its bitter end. Therefore against this human monster, in the name of our poor human joys and also in their defence, I demand the supreme penalty. . . ."

There was a stir in court as Lindon sat down and Judge Jadin had to call order several times to obtain silence. All eyes were turned on Maître Baudet, this unknown lawyer who risked losing his client's head in his first big case. As I said before, Pauline would not have been guillotined, as President Auriol would have pardoned her, yet it seemed certain she would at least be sentenced to death as premeditation appeared clearly proved.

Maître Baudet rose slowly. He looked for a long time with uncon-cealed hostility, if not actual hatred, at the Advocate General and at Maître Floriot. He spoke slowly, his voice charged with emotion.

"I raise a lone voice in the midst of excess, for in this case, everything has been excess," he began. "But your excess," he said, turning again towards Lindon, "weighs on my shoulders like lead. You overwhelm me, Monsieur l'Advocat Général, because your judicial mechanism has been so well built and is so precise, that I have nothing with which to counter it but my good will and my sincerity. I am afraid. I am not used to appearing in your cases, but in the course of my career, I have come to love those whom I defend, to love them for themselves, to attempt to understand them. . . ."

Baudet explained Pauline's upbringing and the strange philosophy which her father had taught her, that she only was thirteen at the time of the Dunkirk disaster which took place before her eyes. Then he turned to her love life:

"You stress that the German Colonel was fifty-five years old, Monsieur l'Advocat Général. Are you trying to say that men of that age have no charm left? Surely you're not trying to insinuate that she took this officer by force, that she raped him! The same goes for the lovers who followed, they were not forced into Pauline Dubuisson's bed!

"She was a loose woman, you say, because she had lovers. Monsieur l'Advocat Général, would you dare go through the courtroom with me and say that she is the only one of her kind here?"

Lindon looked uncomfortable. He had not expected such a biting frontal attack from this little lawyer whose words, ringing with sincerity, were having their effect. Maître Baudet swung to face René Floriot: "How did she kill? I was appalled, listening to *you,* Maître Floriot. . . ."

It was Floriot's turn to look uncomfortable. Pauline had turned her gaze to stare at him, too, and he must have felt her cold eyes boring into the back of his head, for he turned quickly to look at her. But he turned back quickly as Maître Baudet continued:

"Yes, appalled, Maître Floriot. You can make a dossier say anything you like, I see, with a little intelligence, enough imagination and a lot of talent. We only *know* one fact, that it all happened very quickly. Witnesses who heard the shots say that they came one after another without any interruption. So myself, I am going to launch a theory as well. I have the perfect right to do so because you have done it. Leave the first two shots aside, I am going to speak of the third shot which you have indifferently termed the *coup de grâce,* the killer's bullet, or the executioner's bullet. Pauline Dubuisson has fired and Félix Bailly falls. Who can say that as she rushed to support him, the gun in her hand did not accidentally come into contact with his head? Who can say that it was deliberate? Nobody. You, you've come to the conclusion that it was deliberate simply because you have decided that everything must be horrible about this crime."

And Maître Baudet concluded:

"For Pauline and in her name, I beg pardon for this proud being who, desperate, in the cold night in her cell, did not want to accept your justice and thought it her duty to choose death instead. I beg pardon for all those parents who believe they are educating their children in bringing them up in their own image. I beg pardon for the manner in which she made her confessions and for their clumsiness. Finally, I beg your pardon for him she chose as a lawyer, a useless accessory of justice, who, if he refuses you the emotion of his tears, at least gives you the spectacle, even when he is pleading with you, of dignity."

As Maître Baudet sat down, Pauline bent forward and touched him lightly with her hand. The lawyer felt for it and held it for a brief moment.

Then Pauline broke down into tears. She had remained passive and indifferent before the cruelty of the Advocate General and Maître Floriot, but before kindness, before Maître Baudet's touching appeal and his strange apology, she could no longer hold back her emotion. Judge Jadin gave her time to recover and then asked the ritual question:

"Have you anything else to say?"

Pauline pulled herself together with a terrible effort and said in a strangled voice:

"I have nothing to add for my defence. I would like only to repeat the words I wrote when I thought I was about to die. I ask pardon of all those to whom I have done harm without measuring the consequences. . . ."

She left the box between her two huge gendarmes and the jury filed out silently behind her. It was forty minutes before they returned. When everyone had resumed their seats, the foreman of the jury rose with a piece of paper in his hand:

"We find the accused guilty of murder," he said.

Judge Jadin stared at him:

"And the premeditation?" he asked coldly.

The foreman glanced down at the woman juror, Mademoiselle Raymonde Gourdeau, and frowned, then lifted his eyes to the judge:

"We find the accused guilty of murder without premeditation. . . ."

Judge Jadin turned to have a quick word with his two assessors—deputy judges—and then turned towards Pauline. At a nod from the gendarmes, she stood up.

The judge's voice grated unpleasantly across the still courtroom:

"Pauline Dubuisson, you stand convicted of murder. This court hereby sentences you to penal servitude for life as specified under Clause 304 of the Penal Code.

"Remove the prisoner."

A horrified murmur from the spectators greeted the terrible verdict.

But for the very first time since the case began, Pauline Dubuisson smiled properly. The smile showed her contempt for the court. It also showed that despite the months of cell life and prison diet, she was a very attractive woman. She touched Maître Baudet once again on the hand, and was gone. She had received the most severe sentence given in an affair of crime passionel for over forty years. . . .

The sentence was severely criticised in every section of the French press. But perhaps the key to the affair came at the end of a letter written to a newspaper by a certain Monsieur Laurent of Clignancourt, a northern suburb of Paris. He said simply:

"In conclusion, Pauline Dubuisson has paid, has paid very dearly, too dearly, not for the death of Félix Bailly (for other women have received

far lesser sentences for the same crime and have even been acquitted)
but because she transgressed against present-day bourgeois morality."

And for having upset that 'bourgeois morality', Pauline Dubuisson
will spend at least the next twenty years of her life making rough leather
harness in the women's prison of Haguenau.

THE MESKIN HOUND

A Complete Novel by

John H. Latham

THE MESKIN HOUND

ILLUSTRATIONS BY NICK EGGENHOFER

EDITOR'S NOTE

This is the story of how young Jim Tucker grew up to be a man during the months he spent in the hills of east Texas with Sugar Barnett, the one-armed hunter, and Felipe, the hound puppy who understood only Spanish. Warm, humorous and suspenseful, it is a delightfully different novel. In the words of the *Dallas News,* "It goes right alongside *Old Yeller,* and is for the same wide readership."

The author, John H. Latham, was born and raised in the west Texas ranching country. Among other jobs, he has hoed and picked cotton, driven four-mule teams, farmed, ranched, worked as a cartoonist, merchant seaman, policeman, and magazine writer. His home is now at Conroe, Texas, where he publishes two trade journals.

1

THE OLD CAR came careening up the rocky lane, Sam Cleever rolling in drunk again, and from the moment he heard it Jim Tucker was set for trouble. *One of these nights he'll wrap that rattletrap around a tree,* Jim thought, but now he thought it aimlessly, not in the fierce and thirsty way he used to long to see his stepfather split and flayed and hell-fire roasted.

Cleever ran the car into the yard before he slammed on the brakes. He switched off the lights. Jim could hear him mumbling, pawing in the darkness for the door latch. Then he heard a dog growl, and the corn-shuck mattress under him rattled as he sat up quickly.

"Queenie!" he called sharply.

He was too late. The hound's yelp of pain was shrill in the yard. Jim Tucker came up out of bed with a sudden tight feeling inside. Cleever was always kicking his dog, and when he was drunk he made no bones of hiding the pure meanness he meant by it.

"You got no call to kick that dog!" Jim said in a thin, tight voice. His tone was a challenge, and the goose pimples rose along his arms and his back at memory of how Sam Cleever had answered other challenges.

Cleever slammed the car door. "Button your lip!" he growled, as usual, but there was something wrong with him. Instead of a streak of cussing, telling how he'd kick any fool old dog any time he pleased, he stood there wheezing out his breath. Instead of pawing the dirt toward Jim, over on the gallery, he was looking around at the shadows. "Who's been here?" he said. "Was anybody hunting me?"

Jim didn't answer. The light of a quarter moon rising over the Texas hill country showed him palely on the gallery, with only a pair of flour-sack drawers to cover his stringy nakedness. He was standing boldly with arms crossed, fingers gripped on his biceps, but most of the bravery was in the pose. Sooner or later he was bound to have it out with Sam Cleever. Sam would come at him one of these nights when he wouldn't turn and run, and then by God they'd see. But not tonight. Sam had something in his hand, hiding it down beside his leg, and a scarecrow would suspect him.

He made one brash step toward the gallery, then angled into the house. Jim was aware of some other movement in there, his mother or Mary Sue, and he tensed as he waited for voices. But the worst he heard, a little later, was a sound of retching. The tightness went out of his chest then, and only a hint of it came back when Cleever loomed again in the doorway.

He was cussing as he came. "This place is mine," Cleever blustered, "and nobody tells me what I'll kick on it!"

Maybe it was, Jim thought, but there were still memories of the days when the Tuckers had run a cattle spread under their Fiddle brand. Though there wasn't much left, people still talked of the old Fiddle brand. In fact what had changed Cleever's tune was the Fiddle brand carbine tucked beneath one arm and the half jar of bootleg whiskey he was carrying. He came to the edge of the gallery and sat down, dropping a tire iron beside him. This was what he had been hiding along the leg of his overalls, scared of the yard's shadows.

"A convict's two-bit hound," Cleever sneered. "And a convict's wet-nosed kid. Ought to've run you both off months ago."

Jim knew he shouldn't answer. It was his back talk, his mother complained, that no kind of man would swallow in his own house. His bickering only made it worse for them. But something kept goading him into it, sharper than ever lately.

"I've earned our keep," he said. "You've seen to that."

"Shut up!" Cleever lurched toward him swinging the carbine, but it was false pretense. There was more on his mind than beating up his stepson, whacking respect into his hide with a quirt. The big black jumps were riding him, scratching him with mortal terror.

"A damned stir-crazy convict's kid," Cleever said, but his sullen eyes switched away from Jim and he might have been talking to the yard. He took a drink from the half jar, then wiped a bony hand across a two-day growth of steely black whiskers. "Well, I can tell you one thing. First sight or smell of him around here, I'll shoot him down. He can sure bet on that!"

Jim was standing tensely again. Queenie came slinking along the gallery floor to rub against his bare legs, and he reached down and pulled one of her ragged ears.

"That hog-thieving pa of yours," Cleever said, "he never had real good sense. Like they all said at the store, he'd be just the one to lead such a jughead thing—jumping on the work-truck driver, piling 'em all into the ditch. Happened just the other day. Twenty convicts in the truck and more'n half got clean away."

Jim's heart leaped into his throat.

"But I warn you now," Sam Cleever said hoarsely, "that he's as good as dead if I catch him here. I'll shoot him down the way I would a hydrophobia polecat." He'd been talking into the moonlit yard, and now he turned his scowl on Jim. "If you know a thing about him, if you hear a single word, you'll be smart to turn him in. That's what he just told me—August Hershimer. 'You tell that boy he'd better not try to help his pa one lick unless he wants to see hisself in jail.' That's what August said."

It's Pa, Jim thought. *Pa's the one he's scared of.* The thought was warm inside him, and his shoulders stiffened. He tried to put his scorn and contempt of his stepfather into half a sound something like a laugh.

Cleever got up and staggered into the house.

Five years back, when Jim was scarcely turned thirteen, August Hershimer had sent his father to the pen for hog stealing. A year later, his mother had divorced Dan Tucker and married Sam Cleever. That was a thing Jim found hard to understand. Or forgive. For everyone knew it was Cleever's testimony that had brought about Dan's conviction.

Jim stood thinking about it now. He saw his father running through the night, wading some desperate river ahead of the trail cries of the bloodhounds. But he'd always heard it took a good man to escape the Texas State Prison Farms at Huntsville. If Dan Tucker was coming ring-tailed wild to settle up old scores it would need more than a bloodhound pack to stop him.

The mental picture gave him a lift. Times he had lain there with the stings of the quirt hot on his back, crying into his corn-shuck mattress or into the dirt of the yard, some such lift was what he prayed for. He fondled Queenie's head, wondering how he could help if his father did make it back hereabouts. Dan Tucker would be hungry. He'd sure need grub, a place to hide, the help of someone he could trust.

Then sharp reality came back. With everybody watching him, what help could he be? One wrong move would put him outside the law himself, and he was deathly afraid of the law. The sight of August Hershimer, who represented the law in Mason County, made him hear his mother carrying on outside the jail again, and he couldn't forget the time he saw the big squat sheriff take a hammer-lock on Menitole Sanchez and wrench the Mexican's arm out of socket, making him confess the theft of a sheep.

It wasn't right to be so afraid. August Hershimer was just a man, he tried to tell himself, and one man was as good as the next. But the fear always stayed in him, gnawing away, the same as it did each time he tried to nerve himself for a showdown with Sam Cleever.

From around the corner of the house came a whisper: "Jim!"

Mary Sue was motioning to him. Mary Sue was Cleever's girl by his first woman. Jim reached for his pants, pulled them on, followed her across the yard. They went out the back gate, past the garden patch, and around the corner of the barn to a cotton wagon standing at the edge of the field. The canvas sheet was thrown back from the rear-end bows and moonlight shone on a half load of cotton Jim had picked.

Mary Sue climbed into the wagon and flung herself full length. Jim came and sat beside her, his weight sinking him deep into the cotton's fluffy mass.

"What was he mad about now?" she asked.

"What he mostly is—Queenie or me."

"You ought to get shut of that old dog," said Mary Sue. "It don't make sense to keep her around when she makes Pa so mad. And she's no account, anyhow."

"Pa give her to me," Jim said. "I wouldn't take nothing for Queenie."

"Get shut of her," Mary Sue insisted. "Your mother was saying yesterday how you ought to get shut of that old dog. She said it don't look like you want to get along with Sam."

Sitting there in the cotton, Jim could hear in his mind his mother's thin voice. "Old hound-dog's always underfoot, eating a body into the poorhouse. Just like your pa always was—thinking more of a hound-dog than of his own folks."

His mother was right in a way, Jim guessed. Dan Tucker had seemed to think more of dogs, of hunting and prowling the woods, than he ever had of plowing his cotton or making a decent living. But a woman should also be able to see that nag, nag, nag, day in and day out, wouldn't change a man's nature.

"What was Pa saying?" Mary Sue asked impatiently. "I could hear him talking big. What was it?"

Jim wanted to tell about his father. He wanted to brag that likely as not Dan Tucker was right now winding up a bunch of fool bloodhounds in such a tight circle those dogs wouldn't know which way was up. But something stopped him. Mary Sue was all right, but you never could be exactly sure where you stood with her. This wasn't something to share with her, or anyone else. This was purely Tucker business.

"Just same as usual," he evaded. "Cussing me out and telling how he should've run me and Queenie both off the place."

She lay back, stretching, glancing sidewise at him. "Why don't you run off?" she asked. "If I was a man you'd see how quick I'd tell Pa to go to hell. I'd go make me some money and set up on my own."

She put a hand on his arm. Mary Sue was eighteen, a few months older than he was. She had all the Cleever looks, the coal-black hair and high-bridged nose and snapping eyes, and her tongue could bite when she so minded. But she was too smart, Jim had always reckoned, to be another mean and shiftless no-account like her pa. Too smart and too pretty. Even in that shapeless old striped flannel nightgown she looked pretty. Pretty—and something else.

Her fingers played along his arms in a teasy kind of way, and a cool, delightful prickling crawled across his shoulders. Mary Sue was smiling up at him, and now her blue-black eyes widened. She gave a low, reckless laugh, caught him around the neck, drew him down upon the cotton.

In what was a bold move for him, Jim put his arms around her. He drew her close, holding her strongly, and the pound of her heart so close to his own was wild and secret and sinful. He kissed her face, and a sudden tenderness caught at his throat and put a sting of tears in his eyes. Something in the back of his mind told him here was the answer to the fears and doubts and longings that plagued him.

After a moment her face changed. Suddenly she was out from under him, coming violently to her feet. He caught at her hand but she wrenched away. With a full-armed swing she whacked him across the face.

"You!" she spat out. "What gives the likes of you the right to maul a girl!"

"Wait!" he said. "Listen, Mary Sue—"

On his knees, Jim watched her go. She hiked up the skirts of her night-gown, running on long legs around the corner of the barn, everything about her showing honest outrage. Now he had no friends left in this house, no friends left in Mason County, at least to amount to anything.

2

GETTING HIS THINGS TOGETHER, getting ready to go, he kept halfway quiet
though there was no need. A mule kick wouldn't wake Sam Cleever,
flopped out in a bullhide chair. Jim's mother, lying with arms flung wide,
was one of those heavy sleepers who claimed they would never know if
the house fell in. If Mary Sue heard him, she gave no sign. She wasn't
likely to, after what had happened.

It was around two o'clock in the morning when he started down the
lane, with Queenie trotting at Blue's heels. A bedroll was tied on behind
his saddle. A plunder sack hung from the saddle horn. The .30-30 he
had snaked from beside Sam Cleever's chair was strapped under his left
stirrup. Cleever sure would prize things up about that carbine, Jim
reckoned, but let him prize. The brand burned into the gunstock, the
mark of a little fiddle, proved who owned it. Maybe the brand was dead
but there wasn't a man in that part of Texas that didn't know it represented the old Tucker outfit. Any kind of law would admit his right to
take his own daddy's horse and gun.

Heading out, Jim felt a lightness of heart. Why on earth, he began
to wonder, had he put it off so long? Mostly it was his mother, and even
now he had his doubts that this was what she deserved from him, riding
off without a word. He had stood and watched her sleeping, there toward the last, trying to think a long way back and wishing he could puzzle
it out and know just what to tell her. But he couldn't.

The moon was riding high now and a tinge of frost fuzzed the patches
of needle grass out in the openings. Blue threw up his head and snorted,
and from out in the brush came a sniff and the clatter of hoofs. That'd
be a deer, come to graze in the oat patch in the bend of the creek. Outside of little patches of rescue grass, young oats were about the only green
pickings deer got in the fall.

When his mother first married Sam Cleever, he was too young to do
more than hang around and sulk. Maybe he thought that being with her,

sassing Cleever every chance, would bring them together again, Dan Tucker's family, when they set his father free. But he didn't believe that any more, hadn't for years, so why had he let things run on? Working himself to a frazzle, taking Cleever's beatings and never fighting back—weren't nobody's benefit in that.

Maybe he wouldn't have heeded his mother's complaints that he was only a chore to her, like Queenie, if it hadn't been for his father. Dan Tucker had escaped, and he'd be counting on his son, Jim told himself. The need to be foot-loose, to set up a base where he couldn't be watched and followed, made him think of Sugar Barnett. Sugar had been a friend of his father's, and Jim always had the feeling that the wild-hog hunter would be a friend to him, too.

Out in the post oaks a hoot owl started his lonesome booming. Close by, a fox had the nerve to bark at them. Jim had to call Queenie to keep her from chasing the fox. He took a deep breath of the chill air and thought: *I'll take no more from Cleever or anybody else. I'll show 'em I'm my own man!*

Before him the thick foliage of towering live oaks threw a chunk of black shadow across the road. Blue flung up his head. Queenie uttered a growl of warning, and Jim realized he was looking at the dim outline of two cars under the oaks.

In alarm, he saw movements of men getting out of the cars. Behind him he heard the voice of August Hershimer call out sharply: "All right, kid. Which way you heading?"

The big sheriff stepped into the moonlight, holding a rifle. Hershimer was almost as broad as he was long, with a neck so short that his head seemed to rest squarely on his shoulders. He shuffled his boots in the sand, hunting better footing, and asked again: "Where you going, Jim Tucker?"

"I'm heading for Sugar Barnett's place," Jim said. "Why?"

But he already knew why.

The men crowded closer around his horse, and Queenie started growling deep in her throat.

"Shut up!" August Hershimer commanded harshly, and kicked at Queenie. He looked up at Jim. "Don't lie to me, kid. Where you meeting him?"

Jim thought of Menitole Sanchez, and of how his arm had looked when August Hershimer was through with it.

"I said I was just heading for Sugar Barnett's," he answered, his voice tight. "I'm aiming to throw in with him, hog hunting."

August Hershimer laughed shortly. "Hell of a time of night to be leaving home."

Jim said nothing.

The sheriff prodded: "Sugar expecting you?"

"Sure," Jim lied. "We made our plans a while back."

"Uh-huh," August said. "Well, it's damned funny how forgetful that Sugar is. When I talked to him this evening, he was headed for Jess Pickett's place on Little Devil's River in a brand-new Model T. Aiming to do a little catfishing, he told me."

A man Jim recognized as Clyde Turner eased closer. With a quick movement, he slid Jim's Winchester out of the saddle scabbard. He handed the carbine to a man behind him and lifted down the flour sack Jim had hung to his saddle horn. "Here's a big bait of grub," he said to the sheriff.

"Sure," Hershimer said. "His old man could likely use a bait of grub now."

He said it kindly, as if he approved of Jim's taking food to his father. He smiled up at Jim and rubbed the knuckles of the huge hand holding his rifle.

"Get off that horse, kid."

Jim got down off his horse. His knees felt rubbery weak now and he was having trouble pulling enough breath into his lungs. He knew how it was going to be, even before August Hershimer hit him in the mouth.

He had no sense of falling. The world merely turned over and he was lying face down in the sand. There was the salty taste of blood in his mouth. There was gritty sand between his teeth, and he kept grinding them together. Beside him, August Hershimer was gripping his arm and hauling him to his feet.

Hershimer said in a soft voice, terrible in its very gentleness: "Somebody hand me that rope off his saddle."

A man brought the rope. Hershimer shook out the coils and slipped the loop over Jim's head.

The feel of the rope brought Jim to his knees in sudden panic. He clawed at the loop, but Hershimer hit him again, knocking him back down into the sand. The rope jerked tight around his neck. Still conscious, but unable to move, Jim watched the big sheriff rise, step toward the live oaks and toss the loose end of the rope across a limb.

"Get your car, Dave," he ordered.

Dave Michner started up his car and backed it off the road. Hershimer squatted and tied the free end of the rope to the axle.

"Where you meeting your pa, kid?" he said to Jim.

Jim couldn't say anything. He couldn't even swallow.

"All right," Hershimer said. "Move her up, Dave. But take it easy. I don't want his neck broke before he gets a chance to talk." Dave Michner slid the clutch in gently, looking back over his shoulder to where Jim lay. August Hershimer gripped Jim's hands, anchoring him. The rope slid slowly across the tree branch and tightened.

Jim Tucker screamed, but the tightened loop choked him off, pulled his head up slowly, away from his body held fast in the sheriff's grasp. Hershimer, pulling on Jim's hands, watched him out of calculating eyes as he kicked and squirmed.

A rope around your neck is purple. But after a second the purple bursts into a red flare against your eyes like the flare of a shotgun in the dark and with the same shattering blast of sound. Then you know you're dying because your eyeballs are popping out of your head and that's what happens when a rope draws tighter and tighter around your neck, pulling your head away from your body.

Jim came to with his face in the sand, his fingers tugging at the noose around his neck. To suck wind into his tortured lungs was like breathing fire.

"Where you meeting him, kid?"

"Take it easy, August," somebody said. "Hell, the kid ain't done nothing yet. It's his old man we're after."

"And he'll tell me where his old man is," Hershimer said, "or I'll pull his damned head off his shoulders." He kicked Jim in the ribs. "Where is he, kid?"

Jim heard a voice croak, "You can go to hell—all of you!" And Hershimer was ordering Dave to tighten the rope again before Jim realized that the voice had been his own.

He tried to fight then, but Hershimer gripped his arms once more, swinging down with all his ponderous weight.

The water was cold and slimy around him. He could hear Queenie barking as he slid down into the murky depths. The brindle bitch was tugging at his shirt collar, choking him, straining to drag him to safety. But he slid on down and down into the dark water until there was no sight or sound.

They had the second car backed around now, and the lights were blinding bright in his eyes. All Jim could see was a ring of boots around him.

"We damn nigh kilt him that time, August," a man said.

"Hell, I will kill him if he don't open up and talk," Hershimer said. His voice was thick with baffled rage.

"Not with my help," Clyde Turner said flatly. "I'm done ashamed of the part I takened in this. We ain't bothering him no more!"

The sheriff lunged toward him. "By God, I'm running this show!" he roared. "You're a sworn deputy, and you'll take my orders!"

Turner thumbed back the hammer of the Fiddle brand carbine. "Not no more orders like choking this kid to death," he said evenly.

Jim Tucker started crying. His throat hurt so bad when the sobs tore out of his chest that he tried to stop them, but they came anyhow. He felt tears washing down through the dust on his cheeks, scalding hot.

He turned over and buried his face in the sand. He couldn't bear to have them see him cry.

3

LATE THE NEXT AFTERNOON, Jim located Sugar Barnett's camp on James River, a quarter of a mile above the mouth of Little Devil's River. He found a shiny new Model T Ford parked on a grassy bench that jutted out from the canyon wall. A gnarled cottonwood grew against the rock cliff and from under its roots gushed a bold spring that spilled foamy white water over the shelf. Below, the spring water had carved a meandering foot-deep trough through the hard limestone to join the main stream in the canyon. Across the river, a rock wall rose sheer for fifty feet, then slanted back to the top of the hill. A heavy stand of scrub cedar covered the slope.

Jim dismounted and looked around, then stripped the gear off old Blue and staked him where he could get water and good graze. He rifled through Sugar's chuck box wedged in the forks of a cedar and started up a fire.

If his mouth and throat didn't feel like eating, his belly sure did. Clyde Turner had put the .30-30 back into its scabbard but he never knew

what happened to his plunder sack of grub. He made coffee, chewed cold
venison and biscuits, and topped it off with a batch of honey he found
in a battered tin bucket. It was wild honey that Sugar had cut out of
a tree somewhere, the dead bees and shattered bits of bark in it told
that, but it went down smooth. It had a good flavor—catclaw, Jim guessed
—and he ate a filling bait of it.

His full stomach made him drowsy. He got himself a cold drink from
the spring and spread out his bedroll near the Ford. He slept till long
blue shadows were filling the canyon. There was still no sign of Sugar when
he woke, so he left camp afoot and worked down toward the mouth of
Little Devil's River. His bruised lips and neck were swollen and feverish
and he stopped once to bathe them in the cold spring water.

He found Sugar Barnett knee-deep in a clear rock-rimmed pool, using
a dead sotol stalk for a pole and a jack-rabbit liver for bait. Sugar was
a one-armed man and he handled his tackle much like a fly fisherman.
He'd pull his bait from the water, whip it behind him, then flick it forward
again to drop gently and neatly against a lily pad where the spotted tiger
bass or blue channel cat lay in wait.

A bass struck just as Jim walked up, and Jim marveled at Sugar's
speed and dexterity in landing and releasing his catch. A man with two
hands couldn't've done it any faster.

Sugar grinned at Jim over his shoulder as the bass flopped back into
the pool. "It's just too good to quit!" he said. "They'd come out on the
bank to hit a bait today. Been tossing 'em back for the last hour."

He rolled the pole between his fingers, winding up his line, and started
wading to the opposite bank. "Got a good mess for supper tied up in a
grass sack at that willer yonder," he said.

Jim watched him wade toward the willow, and recollected a night,
years ago, when his father had brought Sugar in, moaning drunk, with
nothing left of one arm but a bleeding stub. Sugar and Jim's father had
been working wild hogs up on the Candace place near San Saba and that
night Sugar had let a jug of Wild Lucy wine get the upper hand of him.
He'd wandered out into the dark and fallen into a pen with a bunch of
range hogs. Dan Tucker had heard his first scream, but by the time he
could get the hogs fought off, Sugar's left arm was eaten off nearly to
the elbow, and there was a bad slash across his left jaw.

Sugar wore a stubble of beard to hide the disfigurement, but he was
not bad-looking. He was always full of joke and josh, and Jim Tucker
liked him. Women sure seemed to like him, too.

Sugar lifted a dripping tow sack out of the water and Jim could see
the fish flopping about inside it. He went around to carry the sack and

Sugar saw his face. "Blessed Jehoshaphat!" he said. "What got hold of you?"

Jim didn't much want to tell him. But he knew Sugar would learn it sooner or later, anyhow, so he told him the truth. Only, he didn't mention about how he'd lain there in the road sand and cried like a baby. That part was too ugly. The very memory of it made him cringe.

"The sons of bitches!" Sugar growled. "The dirty, stinking sons of bitches. Come on up to camp and I'll make you a pear-root poultice."

In camp, Sugar got a short-handled shovel out of his car and went back up on the ridge and dug among the rocks till he'd unearthed a prickly-pear root about the size and shape of a sweet potato. He brought the white root down and washed it in the spring, then dropped it into a clean flour sack. He laid the sack on a flat rock, and went to pounding the tuber with the back of his ax. When he had it beaten into a pulpy mass, with the juice seeping through the cloth, he made a poultice out of the sack and bound it around Jim's swollen neck.

"That'll draw the swelling down," he said.

The poultice felt cool and Jim was instantly conscious of soothing relief.

Jim cleaned the fish and rolled them in corn meal. He fried them in a skillet of smoking-hot hog fat while Sugar mixed a batch of sour-dough biscuits and put them in a Dutch oven to bake. The coffee Sugar made was strong and bitter, and it went fine with the fish. They ate quickly and in silence, while night closed down in the canyon.

When they'd fed Queenie and cleaned up the dishes, Sugar went to sit on the running board of his new Ford and began to pick his teeth with the blade of his pocketknife.

"Ain't these new models the dilly?" he remarked. "This '22 is the best un old Henry Ford ever put out."

"It sure looks fine," Jim agreed. "Them seats, they look like they're real leather-covered."

"Imitation," Sugar said. "But the women, they don't know the difference."

When Jim didn't laugh at the joke there was a short silence. Then Sugar said: "Be dogged, I can't hardly believe it about Dan."

"You mean about his breaking out?"

"That's right. Dan ain't nobody's fool. His time's up in another five or six months. It don't stand to reason he'd bust out now and risk going back for a longer stretch. Less'n he went stir-crazy."

"Stir-crazy?" Jim repeated.

"That's what they call it," Sugar said somberly, "when a man used to the open can't stand prison no longer. Now and then one cracks and gets batty as a loon."

Jim thought of his father, slack-jawed and empty-eyed and running like a summer fox. He shuddered. "That's what scares Sam Cleever," he said. "I reckon that was why the sheriff bore down so hard on me."

"August Hershimer don't need excuses to skin a man alive," Sugar said. "He was born a mean devil."

He got out his sack of Black Stud, slipped a paper from the pack and laid it on his knee. By the light of the campfire he sifted tobacco into the paper and rolled a neat cigarette with unbelievable speed. He lit up and drew thoughtfully.

"What you aiming to do about Dan?" he asked bluntly.

"Why, I don't know much to do," Jim said. "Had it figured that if he had broke out, he'd maybe try to get in touch with you, seeing as how you all used to run together a heap."

Sugar nodded. "Could be he would."

"Figured too," Jim said hesitantly, "that you'd have a hog-gathering job for the winter and I could maybe help you out." He broke off to add hastily, "That is, if you can use me . . . I'm sort of out on my own now and I'd like to get a start somewhere, making my own way."

He waited anxiously for Sugar's answer. He hoped it didn't look too much like he was trying to horn in on Sugar.

The hog hunter studied him speculatively while Jim stared into the fire. The boy was already taller than Dan Tucker, and he'd soon be thicker through the chest than Dan Tucker had ever been. His shoulders squared unobtrusively under his old hickory shirt. He had a lean dark face and friendly eyes, but at times, such as now, those eyes could turn hangdog with sullen bitterness.

But what else would you expect from a boy raised under Sam Cleever's thumb? He'd been forced to become a man too quick, so now he figured every hand in the world was turned against him.

Sugar scratched a knuckle on his chin. "Well, could be," he said. "I'm on a deal right now with the Kline Brothers & O'Toole outfit to work their range. They figure on stocking with Angora goats, come spring, and want to clean their pastures. Old hogs'd eat up them kid goats faster'n the nannies could drop 'em . . . I'll know about it in a couple or three days."

Jim didn't look for sleep to come quickly, after the nap he had, and when they finally turned in he kept shifting around in his bedding. Every way he turned, he found new soreness. With his eyes closed, stretching himself, he could almost feel the brutal weight of August Hershimer fastened to his arms. The memory of his weakness, sobbing into the sand, flooded new weakness into him and he found that he was shivering.

On his back, staring into the night, he clenched his fists against his chest. Presently he felt easier. It was clear and cool and the air was fresh on his face. He could hear the splash of the spring and soothing sounds from the river. If he turned his head he could see the shape of Sugar sleeping yonder, and starlight glinting from the Model T. *The stars are no closer or brighter than from the gallery,* he thought, *but the room around 'em here is all the difference.*

Sugar let him sleep late. When he did get up, Sugar saw how stiff he was and set out treating him like a sick man. While Jim was eating, he went off for more prickly pear to freshen up the poultice.

"What I'd sooner have is some of that whiskey the Meskins 'still through three-four times," he said. "That'd really fix you. But I don't know where I could put my hands on none, unless—now, let me see."

"I'm all right," Jim said, embarrassed. "I won't feel a thing tomorrow."

Then, as Sugar went talking on, he sensed that there was something in the back of the hog hunter's mind. *He wants to get shut of me,* Jim thought, *without plain-out saying it.*

His heart went down to his boot tops. "I expect you're right," he said in a moment. "I'll sit around and take it easy. But don't let me be a drag on you, Sugar."

Sugar took off cheerfully around noon. As soon as he left, Jim started to get his gear together. He didn't know which way to head but he didn't care as long as it took him away from Sam Cleever's. Then, with old Blue's tie rope in his hand, he thought: *Be dogged if I do! I'll stay and tell him like a man!* He shucked out of his shirt and pants. After he had washed them, scrubbing hard on the blood smears, he laid them out to sun-dry and took a chilly swim. Kicking against the current, diving deep in the eddy, he could feel the hurt easing out of him. He had just finished rubbing down the Fiddle brand carbine when Sugar came back, midway in the afternoon.

He was so grinning and lively that Jim thought for a minute he'd found some Mexican whiskey after all, but Sugar had forgotten that.

"Sun's just right to hit that lower pool another lick," he said. "You with me?"

Jim looked up at him. He knew about what he aimed to say—how he didn't blame Sugar at all and hoped they'd keep on friends—but the words didn't want to come out.

"Come on," Sugar said. "It's what you need. Worst thing to do for stiffness is sit around and let it cramp you. Like me today. If I piddled away my time at camp I'd have missed what I come up here for."

He kept his voice solemn but his grin stretched as he talked. "Jess Pickett left out for San 'Tone with a truckload of old cull cows this morning. Won't be back till sometime tomorrow. His woman's liable to be lonesome as all git-out."

"You go on about your business," Jim said nervously. "I'll stay and look after camp."

"Like hell you will," Sugar snorted. "You're pulling off that pear poultice and coming with me. If we're partnering up, you've got to help out in the social department."

Jim knew Jess Pickett. He'd seen him around town a lot on Saturday afternoons. Jess was a tall, stooped man with thin skin that never tanned; it merely reddened and kept peeling off, winter and summer. He had buckteeth and a stammering tongue, and a lot of Mason County folks said it was a puzzler how any man that ugly could have ever got a woman as pretty as his wife Myrtle.

Jim wondered about it, too, when she came to the door. She was about thirty, plump, dark-eyed, black-haired. He thought she had the jolliest smile he ever saw on a woman's face.

"Y'all come in," she invited. She laughed at Sugar and said, "I've been expecting you," like there was a special joke they shared.

Jim reckoned she had been expecting them, for she had a coconut cake baked—Sugar's favorite kind. She gave them both big helpings, with cream to pour over it and cool milk from the springhouse to wash it down. Jim wondered briefly how Sugar always knew when Jess Pickett was gone from home, but he didn't let the thought bother him. He was busy enjoying Myrtle's cake.

"Myrtle's the best danged cook in six counties," Sugar bragged, between mouthfuls. "Bar none!"

After a while, Myrtle went to a corner table and put a record on the gramophone. Sugar slid the rag rug out of the way, and he and Myrtle danced. Jim changed the record when it ran out and waited for them to dance again. But Myrtle shoved Sugar aside and said, "You change the records awhile. I want to dance with this young man."

Jim, grinning a little self-consciously, got up to dance with her. He danced awkwardly at first, and had to swallow regularly. Then she smiled encouragingly at him, and that seemed to give him assurance, so that he got the rhythm of the music and executed every step as easily and confidently as if he'd been an old hand at dancing.

"Swing your partner and pat her on the head;
If she don't like biscuit, feed her corn bread.
The girls on Big Creek are about half grown;
They jump on a man like a dog on a bone!"

The gramophone ground on and on. Sugar kept changing records and telling Myrtle Pickett it ought to be about his time to dance. But she'd just laugh at him and shake her head and keep on dancing with Jim.

"Well, great Jehoshaphat!" Sugar finally exploded in exasperation. "Take him on in yonder and get it over with. I can see now that I'm playing second fiddle tonight!"

Jim flushed and suddenly he dropped Myrtle's arm and rushed from the house with Sugar's laughter rollicking after him. As he struck out along the trail toward the James River camp, he told himself he'd gladly bash that fool Sugar's head in with a rock. Saying something like that to embarrass him in front of Myrtle!

But before he'd gone a mile, Jim had walked his mad off; and suddenly he burst out laughing.

Do Jess Pickett come home unexpected, he thought, *Sugar'll likely leave faster'n I did!*

4

THEY LEFT BLUE AND QUEENIE staked at the camp site and drove the Ford toward Sugar Barnett's place at Todd Mountain. New automobiles had played little part in Jim's life and this Model T was a shining beauty of brass and black. He had been longing to try it out with Sugar. They were in a holiday mood for that morning Lewt Scuffles, a rider for Kline Brothers & O'Toole, had showed up at camp to tell Sugar that he had the contract to gather hogs off the James River Ranch.

Sugar was jubilant over the deal. "We'll make a killing there!" he told Jim excitedly as he gunned the Model T up the river canyon toward the main road. "I figure there's better'n a thousand head of hogs wearing their mark. We git four bits a head for every hog delivered in town alive. Come spring, and we'll have money to throw to the birds!"

Jim was as excited as Sugar, but Sugar's driving had him bothered. By nature Sugar was an open-the-throttle-and-let-her-go type of operator and this morning he felt extra lively.

"We'll round up what needs to be done at my place," Sugar said. "Git the dogs and be ready to hit the brush quick as they deliver me some saddle horses down at their pens."

They whipped around a boulder pile, bounced across a gulley and skidded out into the main road, the rear wheels flinging a sheet of red dust high into the air. They tore out across the ridges, with Sugar talking like a house afire. Now and then he lifted his one hand from the steering wheel to point out some landmark, or a wild animal scurrying for cover.

A startled buck deer leaped across the road from a high bank on their left, barely clearing the engine hood with his hind feet.

"Dog-taked scogie's fixing to git himself kilt!" Sugar exclaimed. "Git an old deer fear-rattled like that and he ain't got the brains of a blind goose in a hail storm. Puts me in mind of a time me'n your daddy is hog hunting up on Calf Creek.

"We're out of fresh meat and Dan claims he knows where an old buck's got him a hideout in a bee-brush thicket. One man can't get to him, he says. Claims if I'll come into the thicket from the far side, he'll make the killing shot when the old boy quits cover.

"I agree, but that brush is thick as hair on a dog. I'm down, crawling on my all-fours half the time. Yonder goes the buck. I've jumped him. He's popping the brush in Dan's direction. I hear Dan's gun speak, but know he's missed 'cause here comes that buck back through the thicket again.

"Which way is he coming? I squat, trying to see, and don't never raise from my squat. Dang fool buck runs square over me, knocks me flat of my back, stomps me in the belly and is gone.

"All I lack coming out of that thicket a cripple for life is a pair of shaded specs and a tin cup for people to drop their money in. And we ain't got us no fresh meat either!"

Sugar threw back his head to laugh and drove straight through a barb-wire gate. There was a rending crash and the screech of steel barbs clawing the side of the car. Jim ducked a piece of wire that rapped the windshield.

The Ford slowed to a stop. Sugar got out, a startled look in his eyes. "What d'you know," he said. "I clean forgot that old gate!"

He went around to the front of the car and lifted a shattered head lamp that was still attached to the light wire. Sugar tried to fit the lamp back in place, as if he expected it to catch and hold. It didn't. He pushed back his hat and scratched his head.

"Dog take it!" he said. "That belly-buster latch on that old gate knocked the wind out of me on my way out. Now it's gone and tore a light off."

He dropped the lamp and went around to the side of the car and ran his fingers along the scratches the barbs had made in the black enameled paint. He shook his head. "I ought to have been looking out for that old gate. This here is a brand-new car."

Jim got out and inspected his side of the car. There were scratches all along that side, too. He said to Sugar: "Maybe we can get the light fixed in town."

Sugar's frown cleared. "Sure," he said, grinning now as if everything were settled. "We'll just put it in the back seat and git one of them town mechanics to fix it up."

He tore the light loose from the wire and tossed it into the back seat. Jim got in, appalled by what had happened, but biting back a grin, too. Sugar started the motor, yanked the gas lever down, and they went careening along the crooked hill road at the same reckless pace.

Sugar's place at Todd Mountain was as careless as his driving. The fences were all down. The roof of his two-room shack sagged and the whole log structure leaned drunkenly in the direction of a huge post oak. There was a well under the oak, and a pulley hanging from one branch. A frayed rope dangled from the pulley into the well.

The blue-ticked dogs barked joyously and lunged against their chains as the Ford drove up. Chickens came fluttering out of the open door to race around the picket-pole yard fence, cackling excitedly. Sugar leaped out of the car almost before it stopped. He raced into the yard, hemmed a hen up in the corner and caught her.

"Got to catch all these old chickens," he said. "Got to catch 'em and sell 'em off. We're liable to be working hogs all winter and there won't be nobody to look after them."

He held the hen under the stub of his left arm and deftly tied its legs. The other chickens scattered all over the place, squawking loudly.

"Reckon we'll have to run them down," Sugar said to Jim. "Got a couple of old shoats in the pen down yonder, too. Just as well catch and haul them in."

Jim made a run at a speckled rooster. The rooster darted around the fence. A half-grown pup, part hound and part Airedale, came streaking out of the brush, yelping eagerly. He lunged at the rooster, knocked the bird down, then flung himself upon it. He held it to the ground with his forefeet, grinning up at Sugar excitedly.

"Be dog!" exclaimed Sugar. "First time I ever knowed that pup to be fit for anything besides dodging a throwed rock!"

He caught the squawking rooster by the legs and lifted him up. The pup leaped high, to flop a wet tongue across Sugar's face.

"Git down, confound it!" Sugar said irritably, running back and whipping at the pup with the rooster. "I'll git a rock and bust your tail for you!"

The pup cowered to the ground, looking pleadingly up at Sugar.

Sugar said to Jim: "That's Felipe. Damned bottle-butted thing ain't got the sense the Almighty promised a pissant. Got him off a Meskin here awhile back and that's all he can talk. Don't know a word of English. I aim to make a hog dog out of him if I can ever learn him English."

Jim made a run at another chicken, calling to the pup. The pup lay where he was and paid no attention. He kept looking up at Sugar and beating the yard dust with his tail.

Sugar said: "All right, dang it! If it's me you're waitin' on, git up and git at it!"

He kicked the pup smartly in the rump, boosting him to his feet. The pup darted past Jim. He caught the chicken but growled when Jim reached for it.

Jim said, "He don't aim to let me have it, Sugar. He's holding it for you."

Sugar shouted at the pup: "Turn that chicken a-loose!"

But the pup wouldn't; he growled at Jim again and Sugar had to come get the chicken. Sugar boxed the pup's ears and said, "What the hell! I ain't the only man alive!"

But the pup Felipe couldn't see it that way. He caught all the chickens for them in a hurry, but Sugar had to go take each one from him.

"I'll be confounded if a Meskin-talking dog ain't a sight of bother," Sugar complained.

They tied each chicken's feet together with strings from an old shirt that Sugar tore into strips, then tied them all to a rope and piled them into the back seat of the Ford. They drove down to the hogpen and caught out a couple of slab-sided shoats and tied their feet up and loaded them into the car between the seats. Back at the house again, Sugar brought out a couple of guns, some extra clothes and grub, all of which he stowed among the chickens. He unleashed the two old dogs. They climbed eagerly into the front seat. The pup was afraid of the car so Sugar had to chase and catch it.

Sugar worked his way in under the steering wheel and surveyed his load. "Well, Jim," he said, "if you can hang on the fender, I reckon we can make it!"

Jim got on the running board. Sugar started the car with a lurch. With hogs squealing, chickens squawking, and the dogs all baying excitedly, the Model T tore down the road toward town.

They arrived at the Kline Brothers & O'Toole pens on James River a little before sundown, with Sugar still grumbling about tearing a front fender off his new Model T on the way out.

"Be dog if it don't gall me to see good equipment tore up like that," he said to Jim. "But I sure never seen that live-oak sapling till it were too late!"

The fender lay in the back seat, along with the head lamp Sugar had forgotten to have repaired while they were in town.

The pens stood on a high dirt bank above the river. They were built of brown sandstone slabs, one slab stacked upon the other so that the fence wall stood six feet high and two feet thick. No mortar had been used, but the workmanship that had gone into laying the rocks had been such that the wall was almost as solid and unshakable as reinforced concrete. Sugar said some of the early German settlers had built the pens, back in the days of Texas longhorn cattle.

"I never seen a cow what could jump out of them pens," he said, "but I've seen old wild hogs what could climb out. You corner a boogery old range hog and he can dang nigh do anything except maybe play a pianner."

They camped just across the river in an abandoned two-room cabin that looked to have been built about the same time as the pens. The cabin was roofed with split shingles, black and curling up at the edges, but not a crack showed between them yet. Sugar guessed the cabin had been built by the same German settlers who built the slab-rock pens.

"There's one thing you can say for them squareheads that first settled these Mason County hills," he remarked. "They was builders. They're bullheaded and hard to reason with. They ain't got no more sense of humor than a thicket sow with pigs. But when they set out to do something, they'll hang and rattle till the job's done."

He stood just inside the door, admiring the cut-stone structure while Jim unloaded the Ford and packed their camping plunder inside.

"You take this old house now," he said. "An earthquake would wear itself to a frazzle trying to crack a wall."

From the cabin, the hill slanted off sharply to the river bed. Jim took a bucket and went down past a dilapidated shed to dip water out of a spring that flowed from a fissure in the rocks. A couple of green-winged teal rose from among the cattail grasses bordering a river pool and winged their way up the canyon.

Jim stood with a dripping bucket and watched them out of sight, wondering why the sight of wild things always gave him such a lift. It didn't have to be anything as pretty as those wild ducks. Just an old scaly mountain-boomer lizard skimming across the rocks thrilled him the same way. Or hordes of leather-winged bats that came pouring out of that cave a mile north of the cabin every evening to go twisting and spiraling off down a brushy canyon, looking for all the world like a wind-whipped plume of black smoke. It could even be just a hog-nosed skunk catching grasshoppers or a dry-land terrapin rattling along over the rocks. Anything alive and wild. That's what he liked. He wished sometimes that all he ever had to do was just prowl the woods, looking at the wild creatures and seeing what they were doing.

As he turned toward the house, his face was marked by what he had seen. For a moment his spirit had soared as high as the green-winged teal, riding wild and free over the hills and canyons and whispering river.

5

LEWT SCUFFLES ARRIVED in time for early supper. He drove up in a light buckboard, hitched to a couple of saddle horses nervous in unaccustomed harness. Baled hay and extra saddles were in the wagon and a couple of saddle horses were on rope leads behind.

Jim helped Lewt unhitch and roll the buckboard under the shed and turn the horses into a wire-fence trap nearby. Then he and Lewt went up to the cabin to squat on their heels around an overturned tomato crate in the middle of the floor. Sugar had supper spread out on the crate.

"That there pecan cake," Sugar warned them, "is deesert and ain't to be et till last. Jess Pickett's woman, she give it to us. I declare, that woman, she's the salt of the earth."

Jim glanced nervously at Sugar, but there didn't seem to be anything but pure righteousness in the one-armed man's bland expression.

"It's a wonder them folks ever have a thing," Sugar went on, "what with the way Myrtle is so bighearted. Give you anything she's got—and glad to. There's an old nester living over on Rocky that'd done been starved out, hadn't been for Myrtle. She's kept him fat for years. Myrtle's always sending Jess over there with a batch of eggs or butter or plum jelly. And she won't let me pass the place without she brings me out some sort of fancy fixings."

Lewt Scuffles said: "When this here hog catching is done, Sugar, you reckon we could hire you, full-time? We're gonna need a man."

"Why, I don't know why not," Sugar said. "If the pay's right. What's the job?"

"Goats," Lewt said. "Boss is fixing to stock this part of the range with two thousand head of nannies. Going to need a man to live here and look after them."

Sugar drew back in alarm. "Goats!" he exclaimed. "Hell, no. You don't ring me in on no job with them stinkers. They'll drive a man crazy enough to strip off his clothes and start running nakid through the woods. Hollering as he goes."

Lewt Scuffles looked concerned. "The hell you say?" he said. "Where'd you ever hear about running goats?"

"Hear about it?" Sugar retorted. "Why, I've had experience. Come damn nigh marrying a whole herd of 'em down in the Medina River country."

He shook his head, like a man recalling a very narrow escape. "They belonged to a widder woman. Prettiest little old thing you ever seen. Independent rich and wanting a man bad. Me, I was giving the proposition a real serious consideration, too, till one day some of her Mexican help quit and she called on me to help her out till she could get more. And that did it. We split the blanket real quick, then."

Scuffles looked puzzled. "What happened?" he wanted to know.

"What happened?" Sugar said. "Why, just the same thing as is always happening to a bunch of goats. They was blatting and stinking and breeding and getting screwworms and birthing kids and not wanting to claim 'em and hanging up in fences and getting hoof-and-mouth disease and needing shearing and needing shelter from the weather. Why, dammit, them things just kept me in one straight long lope from sunup to sundown. And what with calling on that widder woman, it wasn't no time till I was so frazzled out, I couldn't hardly throw a shadder on the ground."

Lewt Scuffles laughed. "Well, he wasn't figuring to bring in no widder woman. All you'd have to do is look after the goats."

Sugar said, "Don't make no difference. I'm done with the goat business. Talk to Jim, here. Maybe you can interest him."

Lewt glanced at Jim. "He's pretty much of a boy," he said. "Don't know if the boss would want to turn over them goats to a boy."

"He's big enough," Sugar said.

Lewt started rolling a cigarette, then suddenly remembered. "Y'all hear about that escaped convict?"

Sugar cut a warning look at Jim Tucker. "No," he said, sucking coffee out of his tin cup with a loud rattling sound. "Ain't heard a word."

"Whole bunch of them got loose at Huntsville during a blow storm the other night," Lewt explained. "They tell me one of them is from this part of the country. August Hershimer is on the lookout for him. Claims he's a hard character and plenty dangerous. I guess you boys got guns?"

Lewt was new to the hill country. Jim reckoned he didn't know Dan Tucker or know that he was Jim's father.

"What's this here hard character in for?" Sugar questioned innocently.

"Never thought to ask August," Lewt said. "Reckon it was murder or something like that, though, from the way he talked. I've warned all our riders to pack guns and be on the lookout for him. These hills ain't safe for a man with a convict loose in the country."

A layer of sweat formed on Jim's forehead. He took off his hat and wiped his sleeve across his forehead. He went to a lot of trouble to smooth out the crown of his hat and dent it just right before he set it back on his head.

"They'll git him sooner or later," Lewt said confidently. "Hershimer's got a posse out and has been warning folks to shoot and then ask questions. That convict won't last long in this country."

Lewt got to his feet and wiped the bacon grease from his fingers against his bullhide chaps.

Sugar nodded. "They likely will," he said. "Seems like the minute word gits out that a convict's loose, every whickerbill in the country grabs his gun and starts looking on hisself as a man hunter. Maybe this convict ain't never been knowed to hurt a fly, but that don't cut no ice. He's just plain buzzard bait to anybody that can get a bead on him!"

Lewt Scuffles stared at Sugar, a puzzled expression on his face. It was plain he didn't understand the meaning of Sugar's words. Finally, he nodded uncertainly and said he reckoned he'd better be riding on back to headquarters. He left the house and headed for the shed to saddle a horse.

Sugar squatted where he was till Lewt was out of hearing. "You reckon if he is out," he asked Jim, "that he'll be fool enough to show up back in these hills?"

"I don't know," Jim said miserably. "I just sure don't know."

A little before sundown, Sugar picked up his Winchester and left the cabin. Jim had ridden off a while before, headed for their former camp at the mouth of Little Devil's River, where he aimed to pick up his roan horse and dog Queenie and bring them into camp. It was four or five miles up there, and Sugar didn't look for him back before sometime after dark. In the meantime, Sugar guessed he might as well see if he could knock over a fat doe. It'd be a neighborly thing to take Myrtle a venison ham the next time they paid her a visit. A fine woman, that Myrtle. Salt of the earth!

The dogs saw him leaving with a gun and set up a clamor to follow, but Sugar wouldn't release them from their chains. A man never would get within gun range of a deer with a fool dog yapping around through the brush.

Sugar crossed a rocky hogback ridge and eased quietly into a tangle of bee brush and thorny agarita. At this time of year, the brush was brown and leafless, but in the low places beneath it, the rescue grass was coming green. Sugar figured that late of an evening like this, he ought to could locate a deer feeding on that tender rescue grass.

By nature, Sugar was a quick-moving, impatient man. But when it came to stalking game, no hunter ever showed more patience. He sized up a clump of autumn-red shin oak down the draw and moved toward it, slow and careful. Any deer feeding in this draw would be about there, he figured.

The deer were there, all right. Sugar got a glimpse of one as it moved to a new clump of grass. But before he got a shot, a sudden noise broke across the ridge behind him. It was the eager yelp of a dog, and the rattle of a chain dragging through the rocks.

The deer vanished with a couple of loud sniffs and the clatter of small hoofs.

Sugar wheeled, dropped the rifle to the ground, and scooped up a fist-sized rock. "Felipe!" he shouted as the pup came tearing into view. "You bottle-butted, Meskin-talking idjit! You git back to camp!"

He hurled the rock. It missed, but Felipe wheeled so quickly he rolled completely over. He came to his feet and lit out for the house, yelping louder than he had on the way out. The chain rattled and flopped behind him.

Sugar left the bee-brush draw in disgust. After all that commotion, he wouldn't get a deershot inside of a day's walk.

"Some day I'll learn that pup something," he promised grimly. "Or kill him, one."

Sugar struck the river half a mile below camp. At the water's edge, he leaned his rifle against a boulder and lay flat on his belly in the green grass to drink.

Lifting his head, he stared straight into the popeyes of a green-backed spring frog squatted on a lily pad in front of him.

"Well, now," he said, addressing the frog, "you're just about the right size for a good fish bait."

Sugar twisted his body till he was lying on the shoulder of his stub arm. With his free hand, he made a lightninglike swipe across the lily pad and caught the frog in mid-air.

He got to his feet, stuffing the crying frog into his pocket. His successful catch had him chuckling. "Hell," he said to himself, "chances are, Myrtle had sooner have a bait of catfish anyhow."

Sugar always packed a fishline in his pocket. Now he searched around till he found the dead stalk of a bear grass growing out of the riverbank above the high-water mark. He twisted the stalk out of socket. He tied on his line, then hooked his fishhook through the seat of his frog.

A few steps above where he'd got his drink was a foot-high rock ledge. A frothy sluice of water overshot the ledge, pouring into a deep clear pool below. Cattails and lily pads rimmed one side of the pool. Sugar walked out on the ledge and dropped his live frog into the churning water.

Sugar expected to get action pretty quick; he knew there was no more tempting bait to fresh-water fish than a live spring frog. But he wasn't prepared for the strike to come so sudden or be so heavy. The frog had hardly struck the water when a black shadow of unbelievable proportions rose from the bottom to engulf it. A forked tail split the surface to slap a sheet of water into Sugar's face. He felt a wrenching surge of weight against his bear-grass pole and heard the pole splintering in his hand.

"Jumping Jehoshaphat!" he exclaimed.

He stared wide-eyed at the foot length of pole left in his hand, then out into the pool where the rest of his pole rode the surface. The pole darted crazily this way and that, as the big fish tried to shake the hook. Sugar dropped the stub of pole and wiped the water out of his face. "Be dog! I've hung Myrtle a regular wampus cat!"

The fish kept working toward the far bank. Sugar leaped across the

sluice of water and ran around the edge of the pool. He waited, squatting on the rocks till the floating pole came within his reach. He caught it up and started leading the big fish toward shallower water, careful not to put on enough pressure to break his line or pole.

He led the surging fish, working it up closer and closer to the shelving bank till he finally got a glimpse of its head, broad, flat, and yellow. Sugar judged he had Myrtle sixty or seventy pound of yellowcat caught— if he could ever land his catch.

The fish saw Sugar now. It wheeled with a splash and ran against the line with such force that Sugar had to release the pole again.

The fourth time Sugar worked the big fish into shallow water, he had his plans all laid out. The big catfish showed signs of tiring now, and all Sugar wanted was another short look at that broad flat head.

Slowly and carefully, he worked the fish through the lily pads, trying to keep out of the creature's sight. The fish was in water less than a foot deep now. Just a little farther, and the top of his head would show.

A heavy back fin split the surface. The big fish gave a weak surge forward. Sugar dropped his pole, put one foot on it, and scooped up his Winchester that lay on the bank behind him. With his one hand, he brought the rifle up to his shoulder, lining his sights on the massive head emerging from the water.

He was squeezing the trigger when the sound of a loose chain dragging across the rocks made him flinch. The gun roared. Sugar was horrified to see the bullet slap water in front of the gaping mouth. The big fish gave a sudden lurch sideways and moved sluggishly back into deeper water, leaving Sugar with a slack line.

"Felipe!"

The startled pup might not be able to understand English, but he couldn't fail to note the outraged fury in Sugar's voice. He wheeled and tore out up the river canyon, yelping his terror long before Sugar could stamp a foot against the butt of his rifle and reload.

Sugar fired four shots at the racing pup before he got out of range. But the light of the setting sun was in the hog hunter's eyes and his bullets merely struck the flat rocks and went wailing on ahead. The crashing echoes of the shots bucked and rolled in the hills.

"That Meskin-talking idjit!" Sugar swore angrily. "Made me shoot my fishline in two!"

6

THEY RODE into the hills at daybreak. The air was crisp and chill. The rising sun bathed the hilltops and upper slopes with a bright yellow light that glinted on the slick green leaves of the live oaks. Cottony-white rolls and twists of fog hung in the draws and canyons. Here and there the tips of red-tinted sumach and Spanish oak thrust up through the foglike spear points of flame. The cedars were dark clumps of green against the white limestone of the rimrocks. The leaves of the scrubby mountain elm were a yellow brown. Off yonder in the distance, the high ridges loomed a hazy blue.

The eager dogs circled the riders, casting wider and wider for hog scent. Sugar pulled a huge safety pin from his pocket and pinned down the flapping end of his empty brush-jumper sleeve. "It's pure-dee hog-hunting weather," he commented.

The air was like wine, lifting Jim's spirits. He couldn't seem to get enough of it. He liked to shut his mouth and pull in all of Mason County in long draughts through his nostrils. That way, he could taste its sharp freshness better, could identify more of the scents it carried. There was the pungent, refreshing scent of cedar in the air. There was the musty smell of rotting wood, the rank and damp smell that belonged to the weed growth along the river, the scent of dew-wet trail dust, horse smell, and leather smell and the sweaty, tobaccoy smell of Sugar riding ahead of him. All these scents Jim could pick out. But they were such a small part of the stirring scents that went into making up the freshness of the air in the wild places. Times like this, Jim envied the dogs their keen noses. He wished he had a dog nose that could sift out and savor each scent separately.

Off in a deep canyon to their right, he could hear wild turkeys quitting their roosts, shattering the stillness of the canyons with their loud gobbling and yelping.

It was good to be out on his own, Jim thought. There were so many things a man wanted out of this life, and most of them he didn't ever seem to get. But now, riding through the hills with a good horse between his legs, listening for the first yelp of a dog scenting hogs, it didn't seem like everything was hopeless.

You take Mary Sue now. Let a man get him a little start of some kind and the chances were he could marry up with her and be his own man. Of course, there'd been a time or two when August Hershimer had come and driven Mary Sue off in his Ford. Jim hadn't liked that. But he didn't figure a girl like Mary Sue was going to pay a gracious lot of mind to a brute of a man like August, big and squat and mean as he was. A heap older than Mary Sue, too. She'd told Jim that she didn't. "It's just that August has got a car and can take a girl out now and then," Mary Sue had explained to Jim. "A girl can't just hang around the house all the time and never go nowhere."

Jim guessed that now he could borrow Sugar's Ford any time he wanted to take Mary Sue out for a spin. He'd do it, too, first time he got around to it.

Then he thought of his father, and the pleasure was suddenly gone from the day. Dan Tucker wouldn't be enjoying the fresh, crisp November air. He was on the dodge. He might even be dead somewhere. In the harsh reality of sunlight striking rock and river and hill, such a thing wasn't hard to imagine. And it was a nagging worry that had been in the back of Jim's mind since Cleever had brought news of the mass break.

But there didn't seem to be anything Jim Tucker could do about it. That was the trouble. Jim Tucker couldn't think of a thing he could do. . . .

Across a deep draw to the right the eager yelp of a dog rang out, shattering Jim's thoughts. He swung in his saddle. Yonder went a long-eared jack rabbit across a bald ridge, with Felipe hard after it.

"You Felipe!" Sugar roared. He spurred his horse into a run, clawing a rock out of his saddlebags, but he couldn't follow the pup far because the draw was rock-walled and too deep to jump his horse off into.

Sugar leaped down out of his saddle and hurled a rock after the pup, but already the dog and rabbit were out of his range. He climbed back into his saddle, growling, "That rabbit-running idjit. I don't see how come I ain't already kilt him. . . . I'd a-done it yesterday, too, if the sun hadn't been in my eyes. Making me shoot a fishline in two!"

He rode on, telling Jim about the big fish he'd lost in the pool below camp. "That scogie's laying up in a cave under the ledge," he said. "I'll git him for Myrtle yet. You wait and see."

The dogs rallied the first bunch of hogs in a blue-brush thicket at the edge of a prickly-pear flat—three barrows, a high-shouldered black sow and four shoats. The hogs had been feeding on the red fruit of the prickly pear, and their snouts were stained a bloody red and bristled with the long yellow spines of the broad-leafed cacti. They stood in the thicket, rumbling their wrath at the barking dogs, popping their teeth threateningly. Their coarse hair stood up along their backbones and their beady eyes flamed their hate.

Sugar rode a wide circle around them, telling Jim to follow.

"You can't drive a wild hog for hell," the hog hunter explained. "Try to drive him, and all you'll do is git your horse cut up and lose your hog. You gotta let your dog lead him in. You watch that Queenie now. She used to know how it was done."

Jim followed Sugar and kept his eyes on Queenie. The speckled bitch and Sugar's two dogs kept dashing in, baying the hogs, till finally they got a barrow to charge them. Instantly, the dogs turned tail and raced for the next thicket, the angry hog hard after them. Seeing the dogs so easily routed, the rest of the hogs charged, too.

"Come on," said Sugar. "We got 'em started."

Slowly, from brush thicket to brush thicket, they worked the hogs down one draw into another and still another, moving them gradually and in a circuitous route toward the rock pens on the riverbank. Sugar left Queenie in the lead and called his two dogs back to work the hogs from behind. He wouldn't let the dogs crowd in, but kept them back with him and Jim so that the natural thing was for the hogs to keep drifting away from them.

The hogs were lean, wary, quick-moving as deer in the brush. Wilder than deer, Sugar said. "Ain't a critter in the woods as wild as an old range hog," he said. "And for mean, they can lay a rattlesnake in the shade."

They followed along, Sugar telling about the time he'd ridden up on a bunch of range hogs and watched them catch and eat a live rattlesnake.

"An old sow had that big diamondback caught right in the middle and is eating him alive. Old snake bites her all over the head and shoulders before she's got too much of him eat up. But it don't stop her. And if she ever swells from the bites, I don't know it. Reckon there's too much hair and hide and fat for the poison to git through."

Jim reckoned Sugar wasn't lying to him about that. He'd heard his father tell the same sort of snake-eating story. It was sure a caution, all right, how wild and mean a hog got once he was thrown out on the range to rustle for himself. Didn't hardly seem possible. Take an old pen-raised hog now; he just got fat and stupid. Didn't look like he had the sense and getup of a dry-land terrapin. Just lie around and eat and get fat and squeal his head off the minute he thought more corn ought to be thrown to him.

But put him out in the woods and all that changed. He slimmed up. He got quick-footed and smart. He learned to get food one place or another, one way or another. If he couldn't get acorn mast and roots, he fed on the carcass of some dead animal. If he couldn't find a carcass, he caught and killed a calf or a snake or a kid goat. He learned to fight off wolves. He learned to tell when a blizzard was coming, and to fix himself a warm bed ahead of time, building it out of leaves and bark and weed stalks that he gathered and piled up in a sheltered thicket. He learned to lie in the mud and soak the screwworms out of himself before they ate him up. Corner him then, and he'd fight you as long as he could draw a breath. Cut you to pieces before you could draw one.

"Ain't nothing can cut you up quicker'n hurt you worse than a bad hog," Sugar remarked to Jim, time and again.

Sugar claimed it was old Mama Nature working on a hog that made him so vicious when you turned him out on the range. "He ain't got no choice," Sugar said. "He gits tough and mean or he dies."

Just thinking about working animals as vicious and dangerous as those wild hogs bothered Jim. He wondered, if he'd had an arm eaten off, like Sugar, could he have the nerve to keep on working them. It didn't seem to bother Sugar, though.

When Queenie finally worked the little band of hogs inside the pen and they got the gate shut on them, Sugar went right into the pen with the hogs to open a gate into a second and smaller pen.

"We got to crowd 'em into this second pen," he explained, "so they won't git out while we're trying to pen another bunch."

The hogs stood huddled in the far corner of the pen, eying Sugar wickedly. They held their long snouts high and sniffed at him, whistling keen as deer. Now and then, one popped his teeth, making a quick, clacking sound that sent cold shivers down Jim's spine. White slaver dripped from their razor-edged tusks.

"All right, Queenie, bring 'em in!" Sugar called.

He stood by the gate, waiting to close it, while Queenie bayed the hogs in a clear bell voice, working them closer and closer to the gate. She leaped into the face of a big spotted barrow, snapped at him, then wheeled and dashed through the gate when he charged.

The rest of the hogs charged after the first. All but one; he wheeled suddenly, with a coughing roar, and made for Sugar. Sugar laughed and scrambled to safety on top of the rock fence. The hog jumped as far up the side of the fence as he could, then fell back.

"You fight-talkin' scoun'l," Sugar called down. "You wait till I knock them cutters outta your head. That'll tek some of the mean out of you."

They rode down into Devil's Nest, where Salt Branch ran head-on into a mountain and made a deep horseshoe bend. The cliff walls stood a hundred feet above their heads, broken and weatherworn. Sticking to one cliff wall, beneath a high overhang of rock, were thousands of abandoned mud nests of the cliff swallows. Looking up at the nests, one mud segment jam-packed against another, Jim was reminded of a huge wasp nest the size of a house. He reckoned it took a gracious lot of mud gathering for them little old birds to build so many nests.

A long deep pool of water lay near the cliff. Between it and the wall itself grew tall live oaks and pecans. The old nests of white and blue herons were like trash piles in the oaks and farther along the herons themselves rose from their perches at the approach of the riders. They spread great wings and drew in their long necks and legs and circled above the trees, uttering raucous cries.

The dogs rallied a big bunch of hogs in the thickets there and Sugar said they'd sure have to work it careful if they ever aimed to move that bunch without scattering them.

The nearby cliffs coarsened and magnified the voices of the baying dogs, making them sound as if they were baying in a barrel. The wild hogs gathered into a tight huddle in the center of a dark thicket and rumbled their wrath and popped their teeth at the dogs.

Nothing had been seen of the pup Felipe since he'd chased the jack rabbit across the ridge earlier in the morning. But at the first barking of the dogs now, here Felipe came, barking eagerly, wild to get in on some excitement. He tore past Sugar, headed for the hogs.

"Felipe!" Sugar yelled and grabbed for a rock in his saddle pocket.

Without a pause, Felipe flung himself upon the nearest hog, baying his mightiest.

There was a sudden rush and a roar of sound. Felipe fell away as a huge boar knocked his forelegs out from under him. Before he could move, more hogs were upon him, slashing and cutting, filling the deep canyon with their savage grunting roars.

"Gracious Jehoshaphat! Keep out of there, Jim!" Sugar cried.

Jim halted, undecided. "But they're killing him, Sugar!"

"Let 'em kill the Meskin-talking fool. He asked for it. Ain't no sense getting your own guts cut out and scattered all over that brush."

Above the crashing and popping of brush and the roars of the hogs, Jim heard Felipe's terrified wailing.

"Queenie!" he called and felt a surge of pride as the hound leaped into the melee and clamped her jaws down on the ear of the largest, a sow.

The sow fell back, roaring with surprise. She slashed with lightninglike thrusts of her gleaming tusks. But Queenie had flung herself out in front now, hauling back and shaking the ear, her forefeet held far under her body, out of reach of those tusks.

The sow started squealing. Sugar's dogs, Spot and Riley, piled in, each grabbing a hog ear, shaking and growling.

The squeals of the caught hogs halted the others. Suddenly, they broke and scattered, leaving the mangled Felipe lying in the leaves.

Jim swung down out of his saddle. Sugar stayed in his, cussing fit to kill. "I hope they've kilt him," he said. "Hell, I've got more sense'n to jump into a bunch of proddy hogs thataway."

Moving warily, Jim closed in behind the struggling sow that Queenie held by one ear. He made a quick grab for one of the animal's hind legs. He caught it, jerked it high and hard with a twisting, wrenching motion, and rolled the sow off her feet onto her back. Instantly, he was down on her, using his full weight to press a bent knee into her lank belly, holding hard against that sudden wild surge of fear-impelled strength given to all creatures in time of distress.

Some of that wild fear was transmitted to Jim, lending him added strength to hold the frantically squealing sow. For once he'd grabbed that leg, he'd committed himself. One slip now, and he'd be a goner. Let that sow get her feet under her, with him this close, and Jim couldn't possibly move fast enough to escape those yellow tushes.

A certain pride, however, forced him to keep the strain out of his voice when he spoke. "I've got her, Sugar," he said. "Bring a hogging string."

Sugar got down and helped Jim pull one of the sow's forefeet back and tie it to the hind ones.

"Can you tie a hog-knot that'll hold?" he asked.

Jim nodded. "Pa showed me."

"Good," said Sugar. "But you always want to be sure. Me, I'd sooner try to git clear of a woman with a razor than a wild hog that's slipped a tie."

Together, they caught and tied down the other two squealing hogs that Sugar's dogs still held by their ears.

"Lost all them others," Sugar complained, straightening from the work. "And now we'll have to drive a wagon all over hell and creation to haul these in. All on account of that damned Meskin-talking idjit. Might a-knowed he didn't have no more sense than to pitch in and scatter 'em from here to the county line."

Jim turned to the pup. Felipe was struggling to his feet now, trying to walk. But his left front leg hung strangely, there and yet no part of him. He was bleeding from a dozen cuts and slashes. As Jim bent over him, he whimpered and slid down, all the puppy life gone out of him.

"He's sure hurt bad, Sugar," Jim said.

Sugar glanced at the pup, then away. " 'Course he's hurt bad," he said callously. "What else could he expect? Git you a club and finish him off."

"No, wait!" said Jim. "Maybe if we patch him up, he'll live."

"Patch him up!" Sugar yelped. "What the hell do you want to do that for? If he did live, all he'd be fit for is knocking in the head."

Jim reckoned maybe Sugar was right. Still, that pup had caught chickens for them the other day. And then wouldn't let anybody else touch them but Sugar. Seemed like there ought to be some good in a dog as loyal as that.

He picked the pup up, holding the broken leg. Felipe lay in his arms and stared up at him out of pain-filled eyes. But he didn't whimper.

Jim said, "I could whittle him a splint, but I got no rag to tie it on with 'cept my shirttail. There's some folks moved into that old Johnson place across the ridge there, just lately. I kin likely borry me some rags."

Sugar snorted. "It's a waste of time. I'd knock the Meskin-talking fool on the head. Don't know a word of white man talk."

7

THE PUP kept whining and whining. It hadn't whimpered a bit back there at Devil's Nest when Jim first picked it up. But now it couldn't seem to stop. Jim shifted it in his arms, trying to hold the bones in the broken leg together. But that didn't appear to ease the pup. He guessed the movement of the horse was jostling it too much, but if that was the case, he didn't know what could be done about it. The Johnson place, over on the Llano, was still a couple of miles across the hills.

Jim guessed Sugar was right. He guessed he was a fool to think you could save a dog after it'd been cut up by hogs and had its leg broke. In all his life, he hadn't known many four-footed animals to live after a broken leg. He'd seen a three-legged cow once, hobbling about incredibly. He remembered a coyote called Old Three-Toes, that got about on just three feet and a stump. There'd been a dog in Mason that hobbled around with its hind leg cut off close to the hip.

But mostly when a four-footed animal got its leg broke, you either killed it or it died. Jim reckoned the pup would die. Still, he couldn't help wanting to save it. Felipe was ignorant and harebrained as an inbred horse, but there was something about him being an outcast, an unwanted thing, that tugged at Jim's heart. He knew what it was like to be an outcast.

Blue jogged down a rocky, shelving slant into the bed of a canyon. The game trail swung upstream for a little way before leading out through the Spanish oak on the other side. Just beyond where the trail turned up the other slope was a little pool of water. The spring feeding the pool was just a wet-weather seep. The water didn't flow on down the stream bed.

Sight of the water brought a thought to Jim. Maybe the pup wanted a drink. He held old Blue to the stream bed and swung down at the pool, his movements slow and gentle, so as not to hurt the dog. Gripping the broken leg firmly, Jim held the pup down where he could reach the water. The pup lapped eagerly. He tried to wag his tail, every now and then stopping to twist his head about and lick Jim's hand.

Jim was back in the saddle again when he noticed the tracks. They were plain in the soft mud at one side of the pool. The tracks of a barefooted man.

Jim stared down at them for a moment, puzzled, trying to figure a reason for a man's being barefooted out here in these hills of rock and catclaw and prickly pear. The answer, when it came, was like a solid blow.

Somebody was hiding out near here. He had slipped down to the spring for water. Whoever it was had a crippled foot, or maybe no shoes at all. He couldn't be far away.

Jim's heart kicked hard against his ribs. He looked around carefully at the high bluffs, the tumbling hills, the thickets of Spanish oak and scrub cedar. He searched his mind for half-remembered details of the country. He'd hunted in here, back when his father used to take him out.

Half a mile up the water course was that bat cave, he recollected. A man—a desperate, hunted man—might hide in there, making himself live, for the sake of safety, in the awful, suffocating stench of thousands of bats.

Jim swung old Blue back on the trail and rode him out over the ridge. His heart kept hammering. He was full of a new, sharp awareness. His eyes moved quickly from one landmark to another.

The pup lay in his arms and kept licking and licking at Jim's hand with a hot, wet tongue. He wasn't whining now.

But Jim wasn't even thinking of the pup as he rode on toward the Johnson place.

The log house squatted on top of a high ridge back from the river a quarter of a mile. It was a long, low structure, the logs weathered black. The white mud chinking between the logs was broken and spilling out in places. A once elaborate, but now ramshackled, system of sheet-iron gutters hung under the eaves, the rusty pipes leading to a concrete cistern near the chimney. There was a wide gallery across the entire front of the house. A number of buckets hung from the gallery rafters on long lengths of baling wire. Each bucket held a potted plant of some sort. It was November, but the flowers were in full bloom.

Sight of those bucket flowers told Jim there were womenfolks about. Wasn't no man ever going to all the trouble of toting flowers inside every night to keep them from freezing, then bringing them back out next day to hang in the sun.

Jim rode up to the yard gate and hollered, "Hello the house!" He waited a bit and hollered again.

The door opened on a creaky hinge and a girl stepped into sight. She was dressed in blue denim pants and a man's shirt of gray. The shirt and pants were old and wash-faded, but they were clean and freshly ironed. The girl looked to be sixteen. Her corn-yellow hair was drawn back smoothly from her forehead. She stood in the door and looked at Jim.

"Howdy," Jim greeted.

The girl said, "Pa's not home."

She kept looking at Jim with such a direct, disconcerting gaze that he shifted uncomfortably in the saddle.

"I got me a dog to patch up," he explained. "I'd like to borry some rags."

The girl turned and went back into the house without saying a word. Jim waited, not knowing what to do.

Damn a body that would look at a man like that and not tell him a thing!

The girl came out of the house and walked through the gate toward him. In her hand she held strips torn from a clean white cloth. She lifted her arms.

"Give him to me," she said.

Jim, startled, laid the pup in her arms and swung from the saddle. The girl carried Felipe to the gallery and eased him gently to the floor.

"What happened to him?" she asked.

"He got cut up by hogs," Jim answered, beginning to feel important for the first time. "Me and Sugar Barnett's gathering for Kline Brothers & O'Toole. Fool pup don't know nothing about bad hogs. Jumped right into the middle of a big bunch. . . . Sugar said it served him right. Sugar said I ought to knock him in the head."

The girl turned to look at him with that level measuring gaze again. "But you didn't want to?"

"No," said Jim, and didn't elaborate. He wished his face didn't start burning every time she looked at him.

The girl bent over the pup.

"His leg's broke," she said.

"I know," said Jim. He added, "I guess he'll die, all right. I guess I should have follered Sugar's advice and knocked him in the head to git him out of his misery."

"We might save him," said the girl, "could we keep him from walking on the leg until it's healed."

"That's what I figured," Jim told her. He squatted down and smoothed off the ground to draw a picture. "I figured to cut him a splint that would be a kind of crutch—like this. I aimed to whittle it out of a dry forked stick that'd be light but stout. I reckoned on padding the forked part, to hold him up, and leave the lower part a couple of inches longer'n his leg so he couldn't put his weight down."

He looked up at the girl, expecting her approval, but she had already turned away.

"You whittle a stick," she said, over her shoulder. "I'll doctor his other hurts."

Jim scowled. He got quickly to his feet and walked off down toward the river, hunting a piece of sun-dried driftwood that suited him. The way it looked to him, he was about as popular with this new girl as the measles!

When he got back to the house, the girl had rolled her shirt sleeves up to her elbows, revealing smooth brown arms. Her forearms were small but strong-looking. She was rubbing axle grease into Felipe's numerous cuts and gashes and the pup was trying to lick her hand.

Jim studied her, thinking this was the first girl he'd ever known who didn't go into a walleyed fit over a wounded animal. His eyes moved up her arms to the low V of her shirt. He looked quickly away, with a vague sense of guilt.

"Did you find what you wanted?" she asked.

"Yep," Jim answered. "I got it whittled flat on one side, where it'll fit his leg."

The girl glanced at the crutch he'd fashioned for the pup. "We'll need two splints," she said. "Pa keeps wood in the shed behind the house."

Jim felt foolish and baffled for not having remembered. He went around to the back of the house. Piled neatly in a shed was carpentry wood. Tools hung in careful rows along the wall. The thought occurred to him that these people would make something of the old Johnson place.

He found a thin slat to his liking, and shaped it with his knife. When he got back the girl had finished salving Felipe's wounds.

"Hold his head," she directed.

Jim knelt and held the dog's head with one hand and caught his hind feet with the other, holding him stretched out on his back. Felipe jerked and quivered as the girl pulled at his injured leg to fit the broken bones together. Jim, tightly gripping the pup's jaws, felt more than heard the howl of sudden pain that tore at his throat.

But it was all over quickly as the girl swiftly and competently held the splints in place, and bound them firmly with strips of white cloth.

Felipe didn't realize he was free for a moment. Then he struggled up and took hobbling steps, the crutch tapping on the gallery. He came back to whine and lick the girl's hand.

She smiled. "What's his name?"

"Felipe. He don't talk—that is, he don't understand nothing but Meskin."

"I think Felipe's going to do just fine," said the girl, smiling and petting him.

Jim tried to make conversation. "Me and Sugar are camped up on James River," he offered.

The girl said nothing to that. She was deftly testing the knots on the bandage, making certain it would remain on tight. Jim was racking his brain for a thing to say that would make her notice when she said suddenly: "I hear tell there's a convict loose in the country."

Jim felt his nerves tighten. "Yeah?" he said guardedly. "You skeered?"

She shook her head. "Any reason I should be?"

"A lot of girls would be," Jim said. "When their menfolks ain't around the place."

She looked at him, a hint of emotion showing for the first time in her eyes.

"They're all after him," she said. "Hunting him down. No, I ain't skeered of him. I just feel sorry for him. Sorry for anything that's hurt or hunted."

She drew the pup against her and Jim found his eyes drawn back to the swell her breasts made under her shirt.

"You ever go to dances?" he asked.

She looked up at him. "No," she answered. "But I'd like to sometime." She added as an afterthought, "My name's Lida Blair."

"I'm Jim Tucker," Jim told her.

"I hear tell the convict's name is Tucker," Lida said. "Kinfolks of yours?"

Jim felt his heart sink. He guessed that fixed it, his father being a convict. He started to lie out of it, then thought of his father, likely hiding out right now, outsmarting bloodhounds, law, and all. A pride and excitement and anger rose up in him all at once. Damned if he was going to act ashamed of his father, girl or no girl. "Dan Tucker's my pa!" he said defiantly.

The girl studied him with that direct gaze again. Jim met it squarely, angrily.

"Why'd you ask me if I went to dances?" she asked.

"There's a git-fiddle dance over to Grit Saturday night," he answered. "But I reckon you're too good to be seen there with a convict's son."

He was angry, not at anything in particular, but just full, hot, fighting angry.

The girl said softly, with just a hint of a smile on her mouth, "I don't reckon I'd mind."

Jim didn't know what to say. She confused him. Now he was all mixed up in his mind—half angry still, puzzled at the girl, and yet somehow elated as she turned from him and crossed the gallery to enter the house. She was back after a moment, with a clean towel.

"You want to wash up?" she invited.

Jim followed her along the gallery and around the corner of the house to the cistern. The pup hobbled after them for a few steps, then lay down and whined. It stopped whining and lay panting on its belly in the hot sun.

Jim took the lid off the cistern, dropped the bucket in, and hauled in a rope through a pulley until the bucket came up. The bucket dripped cool water back into the cistern, making soft booming sounds.

"Pour some over my hands," Lida told him and reached for a bar of soap on a bench beside the door.

Jim poured water over her hands while she lathered them, then poured more water for her to rinse her hands. He wondered if she was aware of how close she was to him. It was making his breath come in short, choppy intakes; but she didn't seem to notice.

She poured water for him to wash, then handed the towel to him. The touch of her hand was an unexpected shock. Jim began to feel bolder.

"Maybe I'll be around to take you to that dance Saturday night," he said.

"I'd like that," she said.

Jim shoved his hands deep inside his pants pockets and then took them out again. His face felt hot and flushed the way it did when he had fever or had been in the sun too long. He looked at her lips again and then glanced away quickly, for she was regarding him with that same disconcerting look.

"Damn it!" he said in sudden anger. "What makes you look at a man like that?"

Color rushed up into the white skin of her face and she lowered her eyes. "I—I don't know," she said, embarrassed. "I guess I just—like—looking at you."

Jim stared at her, astonished. Confidence returned to him but he couldn't think of anything to say.

A squirrel saved him the trouble. It came running across the yard, climbed clumsily up a fence post near the girl and hopped off onto her shoulder.

"Be dog!" Jim said in amazement. "It ain't got no more tail than a rabbit." Lida reached up and stroked the head and back of the chuckling squirrel.

"An owl bit it off," she said. "When he was a little bitty thing. He can't climb trees much without a tail. He loses his balance and falls out."

The tailless squirrel stuck its nose up against her ear and held it there, as if he were whispering into it.

Jim turned and went to the gallery. He picked up Felipe and carried him out to his horse and mounted. He looked down at the girl, who'd followed him to the gate. He felt more like a man now, sure of himself.

"Could be," he said, "I'll come around Saturday night. If I can spare the time."

"That would be fine," Lida said. "I'd like that!"

8

JIM SAT on the front gallery of the old rock house and watched Sugar head into the hills with his Winchester. He watched till he was pretty certain Sugar's course would take him upriver and away from camp, then he went into the house and started throwing scraps of food into a flour sack. He guessed he'd better hurry. Sugar had vowed he wouldn't come back till he'd knocked over a fat doe for fresh meat, but that might be soon or late.

Jim took a small slab of bacon, some cold biscuits and a little fruit jar of wild honey and put them into a sack. He knew how hungry a man could get for sweetening. He dropped a broken-bladed case knife into the sack and stepped through the front door.

The dog Felipe got up off a saddle blanket and wagged a tail at him. He took a few steps forward, moving stiff and awkward on the unaccustomed crutch.

"You lay down!" Jim commanded.

The pup looked crestfallen. He turned and lay back down on the blanket.

"He's learnin' some English!" Jim said in surprise.

At the last moment, Jim reached back inside the door and picked up his Winchester. *Could be I'm out after fresh meat, myself,* he thought.

He left the house with the flour sack slung over his shoulder, headed toward the seep spring where he'd seen the man tracks in the mud. Atop the first ridge, he glanced back to make sure Sugar hadn't seen him, then paused, held there for a moment by some unexplained compulsion that had to do with the massive white cloud piled on the horizon and the way the stone cabin nestled between the hills.

It would be hard to find a prettier place in all of Texas to build, he thought. The cabin so fitted into its surroundings that a man could nearly fool himself into thinking it had grown there. This house belonged. And with just a little fixing up inside, it would be as solid and livable as it had been when that early-day German settler first completed it.

Jim thought to himself: *Pa'd like it,* and suddenly the house seemed a haven, a place for Dan Tucker to come back to, a place that would help him forget the hurt and shame of having been a convict.

Jim remembered the proposition Lewt Scuffles had offered Sugar. Maybe he could get that job. He wouldn't mind the work with goats. Not if he could live here, with his pa.

In sudden desperate hopefulness, he decided to hit Lewt up for the job. The Kline & O'Toole foreman had intimated that it would go to an older man, one with more experience and with a woman to keep him home. But he could prove to them he was man enough to handle the job. And maybe he could get him a woman.

Then doubt assailed him. He'd never really had a job until he partnered up with Sugar. Lewt Scuffles had called him a kid. And from the way Mary Sue had turned on him the other night, Jim reckoned she'd be hard put to speak to him civilly, much less marry up with him.

Jim wondered when he'd get grown up enough to handle his problems and lick 'em.

There was a new set of tracks at the spring today, right beside the old ones. That puzzled Jim, even more than his first discovery of the tracks.

"Pa ought to have better sense than to leave his tracks plain in the mud like that," he muttered.

He shook his head. Anybody with the sense of a coyote wolf would have dropped rocks in the soft mud and stepped on the rocks. Jim scooped water up into his hands and drank, then picked up his rifle and went slowly up the draw, searching the ground carefully for more tracks.

He found another imprint before he had gone half a mile. He swung out of the draw and went up a game trail leading through a tangle of catclaw and bee brush. The ground was rocky here. No footprints showed, not even those of cattle or hogs or the wild things. But the cave wasn't far now. He'd bet the cave was the place!

He wondered what his father would look like now. He thought back, trying to recollect his father's face. But it would not come, somehow. He could recollect things his father had told him, the very words, sometimes. He could remember his father's sense of humor, his kindness, how he'd react to most any situation. But the actual picture of his face wouldn't come. It was irritating, because there were times when he wasn't even thinking about his father particularly that his face would pop up right in front of him, clear-cut and distinct. But now, when he wanted it so badly, it wouldn't come.

Jim walked up on the cave, a small opening lost in a tangle of brush. His heart was hammering so loud he was certain anybody in the cave could hear it. He got down on his hands and knees, peering into the dark interior. The musty, overpowering scent of bats hit his face, stifling him for a moment. He didn't see how a body could stand to stay in that cave.

A sudden thought struck him and he moved quickly to one side. *Git to poking around here and git myself shot,* he thought. *If Pa's got him a gun, he might be jumpy!* Jim knew he'd be jumpy if he was hidden out in a cave like this.

"Pa," he called softly.

He felt the touch of movement against one leg. Sudden fright paralyzed him. He couldn't breathe. He couldn't even look around. His heart gave a lurch and then stopped still.

The pup Felipe hobbled up to lick him in the face and all the tenseness drained out of Jim, leaving him weak and trembling.

Damn! he thought. *Why didn't I kill that fool pup when Sugar wanted me to?*

He wanted to laugh now, but there was something in him that made him want to cry, too. He moved a little closer to the mouth of the cave and called again. "Pa," he said. "It's me. It's your boy Jim, Pa!" The urge to cry got stronger and bigger inside him.

The pup bristled suddenly and moved into the mouth of the cave, his hackles raised. He halted and uttered a low growl, then started backing out of the cave.

A chill of fear crawled up Jim's back. "Pa!" he called desperately.

The pup set up a sudden furious barking, backing still farther out of the cave.

There was something or somebody in there. Jim was sure of that. But if it was his father, why didn't he answer? He felt shame for this silent, suspicious man.

Crawling closer, Jim could put his head around the corner of the opening.

"Pa," he said. "I'm coming in, Pa!"

His voice wasn't loud, but it reverberated through the cave like a cannon shot. It bounced back at him: *"I'm coming in!"*

There was no answer. Jim Tucker waited for a long minute that dragged like an hour. He crawled farther into the hole and called out. "Pa, it's me—Jim. Don't shoot, Pa. I brought you some grub."

There was no answer, just the echo of his voice booming back at him.

The following silence seemed deeper and more ominous than ever. Jim heard a movement far back in the cave somewhere, a sort of dragging sound. He heard a soft metallic click, too, like the click a gun hammer makes when it's thumbed back to full cock.

Panic seized him. He jerked back out of the mouth of the cave and came to his feet. He started to run, hesitated, then slung the sack of food as far back into the cave as he could throw it. Whirling, he tore through the brush as fast as he could run.

The panic leaped higher inside him. It was something ugly that dogged his heels in the bright sunlight. A nameless dread raced after him, coming closer and closer until finally he could not outrun it and had to look back and be sure the trail behind him was empty. But the dread did not leave him until he reached the river.

There he lay down in the grass beside the water, his throat and lungs burning from the long run. He pressed his face down into the wet cool grass and breathed raggedly for a long time.

He finally put it into words. *Pa wouldn't trust me. They've made him so wild and jumpy that he wouldn't even trust his own boy.*

A sense of horror at what they'd done to his father washed over him. He lay and dug his fingers into the grass until his nails were torn with pain.

"Damn 'em all!" he burst out, and the sound was so futile he said it again: "Damn 'em all!"

A noise in the brush made Jim roll, reaching for the Winchester. It was only Felipe, whimpering, watching with those sad hound eyes. Felipe whimpered again questioningly and when Jim called, the pup bellied down and beat the ground with his tail.

Jim laughed. Felipe looked worse than any dog or man could possibly feel. Take a hound-dog, nothing on earth could look as sad.

"Come on, boy," Jim said.

Felipe limped forward, his head cocked dubiously.

"You been kicked so much, you ain't sure whether you're coming or going."

Reassured by Jim's voice, Felipe hopped awkwardly to land on Jim's lap, licking his face. Jim put up his arms to fend off the eager pup but the rough Airedale coat felt comforting. It was tough and strong, suggesting Felipe's substance. He put his arm around the pup and held him down. "You damn-fool Meskin-talking dog!" he said.

9

THE NORTHER which came howling across the ridges the night before had blown itself out, leaving the air clean and chill. But there in the rock pens, Sugar and Jim sweated profusely, catching and loading wild hogs into the buckboard Lewt Scuffles had fetched them. The buckboard now had pine-plank sideboards, with two sideboards laid lengthwise along the top. One of these had been pulled back to make a small opening through which the hogs were shoved. The barking of the dogs, the roaring and squealing of the infuriated hogs made a constant din.

Queenie did most of the catching. She was a proud and efficient catch dog. She approached the jam of hogs in a fence corner warily, awaiting her chance, then leaped in to grab an ear. A pig or even a good-sized shoat she'd often lead across the entire pen to the wagon. A full-grown hog she merely caught and held till Jim got his hands on it. Jim would throw it and Sugar would clip off the savage tushes with a pair of horse-shoe pincers.

"Knowed an old cotton picker one time what thought he was a hog man," Sugar said. "This whickerbill loads a bunch of wild hogs into a waggin and don't bother to clip their tushes. Time he hauls 'em into town, they're done bled for butchering. Them hogs has cut each other up till the waggin bed's spilling blood out through the cracks."

Jim caught the hind legs of a lean-flanked sow and walked between them, like a horse between buggy shafts, dragging the squealing animal toward the wagon. The sow's forefeet plowed furrows in the dusty pen behind him. With Sugar's help, he boosted her into the wagon.

For the third time that morning, a big old long-tusked barrow got past the dogs and charged the men, roaring savagely, his little eyes wicked with hate. Jim saw him and shouted "Look out, Sugar!" and went up on top of the rock fence. He turned in time to see Sugar standing his ground, with a half smile on his scarred face.

Sugar balanced on the balls of his feet and then leaped straight up at the last possible instant, throwing his legs wide apart. The charging hog went between them, cutting high with quick slashes of his tusks. Down Sugar came, grabbing a hind leg of the hog and throwing himself sideways, all in the same movement. With a wrenching twist, he rolled the hog off its feet and over on its back, jumped on its head and stood there, holding its hind feet off the ground.

"Come hold him, Jim!" he shouted.

Jim leaped down and got his hands on the roaring hog, astonished at the quickness and daring of the one-armed man.

"Gosh, Sugar!" he exclaimed. "If you'd slipped or something, he'd have cut both your legs to the bone."

Sugar nodded, grinning sheepishly. "It was just a damn fool show-off prank," he admitted. "Knowed an old boy one time got his insides nigh ripped out, pulling that stunt."

"You mean, the hog cut him?" Jim asked.

"Slicker'n a dogie calf," Sugar said. "They better make bacon out of that hog in a hurry if they expect to git any. Wild as that old boy is, you could stand him belly-deep in a pen of shelled corn and he'd starve hisself to death. I've seen plenty of 'em caught out of the brush that'd never take a bite of nothing from the day you penned 'em till the day they died."

They finished loading the hogs and Jim climbed a buckboard wheel to secure the top with baling wire. Beneath him, the wild hogs shoved and fought one another.

Sugar stood aside, studying the load. Suddenly, he beamed. "Well, fan my britches!" he exclaimed. "I've thunk up a dilly!"

Jim looked up from his work. "What's that?"

"Why," said Sugar, "we'll haul this wagginload of hogs to town behind my Ford. Make it there in less than an hour's time with that Ford. Deliver them hogs fresh as dew-wet rosebuds and be back here on the job before night!"

Jim's face showed his astonishment. "You—you reckon she'll pull it, with all these hogs?"

"Pull it!" said Sugar. "She'll make it at a mile a minute. Why, we'll go into town traveling like the dogs was after us."

10

THEY STARTED OFF about three o'clock in the afternoon, with the load of hogs trailing behind the Ford. Sugar had the wagon tongue tied to the rear bumper with twists of baling wire. He drove with what, for him, was great caution till they'd crossed the river and pulled the steep slant on the opposite side. Once they were on level ground, however, and Sugar could turn the Ford loose in high gear, he pulled the gas lever down to the usual notch and relaxed.

"Got a tail hold on her now," he said to Jim and grinned his satisfaction. He threw back his head and started singing:

> "Buffalo gal, won't you come out tonight,
> Come out tonight, come out tonight.
> Buffalo gal, won't you come out tonight
> And dance by the light of the moon!"

Sugar roared out verse after verse of the song as he herded the car along the river canyon with his one hand. Sometimes he stuck to the wagon-rutted road and then again, he'd leave it completely, picking openings between trees and boulders and pointing the car through them at the same unvarying speed.

The road swung down into the river bed close to a limpid pool among the rocks, then away from it. Sugar lifted his hand from the wheel and pointed.

"See that hole of water yonder?" he said. "I'm fishing it one time. Try to pitch my bait under the bank on the far side, and overshoot. Hang my hook in a bush. Ain't nothing for it but to shuck out of my duds and wade across. Only hook I got.

"I'm about halfway across when this here little shirttail cyclone hits. Drops off that bluff behind me with a pop like a shotgun going off. Lands on my duds piled in the grass, picks them up and shoots them straight up for a hundred feet. All but my boots and hat. Kicks the boots off in the water and leaves the hat where she lays.

"There I stand, naked as a jaybird, watching my shirt and pants and drawers circle each other on a cloud-hunt. And maybe you think I don't have a lonesome feeling about it.

"Finally, that twister spouts my duds out at the top and they flutter back to the ground. My britches, I locate about a quarter of a mile down-river. My shirt lands in the water about that far in the other direction. My drawers settle to rest in the top of a live oak too high to climb. For all I know, they're still ornamenting that old tree.

"And you know what, I had six bits and the prettiest sort of a little old Sunday pocketknife in my pockets and they never even—"

Behind them there was a screech and the lumbering crash of rending steel. The Ford jerked terrifically, then shot ahead with more freedom. Jim looked back and saw the wagon veer crazily off the road and plow into a brush thicket. It went out of sight, with the startled hogs roaring and squealing.

When the wide-eyed Sugar finally got the car stopped, they went back to survey the damage.

The wagon had struck a big rock that the car had missed. It didn't seem to be damaged in any way, but the jolt had yanked the rear bumper off the car.

Sugar stood and gazed at it ruefully. "Dog take it!" he said. "Looks like driving careful is just a waste of time. I'm just tearing this Ford all to pieces, anyhow. And it a brand spanking new one, too!"

They backed the wagon into the road, then backed the Ford to it. Sugar unwired the bumper from the wagon tongue and pitched it into the back seat of the Ford along with the rest of the disengaged parts.

"Now, don't let me forget to have all them things fixed back on when we git to town," he said. "I aim to take care of this Ford."

Jim didn't say anything. He couldn't trust his voice. Let him ever open his mouth, and he knew he'd never get his tickle box straight again. He helped Sugar wire the wagon tongue to the rear axle of the car, wondering how much country you'd have to hunt over ever to find another man like Sugar Barnett. He'd like to bet money there wasn't another. He recollected how his father always said that when they turned out Sugar, they broke the mold, and he guessed that's how it was. A man couldn't have a better friend.

They climbed in and started off again at the same reckless pace, with Sugar shouting out some new verses of "Buffalo Gal" that Jim had a feeling he was making up as he sang.

The hogs had been delivered and counted out at the Kline Brothers & O'Toole town pens the other side of Comanche Creek, and Sugar and Jim were behind Sprague's store where Charlie Holt assured them there was no danger of the law showing up.

"Best home brew in the country!" Charlie Holt was saying expansively.

Sugar said: "Now, ain't that the gracious truth!" He popped the cap on his third bottle and tilted it quickly to his mouth before the foaming brew could escape down the sides of the bottle.

"That woman of mine, she makes it," Charlie said. "Somehow, she puts a mule kick in every bottle. Don't know how on earth she does it, but she never fails."

"Make your eyeballs spin in their sockets," Sugar agreed.

Charlie was meatcutter and embalmer for Sprague's Meat Market and Funeral Parlour, which advertised with a huge board sign out in front: FANCY MEATS & EMBALMING.

Charlie was also a guitar picker who, with his fiddling wife Sarah, played for the Saturday-night dances. He had his guitar with him now and kept strumming it a little while he talked. He was a small, spare man, looking both hungry and mournful in the oversized store-bought suit his position as undertaker demanded.

He said morosely: "Me'n Sarah will furnish the music. All you boys got to do is dance and set the girls."

"You reckon there'll be a pushing crowd?" Sugar queried.

"Plenty of women," Charlie said. "Can't tell about the men. Likely, some of them will be combing the hills for that convict." He looked reproachfully at Jim, as if he felt that the boy was cutting into his Saturday-night earnings by having a father who lured paying customers away from his dance.

Jim recollected suddenly. He turned to Sugar. "I'd sure like to run out to the house for a little bit," he said. "I need to get me some warmer drawers and another coat before we go back out."

Much as he liked and trusted Sugar, Jim still didn't want to tell him what he had in mind. A man on the dodge needed something besides convict clothes to wear. Shoes, especially, if he was barefooted and wanting to get out of the country.

"Sure," Sugar agreed. "I'll run you out, myself. Haven't seen your ma and Sam Cleever in a coon's age." He laughed. "Sam got her—and sure saved me a mess of trouble."

Jim's mother made a big fuss over him when they went into the house. She made out that she'd been worried sick over him ever since he'd left out in the middle of the night that way, afraid he'd get wet and take his death of cold, afraid he'd get snake-bit or cut all to pieces by a bad hog.

"I declare if it don't tear a woman's heart out," she mourned to Sugar, "having to stand by and watch a body's onliest son foller right into his pa's footsteps. Wild as they come. I guess it'll be the pen for him, too, before it's all said and done."

Jim felt hot rebellion, but he put it down. This was the same old tune he'd listened to ever since his father had gone away. But he'd cut loose from it at last; there wasn't no call now to get into a big word-fight with his mother.

He turned and went into the back room, hearing Sugar say behind him, "Where's Sam?" His mother's complaining voice answered, "Off somewhere with August Hershimer," and Jim felt a chill squeezing his heart at the news.

He heard Mary Sue come in and make a big to-do over Sugar, as all women, young or old, did wherever the hog hunter went. Jim tried to figure what it was about the one-armed man that caused all women to come alive and excited the moment he arrived. He guessed it was a gift. He guessed the lucky man was born with it and the unlucky one wasn't, and there likely wasn't much could be done about it, one way or another. Jim knew a twinge of jealousy as he heard Mary Sue building up to Sugar with a lot of little-girl sweet talk. Dammit, Sugar was too old for a girl like Mary Sue.

He was wrapping up the bundle of Dan Tucker's clothes inside a ducking coat of his own when Mary Sue opened the door. She came through and shut the door behind her, leaning against it a moment with her head thrown back so that she had to look at Jim through her thick black lashes.

"What you doing, Jim?" she asked.

She came to kneel beside him, closer than she had to. Her eyes opened wide. "What you doing, taking Dan Tucker's things?"

"I'm needing the use of some of Pa's stuff," he said. "I've about growed into them a'ready."

Her eyes swept over him and then caught his own, trying to read what lay behind his words. "You're done bigger'n Dan Tucker ever was," she said slowly. She laid a hand on his arm and whispered eagerly: "Where you taking them clothes to, Jim? You don't have to be afraid to tell *me!*"

Alarm shot through him. "What're you talking about? You gone crazy?"

She gazed at him a long moment. He guessed she could tell he was lying. But she didn't pursue the subject.

"You going to the dance tonight, Jim?" she asked.

"Maybe," he said. He went on tying up his bundle of clothes.

"I got a new dress your ma made me," she said. "I could wear it."

"I likely won't go," he hedged. "I got some business to attend to."

"Like taking your pa's clothes somewhere?" she asked softly.

He whirled on her, his eyes blazing. "You shut up that kind of talk! You trying to get me in bad trouble? You got no call to say things like that!"

"Forget it," she said carelessly. "I'll go with August Hershimer. He asked me last night."

The name froze Jim for an instant. Fear for himself, for his father, gripped him. Then he thought of Mary Sue, his girl, cuddling up to that big fat brute, and he went half wild.

"You keep away from that blubber-mouth sheriff," he said hoarsely. "He's mean! I'll kill him one of these days!"

Her laugh was taunting. "I'll bet you'll kill him," she said. "I can just see you now, killing August Hershimer."

Now that he'd said it, he regretted his words. "Maybe I'll kill him and maybe I won't," he said sullenly. "It don't matter. Just don't be going with him. He ain't fit to be seen with."

"I can take care of myself," Mary Sue told him. "It ain't like I *had* to go with you. There's plenty of others would like to take me."

Jim was sick of the whole argument. "All right," he said, "go with August Hershimer. Go get yourself in bad trouble. But don't come whining to me about it. Anybody would go with that big devil ain't no gal of mine!"

"What if I was to tell him about seeing you pack your pa's things? What do you guess he'd say to that?" Mary Sue asked.

Jim Tucker snaked out a long arm and grabbed her wrist, his fingers clamping down like a vice. She recoiled from the violence of his act.

"I told you to shut up about that," he said, his eyes blazing.

"Turn me loose, Jim," she said, frightened. "You're hurting me."

Jim gripped her arm tighter. Mary Sue looked at him, reappraising. She was discovering a strength and hardness in Jim Tucker she'd never realized was there. It was more even than the physical strength of the grip he held on her. She had a feeling that Jim was a man now, a man who could say no to her cajoling and flirting.

"I won't tell, Jim," she said. "I was just teasing. I didn't know you'd take it that way."

He turned her loose and she rubbed her wrist, not looking at it, but keeping her eyes on Jim's angry face. "I don't want to go to the dance with

August Hershimer. I want to go with you," she pleaded. "If—if you can manage to take me."

Jim studied her. This was the first time he'd ever held the upper hand with her, the first time he'd seen her begging. It gave him a sudden urge to tell her to go to hell, just to see if he could make her cry. But he couldn't afford to make her mad at him now.

She knows about these clothes, he warned himself. *If I let her go with August, she'll tell him, sure.*

"You git prettied up," he said roughly. "I'll take you."

He knew he'd be enjoying his triumph over Mary Sue if it hadn't been for a picture that came to his mind. It was a picture of Lida Blair standing at her yard gate with the stub-tailed pet squirrel whispering in her ear, watching him ride off.

11

IT WASN'T a dance hall, at all, just a house that nobody lived in any more. Once there'd been two large rooms, but now the partition had been knocked out, giving more freedom for the dancers. The floor sagged in places and there were cracks an inch wide between the boards. Bill Price's farm was just up the dry sandy creek a way and his hogs had rooted out a bed for themselves under the house. Sometimes the dancers could hear the hogs grunting and rooting around under the floor.

Charlie and Sarah Holt gave the dances and furnished the music. They charged two bits a man; ladies got in free. Charlie and Sarah sold home brew for two bits a bottle at the dance, but it was general knowledge that they drank up all the profits. Nine times out of ten, Charlie and his wife were the drunkest couple at the dance by the time it was over and Charlie rarely left a dance without a black eye or a battered face. Charlie always felt it his duty to interfere with every fist fight that started, although nobody could ever remember his stopping one.

Sugar brought Jim and Mary Sue in his Model T. Sugar himself never fetched a girl to a hoedown. "It's a sight more fun to play the field," he said.

Yellow lamplight splashed across the trampled weeds in the yard as they drove up. All the doors were open and the strains of "Fiddler Joe" spilled out into the night, crying lonesome across the mesquite and prickly-pear flats.

> "Way down in the valley,
> By a cabin door,
> Just an old man with his fiddle
> Playing this tune o'er and o'er."

Talk and laughter came from the dark corners of the yard. Dancing couples swung past the doors and windows. The house was crowded and people turned and collided and laughed, happy to have it that way after a week of hard work on the scattered cotton farms and cattle ranches. One reveler yelped and stomped hard on the floor and a pig underneath the house let out a startled squeal.

Jim laughed. "Maybe I'd better skin under there after that scogie, Sugar. Could be he's worth four bits if he's wearing the right mark."

Sugar laughed loud, as if that were a special joke between them.

Mary Sue entered the house, holding to an arm of each man. She had her hair done up on top of her head in pretty little tight curls. Her mouth was bright red and long sparkly earrings hung from her ears. She had on a short black silk dress made tight in the right places. Jim stepped proudly beside her. Mary Sue looked older than she was, all prinked up like that; Jim thought she was easy the best-looker of all the women there.

Sugar dropped four bits into Charlie Holt's hat, which rested upside down on a table near the door. Charlie and his wife sat playing on either side of the door. Charlie's round eyes followed the descent of Sugar's coin into the hat, then switched to Sugar's face. He nodded, welcoming them with a morose smile, never halting the rhythmic swing of his body, timed with the beat of the music. Evidently, he'd already been drinking up some of the night's home-brew profits; the sweat streamed down his face and dripped from the tips of his handlebar mustaches.

> "Silence in the valley,
> Silence on the hill,
> For the old bow now is silent,
> And the fiddler now is still."

Jim Tucker slipped his arm around Mary Sue's waist, conscious of the warmth and softness of her body as he whirled her out on the floor. He shuffled his boots for a hop-step that kept time to the music and still kept him missing the wide cracks in the floor. Sugar stood just inside the door and beamed at them.

> "But the flowers still are dancing
> O'er his grave with sweet delight.
> For they hear Old Joe a-fiddling
> Where all things are gay and bright."

The music ended and they followed Sugar out into the dark. The music, the stamp of feet, the laughter and talk, the girl he held in his arms—it all set Jim's blood to hammering a wild song in his ears. He felt grown-up, important, a man among men—and women. He stood straighter. The last awkwardness was gone from his steps. Right now, Jim guessed he had a tail holt on the world and was pulling downhill.

This time when the music stopped, he and Mary Sue stepped to a window and leaned against the sills. Just outside, they heard a dull explosion as someone ripped off another cap of Charlie's wild beer. To one side, a couple of men were talking in low, serious tones.

"Spotted him in the brush up that rocky slant just back of my corncrib. Damned nigh takened a shot at him then. I held off, figuring it could be somebody gobbler hunting. But it wasn't. I trailed him a piece. I could tell he warn't game hunting."

All the excitement and pleasure Jim had felt a moment ago drained out of him now.

"Ain't nobody safe, long as he's loose in the hills," another voice said. "A convict ain't taking no chances. Let somebody come up on him accidental-like and he's got to shut them up. Anybody. Best thing you could a-done was shot the hell out of him. If we don't, he'll git some of us; you can bet on that!"

A blind fierce anger took hold of Jim. He turned from the window and said abruptly to Mary Sue: "Let's get out of here!"

Mary Sue looked at him. "But we only just got here."

Jim caught her by the arm and swung her toward the front door, then stopped dead still. Before him stood Lida Blair, staring straight at him with that calm, dead-level gaze that was so disconcerting. Beside her stood a tall gaunt man with turkey-track creases in the skin around his puckered blue eyes. Her father, Jim guessed. The man looked uncomfortable in a barber-pole shirt with red sleeve garters.

Jim stood silent for a long breath, his anger giving way to confusion and embarrassment. Finally, he forced out a "Hello" and launched into a too-hurried explanation.

"I just couldn't get by in time this evening," he stammered. "Got all tied up with a lot of business—and stuff." He stopped, sensing too late that he couldn't make it right now. He felt the blood come rushing to his face.

The girl's steady gaze held for a moment longer before she dropped her eyes. She said: "You didn't make any promise. You just said you'd come if you could get around to it."

The way she said it gave Jim the feeling that she was talking to herself as much as to him, reminding herself of a thing that she'd already said before.

He searched her face, trying to decide whether she was hurt, disappointed, offended, or completely indifferent to his standing her up for another girl.

Her thick yellow hair hung in long waves past her shoulders. Jim would have given a pretty to reach out and stroke it. Her starched white dress brought out the deep blue of her eyes and the glow of her skin. There was a simplicity and a quiet dignity about her that made Jim suddenly aware that Mary Sue wore too much lipstick and that she talked too loudly.

Damn Mary Sue, anyhow, for getting him into this jackpot!

Lida's father murmured something to her and turned away. Jim became aware of his social obligations. He introduced the two girls awkwardly.

"Glad to meet you, I'm sure," Mary Sue said primly, then added: "That your fella just left? Or did you have to come with your papa?"

Surprise and hurt showed on Lida's face, and Jim felt a quick, protective anger. He spoke up before Lida had time to answer.

"I'd be proud to have this dance, Miss Blair," he said. There was an unexpected Sunday manner and respect in his voice.

Lida looked startled, then grateful. "Why, that would be nice, Jim," she said.

Jim took her in his arms, surprised at the slimness and lightness of her. They danced off, leaving Mary Sue standing alone, her face flushed. Jim knew she was furious and that he'd likely have a fight on his hands later on. But he didn't care. Served her right, getting high-tony with his friends. He wished he could think of the right thing to say that would break down the wall of reserve that Lida now held between them. She hadn't accused him of standing her up for another girl, and she was dancing with him; nevertheless the wall was there. And it didn't look like there was a thing in the world that he could do to remove it.

When the music stopped, Jim thanked Lida for the dance and left, prepared to face down Mary Sue. He was surprised to find her standing alone, apparently more hurt than angry.

"You're sure getting biggity, Jim Tucker," she pouted.

But when he merely grinned at her, she didn't show fight at all. She caught him by the arm and held to him possessively.

August Hershimer came in, accompanied by a plump, pretty girl from Koocksville whom Jim had seen a time or two. Her name was Mabel Robbins.

Hershimer left her standing at the door and pushed into the crowd, affecting a joviality that never showed in his pale gray eyes. He roared like a bull as he made the rounds, shaking hands right and left, joshing with men and women alike. Many of the dancers pretended a welcome for the sheriff, fearing to offend him, then moved away from him as quickly as possible.

Hershimer's eyes fell on Jim and rested there for long seconds with a strange sort of loving malice. His lips parted in a faint, hard smile.

"How you, Jim?"

There was a taunt in his voice, and Jim felt a bitter hate for the man. There was fear in him, too, a cold unreasonable fear that sapped his courage. Always it was like this when he found himself in the presence of August Hershimer.

Jim said reluctantly, in a tense voice, "Hello, August." He hoped the others couldn't see how strained his face got, with the skin drawing tight across his cheekbones. Some of them had to know about the other night under those oak trees when he'd lain beaten in the sand and cried like a baby.

"Seen your pa?" August asked, mock politely.

"I ain't seen him."

August smiled his faint hard smile again. "When you see him," he said, "you tell him we'll git him. Alive or dead. Tell him he ain't got the chance of a little smoke in a big wind."

The music started up. August turned back and got his girl Mabel and swung her out onto the floor. The sheriff's great solid weight shook the floor at every step.

"Who's that girl he's with?" Mary Sue demanded.

"I don't know," Jim said. "Name's Mabel Robbins, I think. It don't make no difference."

"Don't make no difference!" Mary Sue flared, then relaxed. She came into Jim's arms and smiled up at him. "Why, no. It don't make no difference, Jim," she said gently. "It don't make no difference at all."

"Hold my mule while I dance, Josie.
Hold my mule while I get about.
Hold my mule while I dance, Josie—
Hello, Susie Brown!"

Jim didn't see the fight start. He didn't even see who started it. It was just like it was every Saturday night. Somebody got mad and swung on somebody else, and suddenly everybody was mixing into it, with the men shouting and cursing in hoarse angry voices and women screaming and the music petering out as it seeped into Charlie Holt's drunken mind that trouble was on the loose. The fight spread wider and wider, as people shoved against people, trying to get out of the way, or trying to get nearer to see.

A beer bottle came whistling past Jim's head and shattered a window glass behind him.

Sarah Holt was on her feet now, screaming at the top of her voice, clubbing her fiddle and beating men across the head with it. Charlie was staggering up, still too muddled with drink to know what to do. Jim saw August Hershimer reaching and grabbing men by their shirt collars and slinging them aside, as he bored deeper into the fight. Beside him, Mary Sue was jumping up and down, trying to see, and screaming her excitement.

Jim felt a hand tugging at his coattail. "Git a hustle on, Jim. It's time we got out of this."

It was Sugar. August Hershimer's girl Mabel held to his shoulder, smiling up at him with that same light of excitement and adoration that seemed to come into every woman's eyes when she looked at Sugar.

"Come on," Sugar urged. "Where's that Mary Sue gal?"

"I'm here, Sugar!" Mary Sue cried. "Where we going?"

"Places," Sugar promised and broke into a gay laugh.

Jim looked across the whirling, struggling mass of humanity and saw Charlie Holt come alive and rush in, swinging his guitar and screaming something unintelligible. Charlie lifted the guitar high and brought it down over a man's head with a bonging crash. The guitar stuck, leaving the man staggering about blindly. Jim laughed suddenly, as wildly as Sugar.

"Let's get gone," he said. "Dance is over. Charlie's busted his git-fiddle."

They ducked out of the room into the cool fresh air of the night.

"August will sure be mad," the Koocksville girl said, giggling nervously.

"He ain't seen us yet," assured Sugar.

They piled into the car—Mary Sue into the rear seat with the bumper and other paraphernalia that Sugar had never got around to getting fixed back where it belonged. Jim gave the crank a twist. The Model T shivered, then caught. Jim jumped into the back seat with Mary Sue.

They wheeled out into the main road, throwing up sheets of dust into the yellow lamplight coming through the windows. Behind them Jim heard the bull-like roar of August Hershimer's voice lifted in anger. Then something solid slapped into the one front fender that was left and wailed off into the night. Above the rattle and banging of the racing Ford, Jim heard a dull report.

"Hurry, Sugar," Mabel pleaded in a frightened voice. "Hurry. He's done missed me!"

Sugar cut her an astonished look. "He just *barely* missed us!" he muttered.

12

SUGAR SAID he'd deliver this load of hogs into town if Jim would take a hammer and some staples and go patch up that old wire pen at the Red Bluff windmill.

"There's a big bunch of hogs wearing the Kline & O'Toole mark feeding on shin-oak mast in them hills the other side," he said. "We can pen there a heap easier'n having to drive all the way down here."

Jim was glad for the chance. He was worried about his father. It'd been four days now since he'd visited the cave, and there hadn't been much grub in the sack he'd left there.

"Better take an ax, too," Sugar directed, "and start cutting brush to build us a wing blind. Ain't no fence there to help us crowd 'em into a pen."

Sugar made a last-minute inspection of the wagon to make certain no hog could possibly root out between sideboard and wired-down top, then got in the Ford and drove off, whistling a hoedown tune.

Jim saddled Blue, put hammer, pliers, and staples into a morral and hung it over his saddle horn. He tied an ax under one stirrup. He rounded up another sack of food, a bigger one this time, got his rifle and rode toward the cave.

The pup Felipe followed, hobbling a little but getting around amazingly well on his crutch. The bandage about his leg was ragged and soiled now, but Jim didn't plan to take it off until he knew the leg was healed. If he took it off too soon, the place would itch and the pup would gnaw at his own leg.

Jim approached the bat cave cautiously, but the pup limped right up to it and disappeared inside. In a few minutes it came back out, its curiosity satisfied, and lay panting at Blue's feet.

Jim sat his saddle, disturbed, undecided. There was nobody in the cave. Where had his father gone?

After a time, he rode a wide circle around the cave. He wasn't an expert woodsman, but any boy who's game-hunted can read a little sign. Finally in a trail a quarter of a mile away, he discovered a part of a footprint. The tracks of the bare toes were plain in the dust; the rest of the print had been trampled out by cows which traveled the trail to water at the river. The toes pointed north, away from the water hole.

That puzzled Jim more than the man's leaving the cave. He couldn't blame a man for leaving the foul-smelling cave. But where could he be headed in this direction? He'd have to get water somewhere.

Jim followed the cow trail until it faded to nothing in the brush. Near to one rocky outcropping he dismounted and examined another imprint in the dirt. It might have been a footprint or it might not. Some hogs had been along the trail recently. Acorn hulls littered the trail and the hoofs of the hogs had trampled over the sign. Finally, Jim gave up and rode toward the Red Bluff windmill.

The wide wheel of the windmill turned slowly, wailing a dismal complaint for lack of grease. A trickle of water spouted from a horizontal pipe into a huge concrete reservoir. A number of range cattle lifted their heads as Jim rode up. There was a startled *put-put-tureet!* and a flock of wild gobblers fell away from the watering trough on the far side of the reservoir and scattered.

"Be dog!" breathed Jim, falling out of his saddle and grabbing for his Winchester.

The gobblers had got their running start now and were whipping themselves into the air, their ponderous wings fogging the dust beneath them.

Jim swung the rifle to his shoulder, thumbing back the hammer as he brought the gun up. He leveled down on a turkey flying directly away from him. Knowing that in his hurry he'd likely draw too coarse a bead, he allowed for it by pulling down between the bent-back legs of a bronze bird.

At the crash of his gun, a puff of feathers spouted from the gobbler's back. The bird seemed to squat in flight and hang momentarily in the air. Then the big wings folded together above the back, letting the bird drop. It hit the ground soddenly.

"Be dog!" Jim repeated. "First one I ever knocked down a-flying!"

The rest of the gobblers faded like phantoms into the brush, the pup Felipe racing after them, yelping with excitement.

Jim walked out past the trough to the edge of the hoof-trampled dust around the watering place and hefted his kill. It was sure a big old long-bearded gobbler, all right. Shot right where its wings hinged. As good a shot as his pa used to make with that same gun. Everybody in the country always claimed it was a caution how Dan Tucker could knock down a flying gobbler with a rifle. Jim wished his pa could have seen him this time.

He cleaned his kill, opening the bird at the crop and at the rear end and drawing out the entrails. He carried the gobbler to his saddle and looped a string around its neck and let it hang. He climbed up on the concrete tank to wash his hands. He whistled for Felipe to come back, but the pup didn't appear.

He was squatted there on the rim of the tank when he saw the footprints. They were in the dust just below him. Barefoot prints, like those across yonder at the seep spring near the bat cave!

Jim stood stock-still at the sight, holding his body rigid while his wide eyes swept the picket-pole corral and moved on toward the old cabin of weathered logs that stood beyond.

He stood there a long time, his thoughts whirling. Finally, he leaned his rifle against the wall of the reservoir and approached the cabin, his nerves tight as fiddle strings.

He stayed away from the door that gaped half open and peered between the cracks in the logs. The mud chinking had long since fallen, leaving wide cracks between the logs through which spilled yellow sunlight. Jim could see everything inside—half a bundle of old moldy hay, a broken hame string hanging to a nail, the leather dried and curled, a number of worn-out horseshoes and a sack of stock salt. That was all— there was no one inside.

Then his roving eye centered on the manhole leading to the loft under the high-peaked roof, and he caught his breath. Somebody had carried hay up into that loft recently! There were bits of it still clinging to the ramshackle cedar-pole ladder.

"Pa!" Jim said cautiously.

There was no answer. There was no sound. Yet now Jim was acutely aware of the presence of some live thing in the loft above him. He could feel it. Something or somebody was up in that darkened loft, looking down at him. His heart hammered and he had a sudden desperate urge to run, just as he'd run away from the bat cave that day.

"Pa!" he said in a cracked voice. "It's me! Jim! I'll help you, Pa. Me'n Sugar'll both help you!"

There was still no answer.

The thought came to him that he could climb up into the loft and convince his father of who he was. He moved to the door and lifted the hatch. Then his hand froze.

Sugar had said that Dan Tucker might be stir-crazy. He'd said that cooped up there in that pen, a man could go mad as a hydrophobia wolf.

Sweat cracked through Jim Tucker's skin. A stir-crazy convict might shoot anybody—even his own son. Jim knew a kind of blind horror at the thought.

He turned and stumbled toward his horse, sickened by something ugly that reached out of the silence to touch him. He picked up his gun and mounted. He lifted the sack of clothes and provisions from his saddle horn and hung them over the end of a fence post, making sure they were in plain sight of the cabin.

Then he rode away. He did not look back once at the house.

He was six, proud and happy in a new pair of striped blue overalls Dan Tucker had bought and just put on him. He raced outside toward the garden, calling his mother to come and see his new overalls. He hung his bare foot under the tongue of his little red wagon and landed flat on his face in the mud of the irrigation ditch. His mother came to scold him for messing up his new clothes, but Dan Tucker just grabbed him up and dunked him into a barrel of water, clothes and all, shouting with laughter at the suddenness with which the shock of cold water had cut off Jim's crying, then telling him new clothes weren't fit for a boy to wear till they'd been washed one time.

Jim rode up the trail till it circled the shoulder of a live-oak ridge a quarter of a mile away, dismounted, and climbed the slope. He concealed himself among the scrub oak brush, where he could look through the leaves and have a clear view of the watering place.

He waited more than an hour and was ready to give it up when he caught sight of a man stepping cautiously from the cabin door. The man stood near the log structure for a long time with his head lifted and turning this way and that, searching for him, Jim knew. Finally the man dashed

out to the fence, yanked the provisions from the post and fairly flew back
to shelter.

"Oh, Pa!" Jim cried brokenly.

Slowly, Jim picked his way down the brush slope toward his horse
and mounted, his mind running back again, clutching desperately at
scraps of memories that only tormented him once they were captured.

*His pa was calling from the yard. "Come a-running, Jim. Hurry, boy.
Got a sight to show you!"*

*And Jim ran out of the house, aching with excitement, wanting to
know what it was.*

*And his pa turned and led off down the sandy lane, trotting slow, while
Jim's short legs worked as fast as a road runner's, trying to keep up.*

"What is it, Pa? What is it?"

*But his pa wouldn't tell. All he'd do was laugh and tell Jim to keep
a-digging it, else they'd be too late.*

*They came to the grass burs, where Jim couldn't follow barefooted,
so his pa boosted him up on his shoulder then and trotted faster.*

*At last they rounded the corner of the field fence at the creek, and
there it was!*

A whopping big old sow possum with ten baby possums!

*The baby possums clung to the hair on their mama's back and she
had her fat, hairless tail up and each of the little possums had his little
pink tail curled around hers, holding tight!*

*His pa quiet-footed it up close and the old mama never knew they
were there, but the little possums saw them and all bared their teeth at
him in a grin. Every blessed one of the little scogies!*

From the top of the next ridge an old range cow blared and blared
again, the brassy mournful sound seeming to touch off within Jim Tucker
a loneliness too great to bear. Tears stung his eyes and he rode along
down the trail, desperately in need of someone he could talk to, someone
who might understand.

13

SAM BLAIR SAID: "Honey, if you'll just sit on his head, he won't pitch around so much!"

Lida slid down off the shoulders of the struggling calf onto its head.

"Could of had this job done 'way 'long past summer," Blair said, "hadn't been for the confounded screwworms."

He reached for the bloodstained knife Lida held out to him. The bull calf bawled and strained against the rope binding three of its feet together. Just outside the pens, the big red hound rose to his feet between the two saddled horses and bayed sonorously. Blair halted, knife poised.

"Howdy," said Jim Tucker.

Sam Blair nodded. "Howdy," he said.

Lida stared up at Jim, saying nothing.

Jim swung down out of the saddle. He slipped the gobbler's head out of the saddle-string noose and held it up for them to see.

"Fetched over a fat gobbler," he said.

"For us, Jim?" Sam Blair looked surprised.

"For her patching up that fool pup the other day," Jim said and smiled at Lida.

Sam Blair straightened and clicked his knife blade shut. "Why, now, that's sure neighborly, son," he said. "It sure is!"

Sam Blair's pleasure in the gift encouraged Jim. He said with studied casualness: "Rode up on a bunch, watering. They hit wing at the sight of me, but I managed to cut one down." He hung the gobbler on the corral fence.

"You mean you got him flying?" Sam Blair's voice held a note of respect. "With a Winchester?"

"Likely a chance hit," Jim said modestly, trying hard to conceal his pride. But he couldn't resist adding: "But Pa used to kill 'em on wing that way. Plenty of times!"

"Well, now, that's sure some shooting," Sam Blair said.

Lida spoke up for the first time. "Did the pup get all right?"

"Fit as a fiddle," Jim said. "Last I seen of him, he was high-tailing it after the balance of them gobblers—with that crutch rattling and banging on every bush and rock. I reckon he'll make it back to camp, all right. I couldn't call the butt-head thing in."

"Honey," Sam Blair said to Lida, "why don't you give that old gobbler a fast cooking? I could sure do with a mess of baked turkey and dressing."

Lida looked up at the sun. "It'll crowd him ever to get done by supper, Papa."

"Well, crowd him, then," he said, winking at Jim. "Me'n young Tucker here, we're done watering at the mouth."

Lida turned to Jim. "You'll stay for supper, Jim?"

Jim hesitated long enough to show his manners, then nodded. "I reckon Sugar can handle things till I get back."

Lida slung the gobbler over her shoulder and hurried toward the house. Jim entered the pens to take her place.

"Dry, ain't it?" Blair commented.

Jim nodded. "We could sure do with a good rain," he said in sober agreement.

After that exchange, they worked silently in the dust stirred up by the hoofs of the bawling calves.

The dust turned to pale gold as the sun sank toward the ridgetops.

It was late when they ate. The kitchen was warm with the heat of the cast-iron cookstove and golden in the light of the yellow coal-oil lamps that hung on the walls. Polished reflectors behind the lamps threw the light on a man's plate. They ate from a table covered with a white embroidered cloth and from plates and cups all of a white-and-gold pattern. The gobbler lay on his back in a huge platter, his stump legs sticking up. He was browned to a turn. Surrounding the bird was corn-bread dressing flavored with wild onions that grew along the riverbank. There was brown gravy in another dish, and hot biscuits the size and shape of little terrapins, and wild plum jelly and a mountain of fresh butter and a two-gallon crock of cold sweet milk.

Jim ate like a man starved. He stuffed till he felt as if his eyeballs would pop out of his head, but still he couldn't bring himself to refuse another helping when Lida Blair urged him.

Between bites, he studied the girl covertly. She had changed from jeans into a clean blue gingham dress and had brushed her yellow braids out into waves that reached past her shoulders. Be dogged if he ever recollected a woman who could cook like this one or who took such an evident pride in seeing that a man's plate and milk glass were kept full every second. He wished Mary Sue were more like that.

He and Sam Blair finished and went into the next room to sit full and comfortable in front of a blazing log fire in the cut-rock chimney. There was no fuss about who was to do the dishes, like it was at home. Lida didn't expect man-help in the kitchen. She went ahead with the job. Silently and efficiently, and when she was done, she came to sit with them beside the fire and listen to their talk.

She sat on a low stool, her interlocked fingers holding her knees and the firelight playing on her face and glinting in her hair. She watched Jim with the level, unsmiling gaze that had so disturbed him during his first visit. It didn't disturb him now; he was used to it. It somehow encouraged him so that he talked with more confidence, matching the older man's talk with talk of his own.

It was all man talk, hunting and fishing, escapades with wild cattle and bad horses, fighting hogs. This was the first time Jim could remember telling any tales himself. Always before, he'd done all the listening, not being considered man enough to have stories of his own. It was a good feeling.

Blair told one about a night hunt for wild cattle in the South Texas *brasada,* when he'd roped at what he thought was a yearling calf and caught a Mexican lion.

Jim told about the two range bulls fighting near the house when he was a kid; one had hooked the other into the bed of a two-wheeled cart, starting the cart rolling down a quarter-mile slope. The bull had ridden it all the way, too startled to jump out.

Lida put in, wanting her papa to tell Jim about the time he slipped up on a sleeping coyote.

Sam Blair chuckled. "Booger was sleeping right square up on his back," he said. "Belly bared to the sun and all four feet in the air. Got me an idea. Says I, 'Coyotes is always sneaking up on something. I'll just sneak up on this one. Scare him out of his hide.'

"Got down off my horse. Crawled toward him on my all-fours. Got right up to him. Drawed my six-shooter and cocked her. Can dang nigh poke him in the belly with the barrel of my gun. Can't miss.

"Drawed back the hammer and cut down on him. Too sure to take aim. Missed him a foot.

"That gun going off in his ears sure brung that coyote alive. He jumped six feet straight up, scared blind, yowling fit to kill. Down he come. Right square on top of Sam Blair. Raked me with every claw he's got, messed all over me, and quit the country like his tail was afire!"

The talk ran on and on till Jim knew it was long past the time he ought to leave, and reluctantly got to his feet.

Blair told him jovially to come back "any time you can knock another gobbler out of the air with that there Winchester."

Lida went to the door with him. She stepped out onto the gallery and looked up at him. "You will come back, Jim?" she asked.

"I'll sure do that," he promised, conscious of a strange warm glow of happiness.

Damn it, I could have kissed her, he told himself as he rode into the dark. *I sure could have kissed her.*

He wondered why what he'd seen in Lida's eyes had made him shy off and fumble his chance.

14

IT WAS RIGHT at dark when Jim and the dogs worked the little bunch of wild hogs into the rock pens and Jim shut the gate on them. Across the river, he could see the yellow light of their lantern in the old rock house and guessed Sugar was back from taking another load of hogs into town. He rode down into the river bed and toward the light, knowing a feeling of pride in accomplishment. At the rate he and Sugar were rounding up and delivering hogs, it wouldn't be long till they had some good money tucked away. Jim wasn't right certain yet what he aimed to do with his share of it, but it gave him a good feeling just knowing he'd have it for whatever he wanted. He'd never had any money before—not his own.

Maybe if his luck held, he'd get him a start, hog hunting with Sugar this way. Maybe make enough that he could set up somewhere and ask a girl to settle down with him. Jim guessed every man had that dream, of getting a little piece of ground, a place to hang his hat and call home. Even if you didn't own it, the yearn was still there.

Jim hadn't been able to forget the job Lewt Scuffles had offered Sugar. He knew he could handle that job. He wasn't a kid any longer. He'd proved that by holding his own, hunting range hogs with Sugar.

But there was more to it than that. In some inexplicable way, the job was tied up with Jim's fierce desire to help his father, and prove himself a man. It seemed to him that if he could just get the job, everybody would recognize the fact that he was a man. But he hadn't worked up enough nerve to ask Lewt about it yet. It was suddenly too important; and deep down inside, Jim had a feeling of inadequacy and doubt. He was desperately afraid the Kline & O'Toole foreman would turn him down.

It was just a dream, Jim guessed. But, as he rode slowly toward the river, in near darkness, it seemed somehow close and within his grasp. The old stone house, almost lost in the deeper blackness between the hills, was just the kind of place he'd longed for. He knew Dan Tucker would like it too, if he could come back here after the trouble blew over.

Fixed up, it would be the kind of house a woman would like, and Jim had a particular woman in mind for it. It was funny, though, how memory of the other night kept intervening. Instead of Mary Sue, he found himself thinking of how Lida Blair had enjoyed cooking for him, and the way she'd sat listening while he and her father talked.

Jim wished Mary Sue could bake a fat gobbler the way Lida could. A man ought to have a woman who could set him a good table. But Mary Sue would probably want to start with the whole shebang, instead of helping a man build up, little at a time.

Jim wondered, too, why Mary Sue was always either fighting a man or flirting with him. She never gave him a chance to be comfortable around her; couldn't keep quiet and listen while menfolks talked things over.

Come to think of it, it was sort of funny the way he felt about Mary Sue. He'd been hoping she'd be his girl for so long it was kind of a habit. Now he knew she wanted him, his interest had slimmed down.

He guessed that's the way it was; you ached for something till you couldn't rest and then when you finally got it you didn't want it much any more. You started looking around, aching for something else.

But having a place of your own wasn't like that; you always wanted it. Jim knew he'd always want a place like this. And if he could only get the job . . . Maybe some day he could even get the Fiddle brand started again.

Jim sighed and rode on across the river. The horse's hoofs struck ringing echoes from the long shelving of rock. Sugar was outside the camp house, whizzing rock into the brush and cussing a blue streak.

"What's up, Sugar?" Jim called out. "What you after?"

"That Felipe!" roared Sugar. "That confounded, bottle-butted, no-count pup!"

He threw again. The rock hummed through the darkness and crashed into the brush. There was a yelp of pain and a rustling sound of movement as Felipe ran for new cover.

Jim grinned. "What's Felipe done now?" he asked, climbing out of the saddle and yanking loose his girth.

"Done!" roared Sugar. "Why, nothing! Just set on his damned tail and don't open his head when he ought to've been barking. Damn his Meskin-talking soul. If I could see my sights, I'd shoot him right between the eyes!"

The one-armed man came and sat on the gallery where light from the lantern fell across his face. Jim saw that Sugar was really worried.

"What was he supposed to bark at?" Jim asked.

"At Jess Pickett," Sugar cried. "Myrtle's man. . . . But does he let out one yip to warn me? Hell, no! Lays under the front doorsteps, wagging his tail, I reckon, and lets Jess walk right up on the front gallery. Why, I could have just as easy as not got my head blowed clean off my shoulders."

Jim stared at Sugar in astonishment. "You mean Jess caught you making love to his wife?"

"I don't know whether I'm caught or not. That's what's running me ragged. All the way back here, I'm trying to make up my mind if I am or if I ain't." Sugar wiped sweat from his face with a soiled bandana and sat staring at the handkerchief, frowning with concentration.

"Now, Jess don't see me there in the house," he worried. "He can't. For the minute he steps on the front gallery and hollers 'Myrtle!' I'm hitting for the back door while he's coming in the front. The back-yard gate's shut, and it's fifty yards from there to the brush, but I clear that gate in a jump and streak for cover like a tin-canned dog.

"Now, the question is, does Jess make it right on through the house for a look at me as I run off, or does he git sidetracked into the room where Myrtle's hollering 'Help!' at the top of her voice?"

"Where was the car?" Jim asked.

"Hell, I'm in the clear there," Sugar said. "That car's parked out of sight, where I don't have to pass the house getting out. But what d'you reckon that fool pup's doing all the way in? Chasing that Ford just like he wasn't wearing a damned crutch, and barking his fool head off!"

Sugar got up to throw another rock into the dark where he heard the pup whining, but he evidently missed.

"What about Myrtle?" Jim asked. "Won't she tell?"

"What! Myrtle tell?" Sugar looked indignant. "Why, Myrtle won't tell nothing if Jess don't already know. That Myrtle, she's the salt of the earth!"

Sugar walked up and down the gallery floor, running his hand through his hair, frowning worriedly. "Now, if I only knowed what Jess knows."

He stopped and faced about. "Reckon you couldn't mosey into town and find out for me? Jess'll be liable to be in town, stirring up the law."

"Reckon I could," Jim said.

"That'll do it," Sugar said, his face brightening. "Don't ask no questions. Just browse around and see what you can learn. Between now and then, I'll stick to the brush and be hard to find."

Suddenly the hog hunter threw back his head and his rollicking laughter rang out.

"Lord A'mighty! I must a-been a sight to bulge an eyeball!" He squatted down with his back against the wall and shouted with laughter till the tears rolled down his cheeks. "Lordy, if that Myrtle won't give me a hoorawing!"

His laughter cut off as abruptly as it had begun and he added soberly: "That is, I hope she gits the chance."

His face twisted with anger and he leaped off the gallery. He grabbed up another rock and threw it into the brush. Felipe yelped shrilly and ran off, howling with pain.

"I'll kill that Meskin-talking idjit yet!" he promised.

Jim had never driven a car a dozen times in his life, but at that, he was a better driver than Sugar Barnett. He kept his eye on the road, his hand on the steering wheel, and he was willing to slow down for the rough places.

Now that Sugar, he thought as he drove along the hill road, *he's sure got himself in a pickle. Jess Pickett's liable not to stutter a'tall when it comes to pulling a gun trigger.*

He guessed if Pickett had recognized Sugar running away from the cabin, there wasn't a thing the one-armed man could do but quit the country. And do it fast.

He tried to think how it would be if Sugar left, and he didn't like the idea. Sugar was about all the friend he had. Good friend, that is, one who accepted him for what he was and didn't hold it against him because his father had been sent to prison for hog stealing. He sure didn't want to lose a friend like Sugar. And they were just beginning to pile up a little money. He'd hate to have to quit that. But he guessed if Sugar was run out, he'd leave with him—if Sugar would take him along.

Then Jim thought of his father. Dan Tucker was hiding out in the hills. He'd need help from somebody. He was sick in his mind. Jim remembered the two sets of tracks at the spring. No sane man—no man who knew the country like Dan Tucker, that is—would have left those tracks for the law to find. In the old days Dan Tucker would have slipped around with the wary cunning of a mountain cat, covering his sign to where a dog couldn't smell it out.

Despair laid hold of Jim. He couldn't quit the country. He'd have to stay and see if he couldn't help his father. There didn't seem any way to help a stir-crazy convict, but Jim would have to find one. Somehow. Someway.

He came to the road fork leading off to the old Johnson place and swung into it on impulse. Could be he'd learn something about Sugar's case there and save a trip all the way into town. Could be, too, he'd get to see Lida and talk to her for a minute. The thought was warm inside him.

A pair of beady eyes shone red in the light of the Ford's head lamp and Jim slowed in time to keep from running over a skunk. He had to come to a full stop and wait till the striped varmint decided to lower its hairy tail and amble out of the road. Then he drove on, half pleased with the interruption.

Sugar, now, he'd have cussed and raved about having to wait for a fool skunk to get out of his way. Sugar was impatient as all hell about things, but Jim guessed that was one of the things that made him such good company.

Jim drove, smiling to himself. He sure liked that Sugar. But he also liked the wild things. He'd slow up for a varmint any time, just for the chance to see how it acted. He had a feeling that Lida Blair was like that, too, and wished she'd been there with him to see the skunk holding up the show while he took his time crossing the road.

Jim drove the car up to the yard gate of the Johnson place and stopped. He saw Sam Blair open the door and peer out.

"Lida home, Mr. Blair?" he called out.

Sam Blair waited a long time to answer, then asked gruffly: "That Jim Tucker?"

There was an anger in the man's voice Jim didn't like. "Yes, sir," he faltered.

Sam Blair reached overhead and lifted down a rifle from a rack above the door. He jacked a shell into the firing chamber and said, "Sorry, Tucker. Lida ain't home." There was apology in the voice, but there was also finality. Sam Blair meant what he'd said.

"She ain't never going to be home to you no more."

Jim was too stunned to reply. But he guessed he knew what the trouble was. Somebody had told Blair he was the son of a convict. And there it was again! For five years now, every time he'd made a friend or begun a friendship, he'd been slapped down with the same words: "Convict's son." Nobody wanted to have anything to do with a convict's son.

A black wave of despair and futility swept through him. Then he thought of Lida, her gentle ways, her understanding, how her rare smiles had always seemed to give him courage, made him feel there wasn't a mean or cowardly streak in him.

He was unbearably full of a need for her now, and his longing was deep and hurting.

But there was nothing to do but drive on toward town.

15

JIM DROVE into Mason and parked the Ford under the big old three-pronged live oak near the courthouse. There was a man drawing himself a drink of water out of a nearby well when Jim pulled up. The man lifted the bucket out and set it on the curb, looked at Jim, and left the bucket sitting there without drinking.

The man was Sam Cleever. He came in a hurry, climbed into the car, and said excitedly: "Drive off the square, boy. This ain't no time for you to be seen in town!"

Jim started the Ford and drove off back of the wagon yard and parked under a big mesquite tree.

"What is it?" he demanded of Cleever.

Cleever countered with a question of his own. "Where's he at, boy?"

Jim thought he was talking about Sugar. "Out in the brush," he said warily. "I ain't seen him for a day or two."

"We got to help him, boy," Cleever said confidentially. "You tell me where he is and we'll go see about getting him out of the country."

So Sugar would have to leave, after all. "I don't rightly know where to find him," Jim said. He was suspicious of Cleever's wanting to help anybody. "He's just in the hills somewhere."

"They'll git him, then," Cleever said. "They'll shoot him or hang him.

Sure as you're born. Boy, you better come clean with your stepdaddy if you want to git help from him!"

Jim needed to know more. "What'd they say about it?"

"Say about it!" rasped Cleever. "Hell, they told it all. Jess and his woman come driving hell-bent into town, with Sam Blair riding the back end of their pickup with a Winchester laid across the top. I seen all three of 'em pile out and go rushing into the sheriff's office. In a minute, here come August Hershimer out with 'em and the news spreads.

"Somebody's molested Myrtle. She don't know who. Some wild-looking man with hair all over his face. It's late, too dark in the house for Myrtle to know whether she's ever seen him before. But Jess seen him just as he hits the brush back of the house. Claims it was a white man, wearing queer-looking garments. Prison clothes, Jess is willing to bet. So it ain't no question now who done it."

Jim's blood ran cold. "You mean they think it was—Pa?"

"They know it was," Cleever said. He added sanctimoniously, "Dan ought'n to a-done a thing like that, him being on the dodge and all. He must have gone stir-crazy down in that pen. He don't stand the chance of a snowball in hell now. They'll git him if we don't give him help."

Jim wiped cold sweat from his forehead, his thoughts whirling. This was the reason Lida's father had run him off! They thought his father was not only an escaped convict, but that he had— "Lord!" he said weakly.

Cleever went on. "I know me'n you ain't allus hit it off well, boy, but this is sort of a family affair and no time for personal differences. You tell me quick where Dan is. We ain't got no time to lose. They've even got up a reward for him. Two hundred and fifty dollars. He needs help bad."

Jim could hardly get his breath. *A reward out for Pa!* he thought. "I don't know where Pa is," he told Cleever finally. "I thought it was—I didn't know you was talking about Pa."

Cleever caught up Jim's shirt front in his big hand and jerked the boy closer to him. "Where's he at, damn it?" he demanded. "Come on, now. Quit your lying before I knock hell out of you. I've got a bellyful of your damned foolishment!"

There in the dark, Jim couldn't see Cleever's face, but it was no trouble for his memory to tell him what it looked like now. Black dirty whiskers, blazing bloodshot eyes, features twisted with hate and rage.

He brought a hand up and shoved hard against the whiskery face. "You're lying," he said. "You don't want to help Pa. All you want is that bounty money."

Cleever slapped him hard and slapped him again. Jim was thrown off balance, half out of the car. He came to his feet on the ground, his ears ringing.

Cleever started climbing out of the car after him, cursing hoarsely, and for the first time, Jim's hatred of his stepfather was stronger than his fear.

Sell Pa's life for money to stuff in your dirty pocket, he thought and hit Cleever in the face with every ounce of power he could put behind a hard fist.

Sam Cleever fell back into the car with a startled grunt. He started to rise and Jim hit him again. Cleever cried out and started scrambling wildly to get out of the car on the other side. Jim climbed in with him, slugging hard and fast in the darkness.

Cleever screamed now, frantically, and rolled free, piling out over the other door.

His feet hit the ground. He stumbled and fell, but got up again before Jim could get out of the car. He turned and ran toward town, shouting and crying out as if Jim were still slugging him.

Jim stood and stared after him as long as he was in sight, surprised at how easy it had been. *I could have done that all along,* he thought. *Cleever's scared. If I'd fought back one time, I'd never had to put up with another licking from him.*

He was ashamed of himself for never having had the nerve to stand up to Cleever before. But he felt proud, too, knowing that there was one man who'd never make him cringe again.

He passed Cleever hurrying toward the courthouse as he drove the Ford out of town.

Armed riders were combing the hills the next morning. Jim and Sugar sighted two of them crossing a high point of a far ridge as the hog hunters drifted a bunch of hogs down the long twisting canyon that led toward the rock pens. Later Jim sighted one pushing his horse through the scrub live oak, headed straight for Red Bluff Mill.

His heart constricted. They weren't after him, but it gave him a trapped feeling to see them out here, just the same. Would that rider investigate the loft of the old cabin at the Red Bluff Mill?

Jim knew that if they ever found the man who was hiding there, they'd shoot him or hang him, like Sam Cleever had said they would. He'd die, partly because he was a convict and partly because Myrtle Pickett had lied to protect Sugar. He wondered how Myrtle would feel if she caused a man to die for a crime he didn't commit. He wondered how Sugar would feel.

"Sugar, you think they'll catch him?"

"Not Dan Tucker," said Sugar confidently. "He'll make them drug-store cowboys look like a pack of fools. If he's here, he's likely laying up on the rimrock now, laughing at 'em."

"But what if he's really stir-crazy?" Jim asked, reluctant to bring the dread thought into the open. "A man out of his head ain't likely to cover his tracks. You know that, Sugar."

"Hell, Dan ain't stir-crazy!" Sugar scoffed.

"Then why ain't he come to us?" Jim demanded tensely. "Why don't he give some sign so we can go to him?"

"Dan's too smart for that," Sugar told him. "He can make out. And he might figure August'd git it out'n you somehow if you knew where he was. You can count on Dan to lay low. He'll hang and rattle till the cows come home."

Maybe Sugar was right, but the thought held little comfort. The whole country was out scouring the brush for Dan Tucker.

And the hog hunter didn't seem to be worrying about it, Jim reflected bitterly. Sugar seemed completely indifferent to the effects of his escapade with Myrtle, now that he knew the riders weren't after him. Couldn't he see that Dan Tucker would have to take the rap for his own guilt? Or didn't he care? The sickening suspicion came to Jim that maybe Sugar was glad of it.

Sugar rode along as talkative and carefree as ever.

"The time I'm telling about," he said, "I'm hog hunting out on the head of the Nueces. This old bar'-hog is a bunch quitter. No way on earth to git him to drive with the balance. He heads for the brush and I put the dogs on him. They rally him in a shallow cave where I can't reach him with a rope on account of some tall willers growing out in front.

"I think up a smart trick. I quit my horse and climb up the slant and get over the cave mouth with my rope. I chunk rocks down in front of the cave to git the dogs to rush him. When the dogs crowd in, the bar'-hog charges 'em, like I figure he will. I'm standing right over him with my rope cocked. Out he comes, and I latch on.

"Only it don't work out like I figure. That bar'-hog's too heavy and running too fast. Jerks me clean off that ledge. I land flat on my face not three feet away from the devil. He whirls and has my leg cut to the bone before I can move.

"It's the dogs is all that saves me. They pile in and fight him so fast

I manage to git out from under. One dog gits kilt complete and another'n is cut all to hell. But they drag him down and hold him till I can git my knife out and the blade bit open.

"I just kindly cut that bastard's throat and leave some bacon for the buzzards," Sugar finished.

Jim couldn't enjoy this story of Sugar's. He kept thinking of those men riding the hills.

The barking of the dogs rang in the canyon. The wild hogs made streaks of black and gray as they darted through the tall broomweeds from one thicket to the next. Jim let his gaze wander up and down the canyon slopes and down into the steep-walled gorge ahead. It was wild and beautiful country, this part of Texas, with its rock-ribbed cliffs, its steep slants thick with tangled shin oak, with the tall elms and live oaks down in the bottom, all riotous now with fall coloring.

Once these hills had seemed like a refuge to Jim, a place to get away from all the hates and anxieties and hurts he'd known before. A place where a man could live like a man and know a little peace of mind. But now, with armed riders in the brush, with his own father hiding out in an abandoned cabin and hunted for a crime he hadn't committed, the very wildness of the hills seemed to make them fearful and foreboding.

They worked the hogs out of the canyon into the pens. They caught them, clipped their tushes and loaded them in the wagon. Jim let Sugar take them on into town by himself, claiming he still had some work to do on that pen at Red Bluff Mill.

16

NOBODY WAS in the attic of the old house at Red Bluff Mill. Jim didn't have to climb up there to know it. The same instinctive knowledge that had told him the attic was occupied at his last visit now told him the attic was empty.

He stood in the pens a little while, puzzling on that, wondering where the man had gone. He went out and examined the ground around the reservoir. There were tracks there, shoe tracks this time. Made not later than this morning. They looked about right for the tracks of his daddy's shoes. Jim guessed Dan Tucker had sighted some of the riders and taken to the brush. Which would be the smart thing to do. A man would sure be trapped in that cabin, all right, if somebody took a notion to search it.

Jim turned to his work on the pens. He cut new poles out of a nearby thicket of cedar, fitted them into the gaps and wired them into place with baling wire. That done, he shucked out of his shirt and started cutting brush for the long wing that would be necessary if they ever hoped to get wild hogs into the pen. There was too much open ground around the mill and pens ever to expect a wild hog to cross it of its own accord.

The air was cool and he worked fast, cutting cedar and dragging it into place. But he had to go a long way for the brush. The wing, leading out at a wide angle from the gate, grew slowly.

It gradually came to Jim that he was being watched, but he had expected that feeling and didn't pay much attention to it. A man using that old cabin for a hideout would naturally stay close enough to keep a sharp lookout on what went on around there.

It was a complete surprise when August Hershimer rode out of the brush almost on top of him and sat his saddle, staring at Jim with that peculiar and frightening look of loving malice.

The squat sheriff seldom wore a six-shooter. There was a rifle butt sticking out of the gun boot strapped under his stirrup and a pair of handcuffs dangling from his belt. But Hershimer had a brutelike belief in his own physical prowess. He figured there wasn't a man alive he couldn't tame with his own two hands. He liked it that way.

"This time, kid," he said gently, "there ain't nobody along to stop me."

Jim swallowed. "No," he agreed. "There ain't."

Jim didn't move. He stood with the smooth ax handle gripped in his sweaty hands, knowing he was going to have to use that ax. His lungs stirred to a deeper, faster breathing, but he stood his ground, not trying to escape. August Hershimer hadn't come here to let him escape.

"You been seein' him," August said.

"No," Jim answered. "I ain't."

"You packed them things for him at home," August stated. "I found where he'd been in that bat cave. I found the sack you brung him grub in."

So Mary Sue had told about his packing off Dan Tucker's clothes. She hadn't been able to keep it to herself.

August Hershimer took his time about swinging his hulking body out of the saddle. His cold glassy eyes never left Jim's. He started toward

the boy, taking one slow step at a time, licking his lips and grinning a little. The grin didn't show in his eyes.

"You'll talk this time," he said gently, then rasped out: "Or I'll tear your damned tongue out of your throat!"

Jim still didn't move. He let the sheriff come closer. He was within reach of those huge arms now. August was big, and Jim knew he was also fast; fast and dangerous as a wild bar'-hog. Jim's fingers tightened on the ax handle. Using that ax might not be brave, but it was the only way Jim knew to even up the difference in his and August's size. *It's a mortal certainty,* he thought grimly, *I won't get any braver dead.*

"Where is he at?" August asked. An expression of brutal pleasure crossed his face when he saw that the boy would have to be forced to tell.

Jim set his feet wider apart. "I don't aim to tell," he said and swung the ax.

He did not heft the ax first. That would have given August a warning. He'd been holding the single-bitted axhead down and a little behind him. He whipped it forward now in a lightninglike blow, striking with the butt at August Hershimer's fat knee.

The sheriff grunted like a stricken bull. His knee gave way and he fell. He flung his huge bulk forward as he went down, reaching for Jim, hoping to clutch the boy to him in a rib-crushing hug.

Jim leaped back. He swung the ax again, aiming it at one of Hershimer's arms. The ax butt struck solidly, with a soggy, meaty sound.

Hershimer lay on the ground and moved the arm experimentally, his eyes surprised that it wouldn't respond to his immediate command. He moved his eyes away from his arm and looked up at Jim.

"Nobody gets by with that, boy," he said. "You'll talk yet." With a powerful movement, he lurched to his feet.

He moved toward Jim again. The injured leg nearly buckled, but he threw his weight onto the other and kept his balance. The left arm hung loose from his shoulder.

Jim felt his insides churning with fear, but he stood his ground. He had to let the man get closer.

He chopped at the wounded arm again, still using the butt of his ax. The blow rocked Hershimer off balance, but that was all. Jim knew he couldn't bring himself to use the bit of the ax. He struck a third time, driving the butt down between the beefy neck and shoulder of the man, trying for a paralyzing blow.

Hershimer fell to the ground and his fleshy body quivered. Jim stepped back, waiting. He was sure Hershimer wouldn't get up again. No man alive could take a blow like that and get up again.

But Hershimer got up. He got up, grunting and reeling, but he stood and started moving toward Jim again. His eyes never left the boy's face. There was something inhuman about him that put an unnatural fear into Jim. He had seen that same glassy stare in the eyes of a wounded mountain lion.

Hershimer breathed in great gasps.

That stare, the scuff of Hershimer's dragging boot as he pulled along the crippled leg, the sound of the man's hoarse breathing, all combined to shatter Jim's nerve. He struck blindly, without aim. The ax slipped from his hand, clattered to the ground beyond Hershimer.

Hershimer didn't try to pick it up.

"You ought to've used that ax blade, boy," he said heavily. "Didn't you have the guts?"

Jim knew now that he should have. Fighting a man like Hershimer was like fighting one of the vicious wild hogs he'd been working with. A man had to keep the upper hand or be mutilated.

He steadied himself, knowing he couldn't lose his head now. He let Hershimer get close enough to reach out for him, then drove a fist into the sheriff's gasping mouth.

The blow caved in two of Hershimer's teeth. The crunch of them breaking against Jim's hand was telegraphed all the way up the boy's arm to his spine. Jim's hand felt suddenly useless. There was no pain yet where the teeth had cut into his flesh, just an over-all numbness.

Hershimer steadied himself, then started toward Jim again, dragging his wounded leg. "You'll talk, boy," he said doggedly.

There was blood on the sheriff's chin. Jim smashed desperately at the bridge of that broad flat nose and there was bright hot blood spurting down over the wide mouth. But Hershimer kept coming, his pale eyes still on the boy.

Lord A'mighty, can't I ever stop him? Jim thought. *I got to stop him somehow!* He hit Hershimer again, frantic now to hurt the man, to crush him down and stop him.

Something smashed through his guard and slammed him in the chest. The wind went out of his lungs in a shuddering gasp. He fell hard, flat on his back, and lay looking up at the sheriff.

"You'll talk, boy!"

Was that all the man could say? Jim stared up at that battered, bloody mouth and wondered vaguely how words could come out of it. The eyes remained untouched, however. In their pale stare was the same unrelenting power of the man.

Hershimer reached down for Jim and the sight of the huge body coming so near electrified the boy. He drew back a foot and drove a boot heel solidly into Hershimer's stomach. Hershimer staggered back, and pain showed in his pale eyes for the first time. He bent over, emitting a low grunting groan. He reeled, staggered to regain his balance, and fell.

Jim came to his feet. He lifted a boot heel to stamp the bloody head and then became aware of those pale eyes staring up at him and through him, unseeing. He knew a second of hot, savage triumph.

I can kill him now. There ain't nothing on God's earth to keep me from killing him. Then I'd never have to be afraid of him again.

But a feeling of nausea swept over him. He turned and ran blindly toward his horse. He had dragged himself into the saddle when nausea finally overwhelmed him. He clung weakly to the saddle horn and retched till it seemed as if everything inside him would come up.

17

JIM RODE into camp at sundown, unconscious of his surroundings, his mind still in a daze from the shock and horror of the fight at Red Bluff Mill. It was like some hideous nightmare that wouldn't end, even after a man woke up. He failed to notice the saddled horse standing hipshot before the cabin, the bridle reins tied to a mesquite.

The animal turned its head and nickered, and awareness halted Jim in the act of dismounting, so that he stood off in one stirrup while his eyes raked the camp house with a quick hard look. His hands moved toward the butt of his Winchester.

Lida Blair stepped through the cabin door and said, "Hello, Jim." Her eyes held some deep trouble of their own, but Jim was too preoccupied to notice.

He stepped down and moved toward the house without answering and came on up on the gallery, still without speaking. To his fogged mind, it seemed only right and natural that Lida be here. He walked past her through the door and she followed him into the cabin.

Lida said hopefully: "I just wanted to come see you for a little bit, Jim."

The fog cleared in Jim's brain.

"Your pa know where you're at?" he demanded harshly.

Lida shook her head. "No," she said soberly. "That's what I came to tell you about, Jim. He—"

"This ain't no place for you to be," Jim said. "Your pa'll come gunning for me if he finds out you've been here. They're all gunning for me. Hell, don't you know my pa's a convict?" Bitterness made his voice rough and savage.

Lida's lips trembled. "Please, Jim," she said. "That's what I came for. To tell you it was Papa who said all those things the other night. It wasn't me."

"It's all the same," Jim said. He poured water and coffee grounds into a blackened pot and set it on the coals in the fireplace.

"But it's not the same!" Lida said heatedly. "What I think and what Papa thinks are two different things. I'm not holding that against you, Jim. You can't help what your papa done."

His face darkened. "Pa never done nothing."

"I know," Lida said. "Sugar told me how it was."

Jim's eyes moved to her face. "Sugar told you—what'd Sugar tell you?"

"Why, just what happened, I guess," Lida said. "He said your papa was rounding up hogs and some of Sam Cleever's were in the bunch and your papa penned them together to keep from losing them all and Sam Cleever rode up and saw them and claimed your papa was stealing his hogs. They had no right to send him to the pen."

Jim had thought for a moment that Sugar had told the girl about Myrtle Pickett. He adjusted now to what she did know. He said grimly, "But you notice they sent Pa up, just the same."

"I know, Jim," she said, her voice softening with sympathy. "But don't let it make you bitter. Don't let it make you hate people."

Jim said nothing to that. He stared into the glowing coals, feeling the warmth pain his swelling fist. Lida came and stood beside him, not touching him, but standing so close that the perfume of her hair reached his nostrils, faint, but with a flowerlike freshness. Her closeness struck through to his consciousness like a warm caress.

From far down the river came the faint furious barking of a dog.

"Where's Sugar?" Jim asked.

Lida smiled. "He's fishing," she said. "He got to telling me about a big catfish he lost in a pool down the river. I told him how Papa sometimes tied a big hook on a pole and went into underwater caves after big fish when he couldn't catch them any other way. Sugar couldn't wait to try it out."

She looked up into his face and smiled again. "I knew he'd feel that way about it. That's why I told him. I wanted to be with you by yourself."

He looked at her, smiling up at him so close, and the sick, angry look on his face didn't change. The girl's smile faltered involuntarily, she stepped away.

"You don't hate me too, do you, Jim?"

The note of appeal in her voice reached him, shamed him a little. He put a hand on her shoulder. "I couldn't ever hate you," he said.

She moved closer, her face soft and gentle in the light of the fire. Behind them, the coffee started bubbling in the pot. From downriver came the barking of the dog again, high-pitched and excited. Jim lifted his head to listen.

"Then you'll come to see me again, Jim?"

Jim raised his hand for silence. "Hush!" he said shortly. He moved to the door, unaware of the girl's hurt surprise. He stared down the river canyon, listening intently.

The dog had quit his excited barking now, to fill the canyon with doleful howls. A premonition of trouble hit Jim like a blow.

"Something's wrong," he said. "Something's happened to Sugar!"

He left the door and crossed the gallery in two long strides and was on the ground, hurrying toward his horse. He mounted without touching a stirrup, ignoring the stab of pain in his swollen hand as he gripped the saddle horn and swung his weight up. He was wheeling his horse around when he saw Lida come quickly out of the house, her eyes wide with concern.

"I'm coming too, Jim," she called.

He couldn't wait. He roweled the horse heavily. The startled animal snorted and buck-jumped a time or two stiff-leggedly before lining out in a hard run down the canyon.

The canyon trail was rough. It twisted between broken boulders and flood-bent cottonwoods. But Jim never let the horse slack his pace. Above the pop and clatter of his own mount's hoofs, he heard that of the girl's hard on his heels.

He saw Felipe first on the bank. The crutch hardly slowed the dog up as it raced frantically back and forth at the water's edge, running over Sugar's clothes piled up near the water. Felipe's back arched in fear, his tail clamped tightly up against his belly. He halted his running to lift his voice in another wailing howl, then leaped into the pool. He swam out across it.

Jim was pulling his horse out of a dead run, his eyes on the pup, wondering what possessed him, when a hand broke the surface of the water at the far edge of the pool. The hand clutched desperately at the air and went under.

Jim roweled the horse again with his spurs, giving him no time to shy away from the water, goading him straight into it. The horse snorted and reared high, then lunged forward with all his might, as if hoping to leap completely across the pool. He came down into it with a splash that knocked water high above Jim's head. The horse sank deep, almost going under, so that the water reached up under Jim's armpits, shockingly cold against his warm body. Then the animal came up, fighting for buoyancy, and Jim felt the water suck and pull at his clothes as it drained from him.

He felt the horse swimming now and wiped the water from his eyes and searched past the swimming Felipe for that hand. It was almost too much to hope for, but the hand came up again and beat against the water till it touched a lip of rock. It clung there, the fingers clawing, rigid and white with strain.

Sugar's head rose and he gasped for breath, choking on the water he sucked into his lungs. Jim brought the horse up beside him. He reached out and caught Sugar's wrist, tore the fingers loose from their fierce grip. With a quick wrench, he hauled Sugar's body, naked and blue with cold, across the saddle in front of him, almost rolling his horse over in the water with the movement.

The forefeet of the horse struck bottom and he righted himself. He came up out of the pool, snorting and lunging. Jim felt Sugar's body slip from his grasp, clutched at it and missed, and saw the hog hunter land heavily on the flat, slanting rock almost under the scrambling hoofs of the horse.

Jim piled out of the saddle, letting the horse go, and dropped down beside the hog hunter, grabbing him under the armpits in time to keep him from slipping back into the water.

The horse went out across the flat rocks of the river bed, bucking and bawling, slinging loose stirrups high.

Jim lifted the stunned Sugar and started walking backwards, dragging him to safer ground. That's when he saw the heavy fishing cord tied around one of Sugar's ankles and felt the drag of added weight tugging at the man's body.

Jim let Sugar down on the rock again. He went to the edge of the pool, caught the line up from the lip of rock and hauled back on it. Astonished at feeling a live, struggling weight on the end, he hauled back

harder and pulled out about six feet of line, tied to a short pole. On the other end of the pole, a big hook caught firmly in his underlip, was the biggest catfish Jim had ever seen.

Jim gave the line a strong tug and brought the fish sliding out of the water onto the slanting rock where Sugar lay. Jim could only stand and stare at the monstrous fish. It would have weighed at least seventy pounds, maybe more. It lay still on the slanting rocks for a few seconds, too startled by its strange surroundings to attempt escape, its only movement the slow opening and closing of huge gill vents that heaved like bellows.

Jim heard a ragged cough and gasp behind him and turned to see Sugar struggle up into a sitting position. Sugar slapped the pup Felipe, who was leaping all over him, joyously licking his face.

"Git out of here!" Sugar rasped hoarsely. He paused to cough again and suck a long breath of air into his lungs.

"Sugar!" Jim cried anxiously. "You all right, Sugar?"

"Who, me?" Sugar gasped. Water was trickling down out of his hair and over his face. He reached up to wipe it away. "Why, I'm all right, I guess. Just a little short of breath," he said. "And froze stiffer'n a brass monkey's tail."

He sat panting a moment, his thin chest heaving. Suddenly he threw up his head. "What about that yellercat?" he asked. "You didn't let that yellercat git away, did you?"

Jim pointed to the line, still tied to Sugar's ankle. He couldn't speak. He was too near shouting with laughter or breaking into tears. He didn't know which. That crazy Sugar!

Sugar bent over to grasp the line and give it a yank. The catfish came to life, flopping heavily, its flat tail slapping the rock.

"Hold him!" shouted Sugar, struggling to his feet. "Don't let him git back in that water."

Jim caught the line and slid the fish farther out on the rock.

"You know what that scogie done?" Sugar cried with growing astonishment. "He tried to drown me. He sure did." A rigor shook his naked body and started his teeth to chattering. Sugar's hurt astonishment was more than Jim could take. His fingers pulling the line weakened and he began laughing. His body shook with sobs of laughter till he had to sit down and bury his head in his arms. He laughed till the tears rolled down his face.

Sugar stiffened suddenly and leaped to a squatting position behind Jim, clawing at his soaked brush jacket, dragging it from Jim's shoulders. "Blessed Jehoshaphat, boy!" he said through rattling teeth. "You never told me there was no womenfolks along."

Jim looked up to see Lida standing with her back turned to them, her shoulders shaking with laughter.

They put Sugar to bed in the cabin and built up a roaring fire in the chimney. Jim got into dry clothes, and Lida fed Sugar whiskey and hot coffee till his chill-racked body stopped shivering and his tongue loosened.

"It were the cold water done it, I reckon," he told them. "There I am, all rigged up so I can't miss. Got my clothes on the bank where I'll have something dry and warm to put on when I get out. Got my hook tied to my pole to get him with. Got the pole tied to my leg so he can't get away.

"Down into that water I go. Lord, she's cold! Makes my bones ache. But I figure I can stand it if I don't take too long to git that fish hooked.

"I keep my eyes open, like Lida says her papa does, and sure enough, I can see. It's yaller-looking under there and not too plain, but I can see."

He glanced at Lida, sitting on the floor and leaning against Jim's saddle.

"I head right into the mouth of that cave. It's real shaller. There's my catfish, big as a fattening hog, laying on his belly and finning the water slow. Staring straight at me. There's my same hook, still in his mouth from the time I caught him before, when that Felipe made me shoot my line in two. I reach for him, figuring I'll have to be quick to catch him when he starts ducking and dodging. He don't duck and dodge a'tall. Just opens his mouth and comes at that hook like I'm handing him a bait of fresh liver. He grabs it. I give a yank and he's on. All I got to do now is go out on the bank and land him."

Sugar stopped to gulp down more whiskey-laced coffee.

"That's where the fun starts. He feels that hook and goes wild. I start for the top, but I'm too cold and stiff. Can't move nothing, arm or leg, seems like. Paralyzed. Aching plumb through my backbone now. Plumb through my brains.

"Old yellercat hits me. Busts me a good un. Knocks me back out of that cave. Brings me to life a little. But not enough. I can't git to the top, not and pull him, too. And he's gone back in the cave and balked. He's at home in that water and I ain't. Can't budge him but an inch or two, then he goes right back.

"I'm busting open for want of air now. How'm I gonna git it? I can git to the top with my hand, but can't git my head out. I reach for the string to jerk it loose from my leg and the draw loop's slipped out. Lord, I'm like a frog on a string, kicking hard but gitting nowhere. If something don't happen quick, I'll never eat this catfish; he'll eat me. It ain't a cheering thought. I go crazy as that yellercat. I don't know nothing from that time on till I fall off your horse."

The pup Felipe came to the door, his eyes on Sugar, whimpering and whining anxiously.

Jim said, "Hadn't been for that pup, I'd never knowed you was in trouble. Not in time to do no good."

Sugar said, "What? That Meskin-talking idjit? What'd he have to do with it?"

"He barked," said Jim. "He barked and howled. Kept it up till I knowed something was wrong."

Sugar sat up in his bedroll, a look of amazement on his face. "That thing bark? How come he don't bark the other night—I don't believe that harebrained thing had the sense to know I was in trouble."

Jim grinned at Sugar's near slip in front of Lida. "He was coming in after you when I got there," he said.

"Well, blessed bleeding Jesus!" Sugar said. "I been plumb mistaken in that pup. Why, damn me, I ain't been treating him right." He looked at the pup, who was now inching inside the door, getting as close to Sugar as he dared.

"Here, Felipe!" Sugar said. "Come on, boy. Right up here in bed with me. Golly, I wanta say my pardons!"

Felipe hushed his whining. He stopped wringing his tail. He stood and looked at Sugar as if he didn't know what to make of him.

"Come on, boy!" Sugar coaxed. "Come on, now."

The soft words were too much for Felipe. He wheeled suddenly, emitted a startled yelp, and tore out of the house in a tail-tucked run as if Sugar had thrown another rock at him.

Jim threw back his head and laughed aloud. Lida Blair looked at Sugar and then at the empty door and her warm laughter filled the room. Sugar sat and stared at the door in astonishment.

"That Meskin-talking son of a—" He broke off to glance at Lida again, and his face turned red.

"I'll kill that dog yet," he said in a disgruntled voice. He lay back and reached for the whiskey bottle again.

Lida moved reluctantly toward the door. "It's past time I went," she said. "Papa'll be worrying."

Mention of her father brought back all the old worry and bitterness to Jim. He walked with Lida to where her horse stood hitched outside. He was remembering that her father had told him Lida would never be home for him any more. He thought of his own father, a convict, hiding like a hunted animal, running for his life, fighting and always living in the shadow of the law. He might be innocent, but for the way everybody treated him and looked down on him, he might as well be guilty.

Lida mounted and sat her horse, ready to ride home. The lantern light from the open door of the cabin lay gently on her face. "You'll come again, Jim?" she asked.

Jim said uncomfortably, "You know it ain't no use, Lida. Your pa ain't going to put up with the likes of me hanging around. And I reckon he's right."

"I can handle Papa," Lida said. "It'll be all right later on, after—" She stopped, confused, wishing she hadn't said it.

Jim's lips tightened. "Sure," he said bitterly. "It'll all blow over, once they've run him down and hung him."

"Please, Jim," Lida cried out. "Don't be like that."

He looked up, saw tears coming in her eyes, saw her soft mouth trembling. A sullen rancor was building up inside him. Damn a world that denied a man even the right to choose his own girl!

"All right," he said bleakly. "But just the same, you'd better forget about me coming around any more."

Without looking at her again, he turned and walked into the house.

18

UP THE SLANT, where the red-tinted Spanish oaks grew tall and the mountain elms were burnt-orange in the sunlight, Sam Cleever sat in his saddle listening. If he'd figured it right, Jim and Sugar ought to be bringing their hog gather down the draw just over the next ridge. He sat and listened and spoke sullenly to his horse when the animal grew impatient and started fiddle-footing beneath him.

"Be quiet, you fool!" he commanded and jerked the spade bit in the horse's mouth.

His red-rimmed eyes lighted with anticipation as the yelping of dogs came at last to his ears. They were in that next draw, all right, and coming down it, like he'd figured. He licked a finger till it was wet all around and held it up in the still air. When the side of his finger toward the dogs grew cooler than the rest, he nodded with satisfaction, got down and tied his horse, and began making his way cautiously up the slant. The wind was from the right direction; the dogs wouldn't catch his scent.

At the top of the ridge, Cleever concealed himself in a thicket of dry bee brush where he had a clear view of the country below him.

Jim and Sugar came into view, the dogs working a motley band of hogs ahead of them. The barking of the dogs was loud in the still air and now and then Cleever got a glimpse of the wild hogs as they charged swiftly from thicket to thicket. No grunts or rumbling came from the hogs; they merely uttered an occasional swishing snort.

Full of rage and resentment, Cleever kept his eyes on Jim.

Ungrateful no-account. Give him bed and board for five long years and what does he do? Beat up on his own stepdaddy. Try to kill him. Try to cheat him out of a good two hundred and fifty dollars. Ought to open his belly with a .30-30 ball.

Cleever ran his hands over the hard metal of his rifle, but he didn't lift it. He'd wait till he got his hands on that bounty money first.

He watched closely till the riders were past and moving out of sight, then he hurried back down the slant to his horse and rode at a sharp clip parallel to the draw down which the hog hunters were driving their catch. When he was satisfied he was far enough in the lead, he tied up his horse and sneaked to the top of the ridge again.

Jim said, "That Felipe's going to make a hog dog, Sugar."

"He is, for a fact," Sugar agreed, "now that he's rid of that crutch. But he still needs a few more rocks bounced off his ribs. He don't keep his mind on his business."

"He's young," Jim said. "He's got to have time. He'll learn."

"He'll learn or I'll kill him," Sugar said emphatically.

Jim smiled to himself. Sugar was still playing at being hard on Felipe, but long after midnight last night, Jim had awakened to find Sugar taking the splints off Felipe's crippled leg, and studying the leg to make certain he could use it without the crutch. Then Sugar had sliced chunks of meat off a doe carcass they had hanging outside the cabin, and stood feeding the venison to the pup. Jim didn't guess Sugar was going to forget that it was Felipe who had saved him from becoming catfish bait.

Jim's mind switched to Lida Blair, and he felt a twinge of remorse. He reckoned she'd never speak to him again, after what had happened last night.

Riding along, Jim thought of how it could be if things were different between him and Lida. He knew the only life he could offer her would be that of an outcast as long as his father was known as a thief. He knew the feeling too well to want to hobble Lida Blair with anything like that.

But his imagination got the jump on him and he could see himself and Lida Blair riding off, quitting the country and heading for a new life together, Jim getting himself a riding job with some cow outfit, 'way off somewhere where nobody knew anything about him. There'd be good hunting, deer and bear and wild turkey that a man could have for the shooting. Plenty of good fishing. And Lida in a snug little cabin, waiting to cook up what game a man brought in. Fixing it fancy like she'd done with that gobbler. Filling a man till he couldn't eat another bite. Then doing the dishes while he sat by the fire and told her his tales.

Jim came back to reality and swore under his breath. There was no way for a dream like that to happen. In the first place, Lida was through with him. He'd fixed that. And even if he persuaded her, how could they get far enough away? All the money he had was what he would get when he and Sugar got paid off. And even if it were enough to get them out of the country, what about Dan Tucker? A boy couldn't just go off and leave his dad in a fix like Dan Tucker was in. He might not be able to help him much, but he had to try.

Jim felt the bulge inside his brush jumper pocket. That was grub he had wrapped up in an old newspaper to leave at Red Bluff Mill after they'd penned the hogs. It wasn't much, but it would keep Dan Tucker alive another day or so—keep him from starving out so he'd have to take big risks getting food.

Sam Cleever lay in the brush as close as he dared to the Red Bluff Mill and watched Jim and Sugar pen their hogs. He saw Sugar shut the gate and wire it tight, then mount and start riding off. He saw Jim piddling around behind, stooping to pull the ears of the pup, messing with his saddle girth.

Cleever waited, hardly breathing. It was plain as day that his stepson was stalling for time. Then his heart leaped in triumph. Jim was walking quickly around the pens toward the cabin, pulling a package from his pocket as he went. He came to the open door of the cabin, tossed the package inside, then hurried back and mounted.

Cleever sat and grinned smugly as he watched Jim riding off after Sugar. It'd been easier than he'd ever hoped for.

There's two hundred and fifty in the bag, he told himself. *All I got to do is go pick it up.*

Cleever's hands shook with excitement till he could hardly roll himself a cigarette.

19

SAM CLEEVER lifted down his .30-30 from the buck-antler rack over the fireplace. He still couldn't get over how close he'd come to cornering Dan Tucker in that cabin at Red Bluff Mill. The signs were there, fresh tracks around the reservoir, Jim Tucker's bundle of grub pitched into the lower room, that pile of hay in the loft with the imprint of a man's body plain on it. But the cabin had been empty and the only thing Cleever could figure was that Dan Tucker was sleeping in the loft at night and holing up in the brush during the day. That meant night was the only time a man would have a chance to catch him.

Cleever pulled on his gray mackinaw, with the faded red and blue stripes around the middle. The jacket was old, with holes at the elbows and frayed at the wrists, but it would keep out the biting November cold, come night.

"Do I git my hands on that reward money, I'll buy me a new coat," he promised himself.

He pulled down the lever of his gun a little, opening the breech till he saw the shiny brass of a cartridge in the firing chamber, then snapped the lever back into place. He reached into a box and took out cartridges, one at a time, thumbing them into the gun magazine till it was full. He put a fistful of extra shells into his mackinaw pocket and started toward the door.

His woman came into the room, looked at the gun and then at Cleever. "Where you going, Sam?"

"I'll be back in the morning," he evaded.

"Now, you know I don't like being left alone, Sam," she said plaintively. "Not overnight. Dan Tucker was always doing me that way. I git lonesome of a night, here all by myself."

"Mary Sue'll be here," Cleever pointed out.

"Mary Sue ain't no man," Bertha Cleever said. "I git scairt of a night with no man about the place."

"I can't help that," Cleever said. "This is business. A man can't make no money hanging around the house all the time."

His wife didn't question that. She didn't reckon there'd be any use in it. She reckoned men were all the same—sweet-talk a woman to death till they got her. Then lose interest in her right away and go off gallivanting about the country, leaving her to worry and wait and be scairt all night.

"I'll be back in the morning," Cleever repeated. "This is business. The deal's hot and can't wait. I got to close it before somebody else does."

His wife said, "You seen Jim lately?"

"A couple of days back," Cleever said. His face darkened at the memory. "If that kid don't come back here and finish that cotton picking before long, I'm gonna catch him and work him over with a bull whip. That'll learn him to prowl off when there's work to be did."

"Now, don't you go being hard on the boy," Bertha said. "It ain't like he's your own blood son. He's got a lot of his pa in him, and Dan Tucker was a mighty prideful and independent man."

Her voice broke a little, remembering how fine and proud and independent Dan Tucker had been. Sometimes she had a feeling she'd done Dan a wrong, throwing him over for Sam Cleever, even if Dan was in the pen.

She heaved a sigh of regret, not quite certain what she was regretting. But she remembered that Dan Tucker had never been mean-natured. He'd been careless and neglectful, but he'd never been mean-natured.

"Jim's got a lot of his pa in him," she repeated.

"And his pa was a hog thief," Cleever pointed out. He derived a sort of brutal satisfaction from the way she flinched. He added: "Wouldn't surprise me none if Jim ain't stealing a few head hisself. Him and that Sugar Barnett."

"There ain't no bad in Jim," Bertha defended, forgetting how many times she'd predicted that Jim would follow his father to the penitentiary. "He's just high-headed like his pa."

"High-headed, but sticky-fingered, I say," Cleever said, then added with a tone of finality, "There warn't no good in Dan Tucker and there ain't no good in his boy, nuther."

His wife let the argument drop. She saw that talk of Dan Tucker was making Cleever mad, as it always did. She put it down to natural jealousy. It gave her a certain mild satisfaction to think she was still woman enough for men to get jealous over.

Cleever walked sullenly to his Ford, set his rifle inside, then went around and caught hold of the car crank. Before he could give it a spin, Mary Sue came and leaned against a fender.

"You seen Jim Tucker lately?" she asked.

Cleever straightened, his face black with rage. "Jim Tucker! Jim Tucker!" he roared. "My God, is he all you damn-fool women got on your mind?"

"He's worth thinking some about," Mary Sue said, arching her eyebrows. "He's got to be a man."

"Man, hell!" Cleever shouted. "Do I work him over with a bull whip once and you won't think he's much of a man."

"You won't whip Jim no more," Mary Sue said flatly. "Not and git by with it. Jim's big enough to be his own man now. I know."

Cleever glared at the girl. "You don't know nothing," he snapped. "What do you want to see Jim about?"

"We're engaged," Mary Sue declared.

"Engaged?" Cleever roared at her.

"Since Saturday night," Mary Sue said.

Wrath blackened Cleever's face again. "Like hell you are!" he shouted. "I won't have no gal of mine marrying up with the son of a hog thief. I'll take a whip—"

"You won't do nothing but blow off at the mouth!" Mary Sue shouted back at him. "Now shut up and tell Jim I got to see him. Right soon!"

She left him standing there and went into the house.

Cleever looked after her, tempted to go work her over and learn her some manners, but deciding against it. She'd likely fight him like a wildcat. Her ma always had.

But that could wait. Right now, he had to keep his mind on collecting that bounty money. A man couldn't pick up two hundred and fifty dollars in every mudhole he crossed.

20

THE POSSE left town in three cars. August Hershimer drove the first. His face was swollen and puffy; a gap showed where two upper front teeth were missing. His left arm hung in a sling made of a red bandana tied around his neck. He drove with his right hand, his pale eyes, hard and brutal as ever, watching the road.

"That kid knows where his old man is at," August said above the roar his engine made as he took the car up a steep rocky slant in low gear. "The kid's been feeding him. I learnt that days ago. Knowed then he couldn't be far away. But it just come to me tonight where he's at. I've had Dev Blood watching the kid and Dev brought me word that the kid and Sugar penned some hogs at Red Bluff Mill. That's what tipped me off. He's holed up in that cabin out there. Sugar and the kid shoved that bunch of hogs in there to cover up the sign."

"I h-hope I—I git a s-shot at him," stuttered Jess Pickett. "G-git him in my s-sights once and-and-and I'll s-save the l-law a bu-bunch of trouble."

Myrtle's man sat on the front seat beside August Hershimer and nursed a rifle in his lap. His hands were shaking and his face strained and pale. His eyes had a wild glare and probed every bush and thicket clump along the way as if he expected to see the convict hiding behind each one of them.

"If he ain't at that old house," Hershimer said, "we'll take turns working the boy over. He knows, and we'll make him tell. Could give that Sugar Barnett a working over, too."

"Don't n-nobody t-t-try to g-git him ahead—ahead of me," Pickett warned. "H-hit w-were my wife. I-I w-want the f-fi—I want the first shot at the s-son of a b—son of a bitch!" He wiped a tear from his leathery cheek. "P-pore Myrtle!"

The headlights brought into relief the outlines of a deer standing in the road, the eyes of the startled creature burning like two mesquite coals. The deer leaped into the darkness and went crashing off into the brush. An owl dipped down out of a live oak and went sailing through the moonlight, flying low across a prickly-pear flat.

"You told Blair and them others exactly where to meet us, I reckon?" Hershimer asked. "You told them to be at the first crossing on James River, this side of the Kline & O'Toole pens?"

"I-I-I told 'em," Pickett said. "Lewt Scuffles s-said he'd h-have plenty of horses."

"Then we'll git him," Hershimer said confidently.

The car whined in low gear as it climbed a second rocky hill. One of the cars stopped in the road while the men worked hastily to patch and pump up a flat tire. The other two carloads of man hunters didn't wait. Ten miles farther along, they pulled up at a pasture gate on a high bank overlooking the crossing on James River. Below them, the clear water was soft silver in the moonlight.

A man came riding out of the shadows and approached the car.

"Lewt?"

"That's me, August."

August Hershimer climbed out of the car, favoring one leg. "You got the horses?"

"I got the horses," Lewt Scuffles said. He stared at the big sheriff for a moment, then added hesitantly: "Now, August, I want you to understand that I didn't have no idea that Tucker and Sugar Barnett was mixed up in any such doings when I put them to hog hunting. If I'd knowed beforehand—"

"Forget it," August Hershimer said magnanimously. "I know how you feel about it. I got the same feeling. These others has, too. That's how come we're all here."

Hershimer looked toward the east appraisingly. He twisted his head and looked up at the moon. "We better git going," he said.

Lewt rode back and started leading out saddled horses. There was the stamp and shuffle of hoofs and the creak of saddle leather as man after man got out of the cars and mounted. Each man carried a gun, holding it across his saddle in front of him.

Hershimer said, "We'll have to circle the cabin from 'way off and ride in on it, or them fool dogs'll tip our hand too quick. Even at that, you want to keep a close watch. We won't want to lose one of them in the dark."

Ten armed men rode through the gate and down into the river. The hoofs of the horses splashed into the water, setting in motion little slashing blades of golden light. Somebody jacked a shell into the barrel of a pump shotgun, and the metallic sound crossed the water and rattled sharply against the cliffs.

Sugar was squatted on his boot heels before the fireplace. He had a chunk of venison stuck on the end of a long, iron-handled fork, holding it over the mesquite-wood fire. The flames licked up around the meat, frying out juices which dribbled down upon the hot coals, making them hiss and spatter. A tantalizing aroma filled the room.

Jim Tucker came through the door. Without a word to Sugar, he leaned his Winchester against the wall and crossed to his cot. He bent to drag his plunder sack from under it.

Sugar glanced back over his shoulder. He noted the grim, determined look on the boy's face, the stubbornness of his jaw. He sat thinking for a moment, trying to figure what it was that had put his young partner in such a black mood; and while his mind was thus occupied, thoughtlessly withdrew the chunk of meat from the fire and bit into it.

"Blessed Jehoshaphat!"

Sugar flung the smoking meat cut into the middle of the floor. Clapping his hand to his burnt mouth, he charged across the room toward the bucket of water that sat on a rickety table. He plunged his whole face into the brimful bucket, holding it there, while the water spilled down upon the table and then to the floor. A moment later, he lifted his face and wiped it clean of water with a swipe of his shirt sleeve.

"Damned meat!" he exclaimed, incredulously. "It was hot!"

Startled, Jim watched the hog hunter return to stare at the offending chunk of venison as if it were some pet animal that had unaccountably turned vicious and attacked him.

Sugar shook his head.

"I reckon," he grumbled, "there ain't nothing on God's green earth that's better'n a good piece of hot meat."

Sugar circled the meat warily, finally bent and poked it with a dubious finger. A moment later, he'd lifted it from the floor and was gnawing hungrily away at it, as if nothing had ever happened.

Jim turned back and began stuffing clothes into his plunder sack. Sugar eyed him speculatively.

"Speaking of romance now," he said, "if I was all fevered up, like you, be dog if I wouldn't just haul off and do something about it."

Jim glanced at him. "What're you talking about?"

"Why, I'm talking about that little Blair girl," Sugar said.

Jim scowled. "What about her?"

"Now, don't git to ducking and dodging around. Hell, it's sticking out all over you. Plain as a sore rag on a busted toe. What I can't figure out is what's holding you off."

Jim stared at the hog hunter. How'd Sugar guessed? Then his face darkened again. He said, bleakly: "Ain't no use in me worrying about that. I've done tore my britches there."

Sugar grinned. "Don't fret about that. Lida told me all about it. Yep," said Sugar, contentedly, "all the little chickabiddies cry on my shoulder. Stopped by there on my way to town with that last load of hogs, and she wanted it made plain it were her pa, not her, saying you had to stay away."

For a moment, hope rose in Jim Tucker, and then died. He closed the plunder sack with a jerk.

"You think she'd marry a convict's son?" he demanded viciously. "You think her old man's going to let her?"

It was Sugar's turn to look startled. "Marry!" he exclaimed, appalled at the very idea. "Who said anything about marrying?"

Jim glanced at Sugar, then down at his hands. He said in a voice unusually quiet and gentle: "With her, marrying is the only thing I'd want."

Sugar chewed slowly on the meat, considering. Finally, he nodded. "Well, now," he said, "I reckon marrying's all right. Never did cotton to it, myself. Never did seem like a natural way for a man to live, what with a passel of young'uns generally cropping up and having to be fed, and a man not supposed to stray off his private graze. On the other hand, there ain't nothing really *wrong* with it, I reckon. Providing a man gets him the right woman."

He bit off another bite of meat, then nodded again, as if half sold on the idea. "And you know, I'd say that little Blair thing was righter than a rabbit. I sure would."

Jim felt a light warm touch of pride. It was no small thing for Sugar, who could get just about any woman he wanted, to recommend one for marriage. A man could take pride in marrying a woman that Sugar Barnett respected.

Then the impossibility of such a thing struck him with new force. He turned savagely to pick up his chaps and plunder sack, throw them over his shoulder, and head for the door.

Sugar regarded him in surprise. "You fixing to go marry her, *tonight?*"

Jim wheeled on the hog hunter, his eyes blazing. "Hell, no! If I could marry her, how'd I support her? I ain't even got a job."

"Why, you got a job," Sugar said. "Hog hunting."

"I *had* a job," Jim told him. "Till I went to see Lewt Scuffles about getting that goat job. And what does Lewt say? He says I'd better roll my pack. Says he don't like to fire me, but what'll his boss think, him hiring a hog hunter whose pa was sent to the pen for hog stealing."

"Aw!" Sugar exclaimed, then added hotly: "Why, the son of a bitch! I'll quit, myself!"

"Ain't no need for you to quit," Jim said. "It's just me they want rid of."

Sugar asked uncertainly: "Where're you going?"

"I'm going to get Pa," Jim said. "I'm going to get him and take him so far out of this country, we'll never be heard of again."

"No, Jim," Sugar said in alarm. "That won't do. Wait a minute. Let me think. We'll—"

"I'm a-going, Sugar," Jim said flatly. "You can stand there and argue against it all night, but I'm still a-going."

Jim stepped out on the gallery. Moonlight slanted into the river canyon, scattering silvery ripples on the wide pool below the house. Jim scarcely noticed. He went to his horse and tied his plunder sack on behind the saddle. Then, remembering his rifle, he started back into the house for it.

At that moment, the dogs raised a clamor, and hoofs rattled as riders spurred suddenly into the yard. Jim whirled, saw the dull gleam of light on metal, and took a quick step backward. Inside, he heard Sugar's startled voice exclaim: "What the hell's all that?"

A kind of wary panic came to Jim. He thought: *I waited too long!* He took another quick step backward, limned against the outpouring light. His gun was there, leaning just inside the door, and he reached furtively toward it.

A hard voice threw a single word at him: "Don't!" Men piled from the saddles. Jim saw August Hershimer's burly shape, and heard the sheriff call, "Sugar?"

"Yep, that's me," Sugar said, still inside the cabin. "Come in! Come in! Dry up that racket, you clabber-headed dogs!"

Hershimer called back, "You come out, Sugar. With your hands up!"

There was a muted exclamation inside the cabin, then sudden silence. Jim said quickly, over his shoulder: "Douse that light. Get out the back way, Sugar!"

August Hershimer said immediately, "Don't try it! There's men back there, too. Come out, Sugar, or I'll have to come in after you."

There was a short wait, then Sugar stepped to the door. "What's all this about, August?" he asked uncertainly. He glanced at the ring of guns trained on him. "What you got on your mind?"

Hershimer said, "You'll damn well find out what it's all about if you make a crooked move." His boots scuffed the dirt as he moved heavily toward Jim. "You little son of a bitch," he said. "Stick out your hands."

A baffled, helpless anger seized Jim. "You can't arrest us," he said tightly. "We ain't done nothing."

"Stick out your hands!" Hershimer growled.

Fear ran all through Jim—fear and that mounting anger. He said, suddenly, through his teeth: "You can go to hell!" and lunged from the gallery at the big sheriff. He swung from the shoulder at August Hershimer's broad face.

The sheriff staggered back. Jim hit him again, quickly. He hit the sheriff a third time. Then two men, moving in behind Jim, grabbed his arms.

They jerked him back and held him. August Hershimer, very deliberately, lifted a big fist and smashed Jim in the face. Jim's head snapped back. Hershimer, with a curse, hit him again, and Sugar Barnett winced at the meaty sound of the blow. Jim would have fallen but for the men who held him.

With a growl that sounded like boards being ripped from a picket fence, Felipe pushed out from under the house. His muzzle wrinkled ferociously and hair ridged along his back as he tied into August Hershimer with an awkward rush.

"Damn it, take this meat hound off'n me!" the sheriff roared. He brought a big fist down on the dog's neck but Felipe's Airedale blood was up and his long young teeth were well set in Hershimer's leg, just above the ankle. The harder Hershimer hit him the harder Felipe hung, all the while his snarls rising in a crescendo of rage.

"Damme, I'd sure like to have a cussed dog like that," Sam Blair said admiringly.

"He don't scare easy, that's one sure thing," Lewt Scuffles said.

One of the posse came over and, grabbing Felipe by his scruff, choked him loose with his other hand. The dog was dragged off, snarling, rearing up on his hind legs, trying to get back. Hershimer watched. When Felipe was hooked at the end of a chain the sheriff picked up a heavy stick of fatwood and started for the dog.

"Aw hell, let him be," Lewt Scuffles said. "He's only a dog, he don't know no better."

Hershimer paused, shrugged, and turned his attention back to Jim. "I guess I can put the cuffs on this one now," he said heavily. He snapped the handcuffs on Jim's wrists, then went to his horse for a rope. He pitched the rope on the gallery.

"Tie the other un up," he ordered.

Dave Michner picked up the rope. Another man stepped up onto the gallery to help him, and halted suddenly.

"God A'mighty, what a yellercat!" he said in astonishment.

Several others stopped to stare in wonder at the huge catfish, gutted and chilled now, swinging from the rafters of the gallery porch.

August Hershimer said, roughly, "We got no time to waste admiring a catfish. Git Sugar tied up, like I say."

Sugar stood dumbly in his tracks, powerless to move, while two men tied his one hand behind his back, then took a half hitch around him, binding his arm to his body. His eyes bulged slightly.

Blessed Jehoshaphat, he thought. *Myrtle's done spilled the beans!*

Sugar could hardly believe it. Not Myrtle! Why, Myrtle was the salt of the earth. He'd said it a thousand times. How could she ever have done a thing like this? He'd have sworn Myrtle would have stayed with him till hell froze over.

A great feeling of loneliness and self-pity engulfed Sugar at the thought of Myrtle's betraying him.

Then it came to him what the immediate consequences might be, and fright took him.

"Look," he said, frantically. "I can explain this, if you'll gimme a chance."

"Shut up!" ordered Hershimer.

"But I didn't mean no harm," Sugar insisted. "I was just fooling around. You know I couldn't a-meant no harm, Jess!"

He looked pleadingly at Jess Pickett. Jess did not answer him.

"Look, you take that big ol' catfish home to Myrtle," Sugar offered, desperate hopefulness in his tone. "Why, Myrtle ain't the kind to hold a mad ag'in a body. She'll tell you—"

"I—I d-d-don't—don't want a c-c-cat-f-f-fish," said Jess Pickett angrily.

"But hit's yours!" said Sugar excitedly. "You just take it home to Myrtle and—"

"Dammit, I said to shut up," August Hershimer growled.

"But Jess can have that catfish for Myrtle!" protested Sugar. "He knows I was just—"

"I—I d-d-don't want it!" shouted Jess Pickett.

"But Myrtle—"

August Hershimer took a long step and slapped Sugar's mouth so hard the hog hunter's head bumped the wall behind him. Sugar regained his balance and stood in stunned, hurt silence. He couldn't see why the sheriff hadn't let him give that big old yellowcat to Jess. It seemed a reasonable trade to him. That was sure a fine catfish.

"Keep these peckerwoods quiet," August ordered, "while I look around."

He walked through the house, his pale eyes missing nothing. In a little while he returned, to stand in front of Jim Tucker. Jim was shaking his head, as if to clear it. Blood showed at the corners of his mouth. Hershimer said to Jim, "He's holed up at Red Bluff Mill, ain't he?"

Jim Tucker said nothing, but his sudden pallor betrayed him. In his eyes there was a trapped look.

Sugar heard only the tone of Hershimer's voice. He thought: *It's gonna be hell to stand,* and wondered how he'd ever be able to face it.

Hershimer said to Jim, "You know it's ag'in the law to aid and abet an escaped prisoner, and that's what you been doing."

Jim still said nothing, but his lips were tight.

Hershimer slapped him—hard enough to rattle Jim Tucker in his boots. "All right," he said. "You won't talk, so we'll just ride you over there and give you a look at Dan Tucker while we hang him. We'll see if you can talk then!"

The betrayed look left Sugar's face. So it was still Dan Tucker the damn fools were after, not him. Myrtle hadn't squealed, after all. His relief was so great that he felt weak and had to lean against the wall. A great overwhelming warmth for Myrtle washed through him.

He thought: *I done wrong to misdoubt a woman like Myrtle. I sure done her a wrong.* He'd have to make it up to her for that.

21

FEAR, COLD AND CLAMMY, lay heavy inside Jim. It lay all around him, too, in the black shadows cast by the trees, in the openings where the moonlight was pale white on the dead grass and the frost-crusted cow chips glittered like diamonds. It lurked in the darkness of the deep canyons and the brush covering the rock-bench slopes of the hillsides, in the thickets that combed the ridges. Stark, naked, inescapable fear.

They were going to hang his father. They were after him because he was a convict. That was the seed of their violence. But the seed hadn't sprouted and grown in their minds until Jess Pickett had stammered out his story of a man attacking his wife, a man in strange-looking clothes. Convict's clothes, Jess Pickett felt sure.

Jim's manacled, sweaty hands gripped the swell of his saddle. His horse followed at the end of a lead rope behind August Hershimer. Jess Pickett led Sugar's horse. Sugar rode awkwardly in the saddle because of his bound hand. Around them rode ten men. Ahead, across the cold, moonlit ridges, a man slept in the loft of an abandoned cabin. A defenseless man. A man innocent of the crime they would hang him for.

The men rode at a fast jog, grim purpose written on their faces. Rocks clinked and rattled under the hoofs of their horses. Saddle leather creaked rhythmically. Moonlight glinted coldly on gun metal.

He was ten. He came home from school with his nose smashed and bloody, one eye swelling shut—beaten up by the Simmons twins, crying for the shame of it. He could have whipped them, one at a time, any time. Dan Tucker held him close and let him cry it out, then said: "Now, look, boy. You fought 'em with all you had. That's the main thing. You can't win all the time, but you can always fight 'em till hell freezes over. Losing ain't nothing to cry about." Then he'd told the one about old Ike Dodger, who was so scared somebody would steal his watermelons that he stayed up every night, guarding his patch with a shotgun. And one night Ike went to sleep and some boys went into his patch and one boy broke a melon over Ike's head, thinking he was busting it on a stump, and scared Ike plumb out of his own melon patch.

It was an old story and Jim had heard it before, but Dan Tucker laughed so long and so hard about it that Jim couldn't keep from laughing with him, and forgot all about crying any more.

Close by, a rabbit cried out in agony as the claws of a bobcat sank into its vitals. The jeering cackle of a laughing owl drifted from a ridgetop.

The sounds were like a rasp against Jim's nerves. He couldn't let them hang his father. Sugar was the man Jess Pickett had seen run out of the house. But could he tell on Sugar? Stirred up like they were now, they'd hang Sugar. And Sugar was his friend.

Jim's mind darted this way and that. Fear was a brassy taste in his mouth. He crowded his horse against Sugar's.

"You've got to make a break," he whispered tensely. "I've got to tell 'em!"

The one-armed man's face looked gray. His mouth showed strain. He licked dry lips and pleaded with Jim in an undertone. "I be a friend of your'n, Jim," he said. "You ain't forgetting that?"

Jim looked helplessly ahead. Here, a dozen cow trails converged, and the posse split up. August Hershimer sent riders in a wide swing in both directions, to surround the cabin.

"Kill him if he makes a break," the sheriff ordered bluntly.

Jess Pickett twisted in the saddle, glaring wildly at the sheriff. "I—I w-want the first ch-chance at the s-son—s-son—son of a bitch," he stated, as emphatically as he could.

Daylight was coming on, in the face of the sinking moon. The ridge sloped down and ahead of them the cabin, the pens, the reservoir and windmill, creaking listlessly, took on distinct outlines. Some late-prowling animal—a raccoon by its movements—left the watering trough, moved leisurely across the clearing, and melted into the brush. August Hershimer rode more slowly, to give his men time to close in on the cabin.

Jim knew then that he had to do something. Sugar or no Sugar, he couldn't stand to see them ambush his father.

"Wait, August!" he called, sharply. "It wasn't Pa done it. I can prove it!"

"Shut up!" Hershimer commanded, angrily. "Damn you, it's too late. I tried to get you to talk sooner."

"But I tell you—"

"Don't do it, boy," broke in Sugar, almost shaking in his saddle. "I was a friend of your daddy's, too. You ask your daddy. He'll tell you he never had a better friend than old Sugar Barnett."

"But it's my pa, Sugar," Jim said in a choked voice. "I know it is. And they're going to kill him."

"If he's still there," Sugar said.

"I know he's there," said Jim. "And he never done nothing to get kilt over."

Sugar's mouth was loose and quivery as a child's about to cry. There was agony in his eyes.

"All right, boy," he said in a half whisper. "I reckon I ain't blaming you any." He sat slumped like a dead man in the saddle.

Suddenly, Jim knew he couldn't betray Sugar. He couldn't point his finger at a man, and know that man was going to die. The knowledge was like gallwood in his stomach. The wildest, blackest despair that he had ever known swept over him.

Then he was spurring his horse, desperately. The startled animal broke wind and plunged into August Hershimer's mount. With a brutal swing of his manacled hands, Jim knocked the burly sheriff from the saddle.

Clawing for leather, August bawled at Jess Pickett: "Stop him!"

Jim tried to ride the rancher down. Pickett jerked frantically around, trying to swing his rifle to cover Jim. The horses collided. Jim struck at the gun, almost wrenched it from Pickett's grasp. Then his horse was slanting away and going down the hill at a hard run.

In the wire corral the wild hogs came suddenly to life, uttering startled grunts, sniffing loudly, racing around the pen and stirring up dust. Jim's heart gave a lurch. A man had stood up over there beside the reservoir. In the half-light, his body merged with the shadow of the reservoir, so that only his head and shoulder could be seen.

"Git down!" Jim screamed.

The man turned. Jim saw a dull flash of light on metal.

"Look out, Jess!" That was August Hershimer's bull roar behind Jim. "He's got a gun!"

Jim reached the corral and the wing fence he'd built blocked his way. He piled out of the saddle, went over the fence, and was nearly to the corral when the shot sounded.

"Pa!" he yelled.

The man by the reservoir staggered. The gun slipped from his hands, and he turned, apparently trying to walk away. A great, numbing dread hit Jim like an ax, and held him rooted in his tracks.

A second shot slammed into the man across the corral, turning him completely around. He stumbled blindly into the corral fence and crawled upon it. He pitched headfirst across the fence. His heels flew up, and he fell inside.

"You got him, Jess!" August Hershimer shouted. "You sure got him!"

A cold sickness overwhelmed Jim Tucker. Behind him, Jess Pickett fell out of the saddle, to stand weakly beside his horse. August Hershimer walked forward to stand beside Jess. A dozen men waited, staring tensely at the corral.

And then the man in the corral screamed—a high thin wail that cut sharply across the silence. The sound was followed by an angry, rumbling grunt—the sound a greedy hog makes in fighting another away from the slop trough. A sow squealed frenziedly, and the coughing roars of the other hogs joined in.

"Good Lord," cried Sugar Barnett. "The hogs have got him!"

Jim Tucker went a little crazy then. He climbed into the corral and began fighting the hogs with his bare hands.

22

TO SEE A MAN shot down was a thing the posse had come for and anticipated. But to see the body of a dead man torn apart by voracious hogs was a horror they had not counted on. And now the dead man's son was in there among the hogs, trying to fight them away from the body with his bare hands.

By the time the first man reached the corral, Jim Tucker had the dead man's rifle. He emptied it into the hogs. Against the terrific din of their roaring and squealing, the gunshots were barely audible. Jim clubbed the gun to drive the last hog away from the corpse.

Someone pulled him back. A man's voice said gruffly, "Git the boy out of here."

There was a moment's silence. Then Lewt Scuffles reached down gingerly and caught hold of the coat. He pulled, rolling the face up.

"My God!" he exclaimed, recoiling violently. "This here is Cleever!"

Jess Pickett stood stunned, like the rest. But gradually the implications of what he'd done seeped into his muddled brain.

I kilt the wrong man. Lord, God, I kilt the wrong man. In a minute now it'll come to all of 'em that I kilt an innocent man!

He stared wildly around, trying to see by the expressions on their faces if that awful fact had occurred to them yet. What could he do? What could he say? Lord, God, if only Myrtle were there to tell him what to do!

He started shaking all over. Cold sweat popped out on his face. He felt as if he were smothering.

He got up suddenly and threw his gun away. He threw it over the fence.

"Let's lay him up on the reservoir," somebody suggested. "We can't leave him on the ground."

The killing of Cleever had sobered the men. It had frightened some of them. A chill gray dread had laid hold of Jess Pickett's entrails that it seemed no amount of warm sunshine would ever thaw out.

But the solution, when it came to him, was so simple that it seemed a miracle had fostered the thought.

"That's the one, all right," he said suddenly. "It were him that was bothering Myrtle."

The men all switched their attention to Jess Pickett.

"Cleever?" said Hershimer, and gaped at the rancher.

"Had to've been," Jess said positively. He was unbelievably calm now. "I recognized that mackinaw a-fore I shot. That's what looked strange about him when I seen him running into the brush. That gray mackinaw. It's got stripes like a convict's coat. He's the man, all right. It were Cleever."

Somebody gasped, "My God!" Nobody noticed that in his excitement, stuttering Jess Pickett had not faltered on one syllable.

"It were dark there in the house," the rancher went on rapidly. "Maybe

Myrtle don't recognize Cleever. Or maybe she does and won't tell, afeared I'll kill him. My Myrtle, she's a softhearted woman. My Myrtle wouldn't want me to kill a man."

"She sure wouldn't," Sugar Barnett agreed fervently. "That Myrtle, she's the salt of the earth! She wouldn't have her man harmin' a fly, could she help it!"

The hog hunter's voice was so charged with conviction that even Jess Pickett looked at him.

Jess glanced fearfully around the circle of men again and knew a vast sense of relief when nobody seemed to question the truth of his words. He suddenly squatted down, his knees too weak to support him.

"What do you reckon he was doing here?" Sam Blair wondered.

"Maybe fixing to help Dan Tucker git away," somebody offered.

"Don't you ever believe it," August Hershimer said flatly. "He was after that bounty money. Sam Cleever could smell a dollar a day's ride off."

The big sheriff wheeled suddenly and bellowed at the men. "Git around that cabin!" he commanded. "Quick! Before he gits away. Damn! If we've let him git away, we'll never git our hands on him again."

He glared at the men as if it were solely their fault that time had been wasted.

But the excitement of the man hunt was gone out of the men now. That grisly figure of Sam Cleever lying there, torn and mangled, was too disturbing. The fascination had palled. They climbed out of the pen, slowly and reluctantly.

"Git a blanket from under your saddle to roll this up in," Hershimer said to Jess Pickett. "We got to git it away from these hogs."

Jess Pickett's eyes grew round with terror. "I-I can't, Au-Au-August," he stammered. "I-I—you'll have to git somebody else."

Hershimer swore in disgust. "Michner! Turner!" he roared. "Come move this outta reach of these hogs."

Dave Michner and Clyde Turner climbed back into the pen. August Hershimer flung himself over the fence and turned toward the cabin, limping on his bad leg.

He stopped suddenly. Jim Tucker stood backed up against the cabin door. The boy held Cleever's rifle in his manacled hands, slanted across his leg.

"You ain't a-taking him, August," he said flatly.

"The hell I ain't!" August said, moving forward again. "Git out of my way, boy!"

With his thumb, Jim eared back the hammer of the rifle. "Not this time, August," he said. "You and Sam Cleever sent Pa to prison once for something he never done. You ain't a-doing it a second time. We're riding out, together, me and Pa."

Hershimer stood silent a moment, watching Jim closely, studying the hot determination in the boy's eyes, trying to stare him down. Jim's eyes met his, unflinchingly.

"Don't be a fool, boy," the sheriff said. "There's too many of us. We'd git you."

"Maybe some of the others, August. But not you. Anybody makes a crooked move, and you're the first one to go down."

Hershimer gave a short barking laugh. "You want to turn outlaw, like your daddy?"

"I'd be proud to turn outlaw with my daddy."

There was a pride and conviction in the boy's voice that shook the heavy sheriff. He glanced quickly around at the others, with the uneasy feeling that Jim's truculent stand was winning sympathy.

Jim said: "Jess, fetch my horse. Bring Sugar up here and cut him loose. And don't try nothing, without you want to ride home without a sheriff." Then he added in the same warning tone: "August, you better make sure he understands that."

Dave Michner said: "I'll do it, son."

"I'll help him," offered Sam Blair.

The two men caught Jim's horse and the one on which Sugar was mounted, and led them back to the cabin. Sam Blair, with his pocket-knife, cut Sugar loose. The hog hunter stepped to the ground with a grunt.

Through all of this Jim had waited, his eyes never leaving the heavy sheriff. Now he took a step backward. He tapped against the door behind him with the butt of the Winchester.

"All right, Pa," he said. "You can come out now. We're ready to ride."

A moaning groan, like that made by some animal in great pain, came from inside the cabin. A sudden fear gripped Jim. His daddy must be hurt. Maybe he wouldn't be able to ride.

He heard the barely audible rustle of dry hay as footsteps approached. Then he heard the door latch rattle and took a step to one side, giving his father room to come out.

He heard the door open. He caught the look of wonder and disbelief that flashed across the sheriff's face. He ventured a quick look of his own, and almost dropped the rifle at the sight of the man standing beside him.

It wasn't his daddy. It was a wizened little gnomelike man, so old that his black skin was wrinkled and his hair white as a freshly opened boll of cotton.

"A nigger!" August Hershimer burst out. "A burhead nigger!"

The little black man stood ashen-faced and trembling, his eyes alive with terror. Jim recognized his father's shoes on the man's feet. He had on Dan Tucker's pants, too. But for a coat, he still wore the ragged remnant of a convict's prison jacket.

He sidled along the wall, backing away from Jim and his rifle. "Don't shoot, Mistah Sheriff," he quavered. "Ise peaceable. I won't make no trouble. Ise done scairt past all human standation."

He cut his eyes toward the pen where the blanket-wrapped remains of Sam Cleever lay atop the stone reservoir wall and shuddered.

A period of stunned silence hung on, then somebody emitted a high, jerky laugh. Dave Michner's face was dull red with anger as he swung on August Hershimer.

"Thought you said the escaped convict was Dan Tucker," he charged.

August admitted, calmly: "Hell, I thought it was."

He glanced around the circle of men, gauging the resentment and suspicion rising against him. The fools! He'd been doing his sworn duty. A sullen wrath laid hold of him, for in his mind there was never any room for doubt of himself. He felt a sudden great contempt for the whole sorry pack of them.

"You're a bunch of fools!" he said. He stepped suddenly toward the frightened Negro, ignoring Jim's threatening rifle.

"Where's Dan Tucker?" he demanded harshly. "He escaped with you. Where's he at, now?"

The Negro cowered against the wall, too frightened to answer. Hershimer lunged forward, slapped the man's face.

"Where's Dan Tucker at?" he demanded again, getting only a mild satisfaction this time out of his power over another human being.

"Lawd, Mistah," the Negro quavered. "Mistah Dan, he ain't with me, suh. Mistah Dan, he still back there in that prison camp."

"Don't lie to me!"

Hershimer caught the Negro by the collar and shook him violently.

"It's the Lawd's truth," the convict wailed. "Mistah Dan, he don't come. He's a trusty, and he ain't got long to go, suh. He'll wait till his time's up."

"Knowed it!" Sugar Barnett spoke up, confidently. "Knowed it all the time. Dan Tucker ain't no fool. He's a friend of mine."

Hershimer let his glance move slowly from one man to the other, seeing only disapproval and dislike in their faces. They felt that he'd made a fool of them and now they resented him for it. He drew a deep, labored breath. He looked at the frightened Negro standing near him, and his hand suddenly whipped out, striking the old derelict in the face, slamming his wizened frame against the cabin wall.

"That'll do, August," Jim Tucker said. "You got no call to knock him around."

Hershimer whirled. "Look who's talking now," he snarled. His composure broke and he lashed out at Jim. "I'll git that hog-thieving daddy of yours yet. He won't be out of the pen six months before I'll have him back, stripping cane for Uncle Bud again. You hear me?"

"I hear, August," Jim said. "And now you can hear me. You won't touch my daddy when he comes home."

"And who do you reckon'll stop me?"

"I will, August," Jim said. "I'll stop you cold. Just like I stopped you a minute ago. Because if anything ever happens to land my daddy in the pen, I'll get you, August." Then he added a statement that made no sense to the others: "I'll use the blade of the ax!"

There was a quality of conviction in Jim Tucker's voice that checked another outburst from the bulky sheriff. He stared hard at the boy.

There was no capacity for fear in August Hershimer, only an animal-like caution at times. Other men were afraid of him. That's how it was, how it had always been. But now he saw in Jim Tucker's eyes the same thing that had stopped him a few moments before. Jim Tucker wasn't afraid. Not any more. Hershimer couldn't understand it; it made no sense, any way he looked at it. But it was a fact and one that he didn't fail to recognize. Jim Tucker wasn't afraid, and he wasn't bluffing.

"I believe you would," Hershimer said slowly, with a sort of puzzled wonder in his voice. "By golly, Jim, I sure believe you would."

Jim saw a new respect for him in the sheriff's pale eyes. For the first time, Hershimer was looking upon him as a man, not a boy: and Jim wondered why that fact seemed to matter so little to him now.

With an impatient gesture, Jim pitched the rifle at the sheriff's feet. "Take it," he said. "It's empty, anyhow."

When Hershimer merely stood and stared at him, open-mouthed, Dave Michner stepped quickly forward to take the sheriff's keys. He unlocked Jim's handcuffs.

"I been a fool, boy," he said. "So's a lot of other people I could name. But you've made friends. You'll see. I aim to speak to the judge about your daddy tomorrow."

"How will that help?"

"We can get him a new trial. Without Sam Cleever to testify ag'in him, he'll come free. Ain't that right, August?"

August thought it over. He looked at the other men, saw the threatening hostility on their faces, and knew there was only one thing he could say if he wanted to stay sheriff.

"That's right. We'll spring him."

Jim walked blindly, dazedly to his horse. The blood sang in his veins. Sugar paused just long enough to speak for a moment with Lewt Scuffles, then mounted and rode after Jim.

23

SUGAR LAY SPRAWLED on his camp bed while Jim worked between camp table and fireplace, preparing a late breakfast of coffee, sour-dough biscuits and fried doe steaks. The second he heard the coffee bubbling in the pot, Sugar said: "Bring me a cup of that bellywash, boy. Dog take it, riding to hell and gone all over the country before daylight makes me hungry as a bitch wolf with pups."

Jim carried over a cup of coffee and went back to lift the lid from his Dutch oven and take a peek at his biscuits.

Sugar gulped the hot brew and smacked his lips. "You know," he said, "I think we'll knock off work today. I'd sort of like to take that catfish over to Myrtle before it's spoilt."

Jim turned in astonishment and stared at Sugar. "Take it to Myrtle!" he exclaimed.

"Yeah," Sugar said. "You know Myrtle's bound to be all tore up about what's happened. Jess, too, for that matter. I figure it would look real nice and neighborly to take that catfish over to them. Cheer 'em up a little, maybe."

Sugar smiled meditatively into his coffee cup. "You know," he said confidingly, "that Myrtle, she's just the salt of this earth!"

Back there at Red Bluff Mill a few hours ago, Jim had known such horror, despair, and then relief that he'd felt wrung out, as if there wasn't another flicker of emotion left inside him. But now laughter came bubbling up, ready to be shouted out. He held it, however, not wanting to break into one of Sugar's gentler moods.

He shook his head. A man had to hand it to that Sugar. Nothing kept him down. Nothing worried him for long. Nothing changed him at all. From now till they buried him, he'd romp right along, cheerful as a fat coon robbing a trap line, never learning a lesson or even realizing there was one to be learned.

Jim half envied Sugar's ability to take things as they came and shoulder off all responsibility. He reckoned a man could get a sight more satisfaction out of life that way. He toyed with the notion of trying his hand at it once. Be dog, if it wouldn't take a wagonload of worry off his own back right now if he could.

He let the idea rest gently on his mind while he got a long fork and turned the slabs of venison frying in the pan.

Now, a man could use some reason about it; he didn't have to go at it whole hog, like Sugar did sometimes. For instance, he could go stand by his ma while they buried her man. Bad as it would be to have to listen to all the moaning and carrying-on womenfolks did at a time like that, knowing all the time Sam Cleever wasn't worth the powder and lead Jess Pickett had used to blow him down—still a man could do that much for his own ma.

And he guessed a man owed it to his ma to see that she didn't want for grub to eat or garments to wear, now that she had nobody to look after her. But after them things was taken care of, a man ought to could cut loose without his conscience riding him too hard of a night.

It'd take nerve, all right. It'd be fearful for a spell, standing up to them two women—his ma with her mournful complaining and that Mary Sue, with her whip tongue. But if a man had the gall to stand his ground, he could sure cut loose for good, all right. Be his own man for all time to come. . . .

Sugar raised up on his elbow. "Dog take it," he grumbled, "take that grub off the fire before you burn it all up."

The one head lamp of Sugar's Model T was weak, just barely giving Jim enough light to drive by. But he knew the road and as he bounced along over it, he sang a little old fool song his father used to sing to him when he was a boy:

> "Frog went a-courtin', he did ride,
> Ladda bola rinktum akimo!
> With sword and pistol by his side,
> Ladda bola rinktum akimo!"

Around him were the broken, tumbling hills, close, companionable, a haven for the wild creatures, a refuge for a man not afraid to dig into their secrets.

Pa loved them old hills, he mused. *He'll be wanting to gopher around in them, soon as he gets out.*

He planned how it would be, him and his pa, prowling round in the hills. With Sugar, of course. They'd need Sugar to keep things stirred up and going.

And without meaning to at all, Jim suddenly recalled Dan Tucker's face. It stood out plain and sharp in his mind as if he'd seen it last week.

Felipe whined. Stretched out on the front seat, floppy muzzle resting atop the door, he whined partly because the Ford was jouncing his jaw, partly it was just plain contented hound noise.

"Shut up, you Meskin-talking fool," Jim said fondly, laying an easy hand on Felipe's curly rump.

Jim remembered Sugar's words.

"Lord A'mighty, take him why don't you, he's no damn good around here," Sugar had said that evening when Felipe hopped into the Ford. But Jim knew better. Sugar had grown a kind of liking for Felipe. It was a real present Sugar was giving him, Jim figured. Just about the only thing that Sugar had to give.

Jim drove up to the yard gate of the old Johnson place and stepped on the brake. There was no resistance, no response to his pressure. Either the bands were burned out or some bolt was gone.

He was still shoving hard on the brake when the Ford crashed head-on into a post. The one light went out.

Sam Blair stuck his head out the door. "What's going on out there?"

Jim said, feeling some of Sugar's exuberance, "Just trying to knock your yard fence down, Mr. Blair. Lida home?"

Sam Blair said: "You bring along a fat gobbler?"

"Got him here in the back seat," Jim said triumphantly. "Kilt him just before sundown."

"Flyin'?" Blair demanded.

"Well, no," Jim said. "I missed my flying shot this time."

Sam Blair threw back his head and laughed. "Come in this house, boy!"

Jim reached back and got the gobbler. Pausing, he examined the broken head lamp. He saw that Lida was now standing beside her father in the doorway and he felt a stirring glow of excitement and anticipation.

"Now, I'll sure have to git that light fixed up," he said to Lida and her father. "It's a crying shame to wreck a brand-new car like that!"

There was laughter on his face when he walked into the yellow light of the kitchen lamps.